Science in the Cause of Man

SECOND EDITION, REVISED AND ENLARGED

Science in the Cause of Man

GERARD PIEL

Alfred A. Knopf NEW YORK 1962

SEVERAL PIECES in this volume appeared originally as follows:
"Scientists and Other Citizens" in *Scientific Monthly;* "The
Planet Earth" and "The Revolution in Man's Labor" issued as
pamphlets by *Scientific American;* "Science, Censorship, and
the Public Interest" in *Science;* "The Economics of Disarmament" in somewhat different form in *The Bulletin of Atomic
Scientists;* and "The Economics of Abundance" as a pamphlet
entitled "Consumers of Abundance" issued by The Center for
the Study of Democratic Institutions established by The Fund
for the Republic. "The Wilderness and the American Dream"
was included in *The American Heritage of Wilderness: Proceedings of the Seventh Biennial Conference of The Sierra
Club, 1961.*
Of the pieces included in the second, revised edition "The
Illusion of Civil Defense" was published in *The Bulletin of
Atomic Scientists* and in slightly different form in the *New
Statesman.* "On the Feasibility of Peace" appeared in *Science.*

L. C. catalog card number: 62–14760

THIS IS A BORZOI BOOK,

PUBLISHED BY ALFRED A. KNOPF, INC.

DISTRIBUTED BY RANDOM HOUSE, INC.

for ELEANOR JACKSON PIEL

Preface to the Second Edition

"THERE IS NO PANACEA FOR PROTECTION FROM NUCLEAR ATTACK," says
the pamphlet *Fallout Protection*, issued by the Department of Defense. "In a major attack upon our country, millions would be
killed. There appears to be no practical program that would avoid
large-scale loss of life." This is a historic admission by our federal
government. Faced with the prospect of nuclear war, the government declares, in effect, that it cannot carry out the functions for
which it was constituted; it cannot provide for the common defense, much less insure domestic tranquillity. Survival is up to the
citizen. "A sane and sober person," the pamphlet says, ". . . would
draw on his reserve of courage and intelligence—and the unquench-
able will to live—and begin to build again."

Despite its candor on the ultimate utility of the effort, the administration is committed to a $700-million expenditure on civil
defense. The issue is, no doubt, a source of anguish to public officials; it is not surprising that they should want to buy "insurance"
for their constituents against their own inability to carry out their
awesome responsibilities. To the sane and sober citizen, however, it
would seem that the time to summon his will to live, his courage
and intelligence, is now.

The issue of civil defense arises at the end of this book. It comes

vii

last in the chronological order in which the twenty-one essays are arranged—in two essays written since the first edition of this book went to press and added to this second edition. But civil defense has more than a chronological connection with what came before. The choice of life or death puts all other questions in crisis and poses each of them in an insistent and personal way.

The choice of life involves, of course, all kinds of ethical, aesthetic, political, economic, and social considerations along with the scientific and technological. Some of these are discomfiting; they contradict received wisdom and demand the re-examination of buried premises. Some apparently collide with powerful vested interests, or with the short-term view of what those interests are. They also pose enthralling possibilities in the way of social and political enterprise, the kind of thing that distinguishes our pragmatic democracy with its flair for improvisation. The choice, once made by our society, would evoke an unprecedented outpouring of human energy and talent.

The order of the essays in this book is chronological and so, to a degree, biographical. In my capacity as a publisher and editor, I have been a party to as well as a contemplator of the issues I deal with here, and I have been thinking out loud about them in public over the last decade. But perhaps the sequence of my confrontations with these issues is not unique to me. It may be that this book derives something of a plot from the evolutionary succession of the issues during that decade, beginning with secrecy and censorship and culminating in the prospect of nuclear war. In my view, the succession of events sustains a thesis—that is, the need to bring into the framing of private and public policy the scientific understanding and the scientific attitude that have so profoundly transformed man's relationship to nature. The enterprise of science, it is true, has been carried on in an organized way for less than five hundred years; only in the last fifty years has technology made the power of this method of inquiry manifest to all men. Nonetheless, it is at their increasing peril that men and nations have gone on living the same old life histories. They have yet to grasp the new choices, the new ends of life and action, that the change in their relationship to nature has made not only possible but imperative.

Ignorance alone does not stand in the way of this long overdue and essential synthesis in our culture. Habit, compulsion, and explicit preference also conspire to hold the world in the thrall of pre-scientific institutions, myths, values, superstitions, and glories beyond the grave. Surely it was in the spirit of folk magic that our legislators thought to cast the spell of secrecy over the nuclear binding force and reserve it to the purposes of the Strategic Air Command. The same renascence of witchcraft reinstated heresy in our politics during the early 1950's and emptied public discourse of content as well as controversy. This development was of concern to my profession as well as to my citizenship because scientists, as negotiators with the powers of outer darkness, figured notably in the rites of exorcism. On the other hand, in the story of the emergence of the American taxpayer as history's most openhanded patron of science, as told in these pages, one sees the bane of simple ignorance. It took some years before science, as distinguished from technology or medicine, could get regular appropriations from Congress. And the truth is that the entrepreneurs of science have learned not to press the distinction too far when they seek larger appropriations.

In the brief span of the Atomic Age, which has already given way to the Space Age, there has been some closing of the gap between science and public understanding. The press and the educational system have contributed less to this development than their spokesmen like to think. The great adult educator is technology. Some three hundred nuclear explosions have popularized the sense of Einstein's Special Theory of Relativity. Several dozen earth satellites have provided the classical mechanics of Newton with its grandest demonstration.

With public policy diverted by these exploits, our economic and social order has meanwhile been undergoing a revolutionary transformation. The private sector has been producing goods in unexampled abundance and finding more consumers for this abundance among our fellow citizens than ever before. Yet the actual production of goods now employs no more than 30 per cent of the labor force. And the economic activity of the private sector creates not much more than half of the ultimate consumer purchasing power that moves the goods. Local, state, and federal budgets, however, have come to equal 25 per cent of the Gross National Product.

Directly and indirectly, the demand generated by these expenditures certifies the rest of the consumers with purchasing power to command their share in the abundance.

The hugest single element in the demand from the public sector is, of course, the military budget. Directly and indirectly the $40 billion, and now $50 billion, of military expenditures generates some 20 per cent of the total economic activity of the nation. The draining of such a vast portion of the national output of goods and services without recovery into the economic sink of national defense has made it possible for the business system to go on doing business as usual. So long as the war economy keeps the system profitably, though perhaps not fully, employed, there is no need to take note of the transition of our society into the economy of abundance.

But the economic institutions of our society, based as they are on the economics of scarcity, are nonetheless technologically obsolete. This is plainly apparent in any projection of the life of our economy beyond disarmament. It then becomes necessary to allocate to the human and physical resources of the nation the share of the Gross National Product which they ought to have and which is now denied to them. Until then, the high incomes enjoyed by an unprecedentedly large percentage of the population can conceal the stagnation of the economy (its rate of growth has now been surpassed by that of France and Italy), dull the sense of responsibility of those responsible, and put off the day when the social and economic transformation of our country must be reckoned with in our politics.

Preparation for a war that can never be fought for any rational objective has facilitated a corresponding inanition in foreign policy. The Austrian State Treaty, signed in 1955, stands as the single settlement achieved between the East and the West since the end of the Second World War. It may be that the diplomatic stalemate was useful to both sides in the cold war because it was essential to the maintenance of their respective war economies. But the glacier has now begun to move, and the motive force is coming from below.

A sufficiently long historical perspective reveals that the real source of instability in world politics is not the celebrated ideologi-

cal contest between the East and the West, but the long struggle
between the rich and the poor. The struggle has moved onto new
ground. The poor have an objective superseding ancient protest;
that great adult educator, technology, has shown that they need no
longer live in poverty. The poor, moreover, have acquired the political instruments for seeking this objective; the two billion people
who live outside industrial civilization are now organized into
seventy-one national states, including the two most populous ones.
In the skirmishes attending their political liberation, still in progress, they have quickened the antagonisms between the great cold-
war power systems. But the poor of the world have more serious
business ahead: the industrial revolutions that will secure their economic liberation. In the attendant social and political upheavals, the
antagonists in the cold war could well find themselves embraced
not in conflict with each other but in alliance against emerging new
powers. At all events, with international anarchy amplified by the
increase in the number of national states, the cold war must seem
in retrospect a period of peace and security.

The present bipolar stalemate presents a relatively simple situation. The modicum of rationality displayed on both sides has so far
staved off collision. But the major powers have no natural monopoly on nuclear weapons. For small nations these weapons hold
an irresistible attraction; they are the ultimate equalizers. As the
number of nuclear powers increases, nuclear diplomacy must become the more purely a game of chance, weighted ever more heavily on the side of catastrophe.

This intolerable prospect compels the cold-war antagonists to
undertake the negotiation of disarmament. But they must not think
that nuclear disarmament can open the way back to the old-
fashioned, feasible kind of warfare. Conventional war will inevitably escalate to nuclear war. The only way to prevent suicide is to
go forward to the elimination of the causes of war. History shows
that these can be traced to poverty. In our own day poverty still
makes slaves and tyrants of men and turns states into war machines.
It is time, therefore, to recognize that the same revolution in man's
relationship to nature that has made war obsolete has also made
poverty obsolete.

To make a start by the end of the century—to double the income of the world's poor, who will meanwhile have doubled or tripled their numbers—will require a threefold or fourfold increase in world production. No insuperable technological or material obstacles bar the way. But the poor nations will not be able to achieve these objectives by themselves. As the war to end war, the war against poverty will require integration of the world economy to a high degree. To the extent that the rich nations come forward with material aid, they can minimize the repression at home and aggression abroad to which the governments of the poor nations would otherwise be (and are now) pressed.

Within the economy of the United States disarmament implies a similar reckoning with change. The country has already equipped itself to produce abundance. To a remarkable degree it has evolved the social institutions to distribute the abundance. If we have achieved affluence instead, it is because one third of the public expenditure goes to arms. To establish the same compelling claim on the Gross National Product for other public interests, the United States will once again have to set the world an example in social and political innovation.

In the piping times of peace to come, one may confidently envision the restoration in full of our Bill of Rights, starting with the First Amendment. The guarantee of the citizen's sovereignty has particular relevance to the scientist, who can recognize no authority superior to his own judgment.

I have here traced briefly, with the advantage of hindsight, the logic in the events that links the beginning and the end of this book. The essence of my analysis derives from the humane ethic of science; the prescription, from technology. What we need to realize is that life today is quite as feasible as death. Whatever small decency we have in our hearts is just as magnificently capacitated by science and technology as is our willingness to murder. We cannot avert self-destruction unless we take up the cause of man.

GERARD PIEL

February 1962
New York, New York

Preface

MAN HAS TAKEN HIS LIFE IN HIS HANDS: This is a statement to which everyone will readily subscribe, taking it to mean that man has the capacity to extinguish his species. But the statement contains another truth not so easily stated and not nearly so widely understood. In the knowledge that confers the capacity to destroy, man has gained equally the capacity to realize his humanity—to eliminate physical deprivation from every home on earth and to extend to every human being the full possibility of life.

These alternatives are not subjects for deferred or delegated contemplation. They press upon each one of us for choice. We have come suddenly and unprepared to the fork in the road. As each day passes we lose the power of decision and are carried into the road that leads to no future at all. We cannot avert our self-destruction unless we take up the cause of man.

What we need to realize is that whatever small decency we have in our hearts is just as magnificently capacitated by science and technology as is our willingness to murder. Life today is quite as feasible as death.

The choice of life involves, of course, all kinds of ethical, aesthetic, political, economic, and social considerations along with the scientific and technological. Some of these are prickly; they con-

xiii

tradict received wisdom and demand the re-examination of buried premises. Some apparently collide with powerful vested interests, or with the short-term view of what those interests are. They also pose enthralling possibilities in the way of social and political enterprise, the kind of thing that distinguishes our pragmatic democracy with its flair for improvisation. The choice, once made by our society, would evoke an unprecedented outpouring of human energy and talent.

I have been exploring various corners of the large and small questions I have suggested here and thinking out loud about them in public over the past decade. My thoughts are presented here in the order—the purely chronological order—in which they came. That they are not in better order betrays the fact that I am not the master of any one of the formal disciplines that must be brought to bear upon these questions. I am a publisher and editor and have had the good fortune to be engaged in these capacities in putting out the monthly issues of *Scientific American* since May 1948. It is this prolongation of my education that has brought me to grips with the topics on which I have written in these pages.

GERARD PIEL

April 1961
New York, New York

Contents

P A R T III

P A R T IV

PART I

Science and Secrecy

NEWSPAPERMEN CLOSE RANKS as rapidly as any other kind of people when their interests are threatened. They will stretch a point, moreover, and count in a magazine editor when the smell of burning printed matter is in the air. Thus it was that the American Society of Newspaper Editors provided the forum for these reflections on censorship at their annual convention in Washington in April 1950.

The Atomic Energy Commission had attempted to suppress a discussion by a distinguished scientist of the technology of the H-bomb in its relation to the ethical, political, economic, diplomatic, and military questions raised by this weapon, then no more than a dreaded theoretical possibility. The Commission claimed that it was acting to protect military security, and its censors did, in fact, insist upon mutilating the article to the extent of deleting three brief passages from it. What is more, the intelligence agents of the Commission presided at the burning of 3,000 copies of the April 1950 issue of *Scientific American* which had already come off the press with the original, unmutilated article in its pages.

The reader will want to know what the censor deleted. I had to tell the newspaper editors that I could not tell them. The original, uncensored article has recently been declassified. With the substance of what was deleted from the article at hand, it is now possible to settle the question whether the A.E.C. was prompted

3

to this act of censorship by concern for military security—or by some other concern not ordinarily implemented by the power of censorship.

In the censored passages, the author made three technical points. He explained why the heavier isotopes of hydrogen would be employed in preference to the common light isotope of the element in the fueling of an H-bomb. The physical data underlying this discussion had been published in the open literature of physics, much of it by our author himself, Hans Bethe, in the 1930's, before the fission reaction embodied in ordinary A-bombs had been discovered. The editors of *Scientific American*, who have never sought security clearance and have no access to secret information, were able to prepare a handsome table from the open literature to illustrate this part of the discussion.

In connection with this discussion the author observed that an ordinary A-bomb would have to be employed to ignite the thermonuclear reaction in the hydrogen fuel. This was an elementary conclusion that followed from the published knowledge that the ignition temperature is astronomical. Among the items in the record of prior publication on this heading was a book by Hans Thirring, an Austrian physicist, published in Vienna in 1946.

Finally, the author stated that an exploding H-bomb would release a flux of neutrons in roughly direct proportion to its power. Here again the supporting data were in the open literature and were presented to our readers in the table that we prepared from the literature.

The citations of prior publication completely vitiated the censor's claim that the article contained secret information. For this argument the A.E.C. was prepared with the counter point that it is important *who* says what—the same statement can be one man's informed guess and another man's disclosure of secret information. Thus, since it was we who had prepared the illustrations, the A.E.C. let them stand, even though they presented the basic information as to temperatures, speeds of reaction, and neutron flux that had been stricken from the text.

But even Bethe's access to secret information on these matters could not have added a scintilla of additional weight to the evidence so familiar to physicists all over the world. As Albert Einstein once said: "Truth, unlike the Big Lie, does not increase by repetition."

Apart from purely technical matters, the A.E.C. struck a passage expressing the author's doubts about the practicability of the H-bomb and declaring his opinion that it would take "years rather than months" to do the necessary research and development. On this point, the censors could not argue the "who" principle because we were able to show that Bethe had already made the same statements on the radio and in the press. Deletion of this passage was accordingly justified by another shibboleth of security: Information about "rate and scale" is primary intelligence data.

But Bethe's conservative estimate was just the kind of "intelligence" one would want to press upon a potential enemy, to get him to slacken his own pursuit of the new weapon. The fact is that Bethe was soon shown to be much too conservative. His estimate belonged in the category of misinformation calculated to mislead a potential enemy, which is quite the opposite of a disclosure of secret information.

With the censored passages once more in the light of day, it becomes plain that this clumsy act of censorship was not motivated by concern to protect military secrets. The reasons must be sought elsewhere. I believe that they are fairly stated in my talk to the newspaper editors.

My deductions were substantially confirmed four years later by the transcript of the famous Oppenheimer security proceeding. As that record shows, the Atomic Energy Commission in March 1950 was the vortex of a ferocious secret controversy (see "Security and Heresy" and "The New Paradise"). In overriding the technical judgment and moral repugnance of scientists like Bethe, the Administration had determined to keep them from taking the controversy to the public.

The more responsible officials protested, of course, that they wanted only to restrain the scientists' discussion of the "technical" aspects of the weapon—the scientists could talk all they liked about the ethical, political, and other considerations.

This attitude is perfectly understandable. It is inculcated by deep traditions and powerful institutions in our culture that divide the world into the separate realms of the "sciences," on the one hand, and the "humanities," on the other. The attitude is nonetheless false, the root of much of the mischief in the world today. The wisdom of Bethe and his colleagues was grounded in thermonuclear physics. No proper weight could be given to their counsel on the ethical, political, and other headings if the public could not share their understanding of the technical aspects of the new weapon.

SCIENCE AND SECRECY are a pair of opposites. They bring to mind two diametrically opposed and mutually exclusive sets of ideas. Since we must have science and since we must apparently have secrecy also, we are confronted with a dilemma.

Henry DeWolfe Smyth—the scientific member of the present Atomic Energy Commission and a physicist who has wrestled with this dilemma, in his own words, "for most of the last ten years"—said recently: "Everyone agrees that freedom of speech is something we would fight to defend." On the other hand, Smyth said: "Everyone is agreed that the technological details of atomic weapons and other weapons should be kept secret."

Here we have the essence of the dilemma, as we have all come to know it during the past ten years. We declare the essential importance of freedom in science, in speech, and in our press. Then we say *but*. Unfortunately, because secrecy itself inhibits the discussion of secrecy, we in the press have been dealing with the dilemma largely at the level of abstraction for the past ten years.

I have to discuss today a tangible case of censorship which takes the question down from the level of abstraction. I believe it can give us some specific answers, if not to the whole abstract question, then at least to some specific subquestions.

Science and Secrecy

Through the accidental circumstance that 3,000 copies of a magazine were burned, certain new aspects of the A.E.C. censorship policy have been dramatically brought to light and into public discussion. They need public discussion. It may result in our finding some practical standard that will help us to decide how much talk not only can but ought to be permitted on certain topics. We will find ourselves dealing with an equally important question: *Who* can and ought to be permitted to do the talking?

Since we have something specific to talk about for a change, let us get to the facts. The first fact you all know. The A.E.C. is equipped by statute with comprehensive control over atomic information. An atomic secret, by statute, is not the dictionary secret—something you and I know and don't want somebody else to know. The statute defines the term "atomic secret" in a special way. It is "all data concerning the manufacture or utilization of atomic weapons, the production of fissionable material or the use of fissionable material in the production of power, but shall not include any data which the Commission from time to time determines may be published without adversely affecting the common defense and security."

Literally, this language means that any fact or document in this area, even if it has already been published or otherwise become well known, is classified and declared to be "secret," unless and until the Commission decides that it may be published without adversely affecting the common defense and security. As the McGraw-Hill journal *Nucleonics* points out, a publication might be held in violation of the law if it were to publish a scientific manuscript submitted from Russia which contained "restricted data"—although reasonable men would deny that such information is really secret or its publication damaging to our nation.

It is of interest to this audience, furthermore, that the Commission claims that its control over atomic information is im-

7

plemented with the power of injunction. So far as I know, no other government agency claims the power to enjoin publication of material to which it has objection. With this reminder of the statutory background, you will appreciate certain features of the following narrative.

In two telegrams, on the fourteenth and twentieth of March, addressed to its employees and consultants and to the employees of its contractors, the A.E.C. announced a new extension of its censorship policies. The first telegram requested those concerned to refrain from public discussion of "the thermo-nuclear reactions of the Commission's thermo-nuclear weapons development program," whether or not the technical information involved was unclassified. Since such requests from the Commission are taken seriously, scientists engaged in nuclear physics were disturbed by implications that they perceived in this request. There were some protests. The Commission clarified the request in its second telegram, which apologized for what the Commission called the "abruptness and tone" of the first. It explained that its object was "to avoid the release of technical information which even though itself unclassified may be interpreted by virtue of the project connection of the speaker as reflecting upon the Commission's program with respect to thermo-nuclear weapons." It added that this "would still permit unclassified discussion of what might be called the classical thermo-nuclear reactions as long as there is no reference to their relation to weapons." The Commission thus told the scientists, in effect, that they could teach physics but that they could not talk in public about the unclassified—that is, non-secret—technical information concerning the hydrogen bomb—which is, of course, the only information they would talk about in public.

I mention these telegrams because they are related to what follows. Some weeks before, Hans A. Bethe had undertaken to write an article about the newly projected hydrogen bomb for *Scientific American* and the *Bulletin of the Atomic*

Scientists. During the war Bethe was chief of the Theoretical Physics Division of the Atomic Weapons Laboratory at Los Alamos. Long before the war he won world recognition for his work that gave us the thermonuclear explanation of how the sun and other stars generate their light and energy. This work now provides the fundamental theory for the fashioning of the hydrogen bomb. Today Bethe is professor of physics at Cornell University and is employed as a contract consultant by the A.E.C. I can assure you that in considering our invitation to write the article he gave careful consideration to the question of propriety: whether he—as a contract consultant to the Commission with access to secret information, himself a creator of much of the secret information—should enter into public discussion of the issues that surround the hydrogen bomb. I need not assure you that Bethe—as one of the scientists who set up the A.E.C. Declassification Guide, which sets the standards for release of material from the secret status, and as a scientist who has seen his own original work go through the declassification procedure and who has declassified the work of other scientists—gave careful attention to the organization and presentation of the technical information which he found it necessary to include in the article. As is the custom among scientists, Bethe sent copies of his manuscript to a number of his colleagues in physics, not for review but for their information. One of these scientists was a member of the A.E.C., which had just sent out the censorship order to the atomic scientists of the nation.

On March 15, after the April issue of *Scientific American,* containing Bethe's article, had gone to press, we received a telegram from the A.E.C. requesting that we withhold from publication the technical portion of the article.

Scientific American stopped its presses and asked the Commission to specify its objections. After some pushing and pulling, the Commission agreed to do so. Its objections came down to a request to delete several sentences. In order

9

to proceed with the publication of this issue of our magazine, we complied with the Commission's request.

The Commission then asked that all copies of the original article be destroyed. An A.E.C. security officer visited our printing plant and supervised the destruction of the type and the melting down of the printing plates with the deleted material and the burning of 3,000 copies of the magazine which had been printed before the presses were stopped. Thereafter we put the magazine, with the expurgated version of Bethe's article in it, back on the press and proceeded with the publication of the issue.

Since Bethe's original manuscript has now been classified by the A.E.C. as containing "restricted data," I cannot tell you what was deleted. I shall be careful, in speaking of it, not to give you a clue.

It does not violate security, however, to tell you that all of the statements deleted may be classed under four headings. In the first category are statements of fact which previously had been formally declassified by the A.E.C. and are well known to physicists the world over. The second comprises statements previously made in public by Bethe, via the press and radio, which are in your own files. The third comprises statements of information previously published in an article by Louis Ridenour in the March issue of *Scientific American*, the first in our series on the H-Bomb. The fourth includes statements since cleared by the A.E.C. for publication in a speech by Robert Bacher, former scientific member of the A.E.C., given on March 27 in Los Angeles. All of the statements deleted fall into at least one of these four categories. You should know that all of the scientists—including men of the first rank who are associated with the A.E.C. in important consulting and advisory capacities—who read the original manuscript and whom I have been able to consult, concur in this description of the material that was deleted from the article.

My narrative poses an obvious question. For myself, I find logic in this act of censorship only by understanding it as an application of the Commission's telegraphic request to all of its consulting scientists, in the words of one of the commissioners, to "keep their traps shut." In short, the real objection here appears to be addressed not to the statements themselves but to the fact that a particular authority was making them.

There is no question that an employer has the power to impose a gag upon his employees. You can fire your secretary if she discloses business secrets to her husband in violation of an express order. The U.S. Government has similar power with respect to its employees. The State Department can fire people who, without permission, leak information to reporters. But such gag orders by our government are subject to public review by the standard of whether or not they accord with the public interest. Two years ago, Nat Finney, Washington correspondent of the Des Moines *Register and Tribune*, won the Raymond Clapper Award and a Pulitzer Prize for his exposé of a plan to adopt the military system for classifying—that is, imposing secrecy upon—public documents in other, non-military departments of the federal government. This society took action at that time which helped to persuade the public officials concerned to abandon the idea.

Now we have to ask the question: Is the Commission's "shut your trap" request, and its related censorship of Bethe's article, in the public interest? It accords with a familiar principle in military security. This principle says that discussion by the informed analyst—though he restricts his discussion to well-known and non-secret data—must inevitably disclose what goes on inside. Sumner Pike, acting chairman of the A.E.C., explained this principle to the correspondents at the Commission's March 29 press conference. Speaking of the Ridenour article in the March issue of *Scientific American*, he said: "It would bother me a good deal, for instance, if Mr.

Ridenour was still under contract and operating and had written that same article . . . What bothers me is that his readers would say: 'Oh yes, they all come from the open work, but he is there and in the know, so therefore this must be it.' "

Then there is the informed "slip of the tongue." Dr. Smyth discussed this hazard at the same press conference. "I might illustrate this by telling you that during the war we had a course in nuclear physics. We had to look around to find somebody on our staff who had no connection with the Manhattan Project, because no one who was working for the Manhattan Project would be able to separate in his mind what he could say and what he couldn't say."

Finally, there is the hazard that talk at the top starts talk all the way down the line. A public statement by Bethe "pulls the stops" on everybody's discretion, right down to the last P-5 at Los Alamos.

Unquestionably these are hazards that must be considered. But let us consider them. Essentially there are two elements of risk involved here. The first element of risk is the gamble taken by everyone except a few hermits—the gamble on people. This we try to take care of by careful scrutiny and investigation of the people we hire for secret work. Even the extraordinary measures taken at this point for the protection of atomic information failed to screen out Klaus Fuchs. But the ban on public discussion of H-bombs would not have hampered his activities either. In short, people who can be trusted to keep secrets in private can be trusted at least to an equal extent in public. Furthermore, in addressing the public, they can be expected to be aware—even as you and I—of the injunctions and sanctions of the Atomic Energy Act.

The second element of risk is the public forum. How dangerous is public discussion as a channel for the accidental, unwitting disclosure of secret information? This requires examination of the nature of the secrets we are trying to keep. Now that the Russians have the bomb, everybody

knows that there never was one big atomic secret that could
have kept them from making the bomb. We have come to
realize that, although the atom is new and strange to most
of us, the fundamental knowledge of nuclear physics has been
common knowledge to the world community of science for
two generations.

Yet we remain bamboozled by the atom. We give acres of
newsprint to the temporary mislaying of a milligram of
uranium 235. And we give not more than three inches on an
inside page of *The New York Times* to the blundering disclosure, before a congressional committee, of a secret radar
and radio picket line around the Arctic Circle. But that was
just a War Department secret. It takes the chairman of the
General Advisory Commission of the A.E.C. to reassure our
congressmen that we are all made of isotopes and that we are
in no danger, therefore, of disclosing secrets when we send
isotopes overseas for medical and industrial research. But the
magazine *Aviation Week* is credited with a scoop for breaking
the secret that an air force rocket plane had penetrated the
speed-of-sound barrier.

There is no question that there are atomic secrets which
must be protected. We are assured by the members of the
A.E.C. itself that these are secrets of "technological detail."
They are trade secrets, the kind we are accustomed to keeping
in everyday business. They are scoops, like those which one
newspaper hides from another until it hits the streets. They are
the kind of things that Macy's is careful not to tell Gimbels.
The employees of American industry keep all kinds of secrets;
they do so without incurring the surrender of their civil right
to talk about the non-secret aspects of their industries and
their professional knowledge. The technical secrets in the
field of atomic energy are largely irrelevant to public discussion of the issues that surround it. The people do not need and
could make no use of this information in forming their opinions and casting their ballots.

13

If we can cut the atom down closer to its actual size, we can see that the risk we run through public discussion of the non-secret technical aspects of atomic weapons by informed scientists is a small one. That risk is not really significant, in terms of the public interest, when it is compared with the certain harm that public discussion will sustain so long as informed scientists must keep quiet. Unless the public is reliably and adequately informed, and unless the people have confidence in their information, there will be no constructive public discussion.

If you will recall for a moment the reckless and foolish talk that surrounded the subject of the H-bomb during its first few weeks in the public domain, you will realize what a notable service the scientists of the country have rendered in bringing the discussion down to earth. We are indebted to them for placing in the public record a reliable statement of the truth about the technical aspects of the new hydrogen weapon. It is now possible to discuss the super-weapon reasonably and constructively in terms of its relationship to the major areas of public policy upon which it impinges.

In this discussion the most important statements have been made by the two scientists—Bethe and Robert Bacher—whose knowledge comprehends the total picture, including the classified and secret as well as the unclassified, declassified, and non-secret information. It is no reflection on the capacity of Louis Ridenour or Robert Millikan or upon the correctness of their judgments to say that their contributions are not so decisive. All of us must have our reservations about their authority on these matters, because neither of them has been directly involved in the work of either the Manhattan District or the A.E.C. In the case of Bethe and Bacher, on the other hand, the public knows that they know. Consequently, when they discuss these matters we can accept their statements as authoritative, although what they say is, of course, equally well known to physicists outside the project.

Even though we can be equally sure that most of the things they cannot tell us are irrelevant, it is important for us to know that they have had access to that information and know that it is irrelevant. Since Robert Bacher has not been associated with the project for nearly a year, and since Hans Bethe is still actively engaged by the A.E.C. as a consultant, it is a real loss that Bethe's contribution to our information, which we may take to be the best informed, should have been blurred by the censors' blue pencil.

The advances in the physical sciences which now make the hydrogen bomb possible contrast powerfully with our laggard understanding in the social sciences. We take freedom for granted. We have only the vaguest intuitions about the processes by which public debate and open discussions sway the development of public policy. We know that logic is not always on the side of the heaviest mail sack in a congressman's office, that the higher reason does not always win on column inches of newspaper type. Yet most of the time and almost every time it really counts, we can be confident that murder will out and that the people will come to the right conclusion. One thing we do know for sure about this mysterious process is that its decisive catalyst is the truth. Hence our abhorrence of secrecy and censorship. In the words of Lord Acton: "Everything secret degenerates, even in the administration of justice; nothing is safe that does not show how it can bear discussion and publicity."

The truth essential to the H-bomb discussion consists of highly technical information. For this information we had to turn to the scientists, as the members of our society especially qualified to know and judge this kind of truth. We can be sure that what they have told us was already well known to the dullest technician in the laboratories of a potential enemy. Thanks to their public spirit, this important information is now known to the American people. Far from endangering our country, we can be certain that the publicizing of this information will enhance our common defense and security. Now we can talk about the H-bomb constructively and confidently, even though we don't know the first thing about thermonuclear physics.

We have four new essential pieces of information, comprehensible to the layman and relevant to his judgment. First, as against the surprisingly widespread notion that we already had the super-weapon, we know now that there is a possibility that we may not be able to make one at all. Second, as against the idea that its development was just an engineering problem, we know that it is likely to take a long time to solve the scientific and engineering problems in the way. Third, we have reliable estimates of its truly enormous power, which raise considerable doubt whether the H-bomb will be a useful and effective weapon if and when we get it.

The fourth is an intriguing piece of technical information for which we are indebted to Robert Bacher. He tells us that tritium, the heaviest isotope of hydrogen, is produced in an atomic reactor by exposing suitable material to the neutron flux. The same neutron flux in the reactor transforms uranium into plutonium. Evidently, since we have only a finite capacity to generate neutrons, the production of tritium may reduce our output of plutonium. Hence, to produce an H-bomb we may have to reduce our production of A-bombs. Knowing this, we are entitled to ask for some tangible assurance that one H-bomb is a profitable trade for the loss of two or more A-bombs.

In the minds of the scientists, these four pieces of information yield the grave conclusion that the advent of the hydrogen bomb makes our country more vulnerable rather than more secure.

All of this technical information, now that it is known to the public, promises to have far-reaching consequences upon our military planning and diplomatic policy. From Bethe, Bacher, and Ridenour, the issue now passes to the Hanson

Baldwins and the Alsops. It will be constructive to raise again the still unsettled question advanced last year by the Navy: whether our commitment to heavy bombardment aircraft designed in accord with the Douhet concept of strategic destruction of cities and their populations, is a wise and effective military policy for the United States. Since the hydrogen-bomb venture involves the investment of a significant fraction of our human and material resources in this field, we can and we ought to ask whether the same effort and wealth might not get us a bigger return if invested in the development of guided missiles, anti-submarine devices, or a bigger stockpile of old-fashioned A-bombs. Since the public discussion that is to follow will be based upon accurate information, we can be more confident of the outcome.

As it goes forward, the H-bomb undertaking is going to create new issues, on which we are going to require additional information if there is to be constructive public participation in the conduct of the venture. For example, we were informed on March 28 in a speech by Acting Chairman Pike that the A.E.C. is "doing some reshuffling of the projects and personnel in the whole atomic energy program in order to bring the utmost weight to bear on the specific weapons development work which the President has recently directed us to pursue." Two days later we were told by an A.E.C. press release that the construction of a breeder pile at West Milton, Massachusetts, has been deferred, that personnel of the General Electric Knolls Laboratory, hitherto devoted to the development of peacetime uses of atomic energy, have been redeployed to the Hanford Works. The motive in these developments is apparently complicated. The A.E.C. press release of March 30 mentions the desire for "firmer cost estimates" and "the demands of expanded atomic energy production." Now to these considerations a press release dated April 14 adds the disclosure that some of the personnel and facilities made available are to go to work on an atomic power plant for submarine propulsion. Though they are not contradictory, it is not at all obvious that these three announcements are consistent with one another. If any other government agency issued three different explanations for a decision of such major consequence, it would be subjected to exacting cross-examination.

In our dealings with other government agencies, we do not recognize a press handout as an ultimate reference for anything but the policy of the agency that issues it. And we are always mindful that a press handout is important for what it leaves out as well as for what it contains. In the case of the A.E.C., however, we are frequently told that we not only cannot have the information that is left out but cannot be told why it is denied to us. I have been talking up to this point about the H-bomb and the issues related to it. To those who have watched the history of the A.E.C., however, it is clear that the H-bomb represents merely an acute phase in a really chronic condition. For example, the A.E.C. still denies us the report on civilian defense against atomic warfare filed with the A.E.C. nearly a year ago. Nor have the handouts told us why this vital document has not yet been released. We have yet to see the report of the Bikini Evaluation Committee, a report which the chairman of that committee, Bradley Dewey, has declared should be in the public domain. In January 1949 the A.E.C. promised a comprehensive report on atomic power reactors "perhaps in a matter of six weeks." Industry is still waiting for the publication of this important information. And the handouts have yet to explain why it is withheld.

In the absence of satisfactory answers to such questions put to other government agencies, we keep asking until we get either the answers or a satisfactory reason for being denied them. It is indispensable, in this process of probing, that we should be able to turn to honorable and independent authorities for their expert knowledge and opinion. The authorities on atomic energy to whom we might turn today are muzzled. We are left with the handouts. The muzzling of independent news sources is clearly an indirect, but effective, censorship of the press. This aggravation of the already extreme affliction of secrecy is the most regrettable feature of the H-bomb undertaking.

Secrecy has poisoned the relations of the A.E.C. with the scientific community of America. The most recent instance of this to come to light was the announcement by Syracuse University that its physics department would no longer accept secret government contracts. Secrecy has frustrated the effort of enterprising industrial concerns to make their contribution to the atomic energy program. On the testimony, a year or so ago, of the Commission's own Industrial Advisory Group, "a vast amount of non-secret information of potential value to industry is buried in the files and activities of the Commission." Some measures have been taken in response to this prompting. But, as recently as last week, former Chairman David E. Lilienthal cited the lag in development of atomic energy for industrial purposes and attributed this to our failure to attract industrial "American know-how" into the program.

Secrecy holds a long-run threat to the welfare of our atomic energy enterprise. Because it is walled off by secrecy from the legitimate inquiry of the press, the Commission has not enjoyed the advantage of public surveillance and even public controversy through which other agencies take the guidance of public opinion. On this point, Herbert Marks, first general counsel of the A.E.C., has warned us that, if cure of the secrecy problem is too long delayed, "our atomic energy program will almost certainly grow so far out of touch with the American environment that when the forces of criticism finally begin to operate with their customary vigor, they will produce drastic upheavals. By then the public, without the knowledge gained by prior participation in the problems of atomic energy, will not be in a position to ensure the establishment of a sound administration in its place."

Now this situation is by no means to be charged against the

individuals who run the Commission. They will, without question, measure up to the standards of integrity, ability, and courage that we expect of our government officials. It is the institution, not the men. Secrecy is a peculiarity of the A.E.C. with which it was endowed at birth. All of us had a part in setting up this institution, the public and the press as well as Congress. For the pall of secrecy which so dangerously frustrates the legitimate activities of the press, we must blame the press itself as much as any other body. Our newspapers and magazines have sold themselves a gold brick. When you extract a banner in 64-point type out of a mislaid milligram of uranium, you have helped to create an environment in which books are burned.

HOW DO WE MAKE OUR
Alumni Publications Appeal
TO THE INTELLECTS OF
OUR ALUMNI

THE TITLE was suggested by the editors of the alumni publications to whom these remarks were addressed at their annual meeting at the Johns Hopkins University in July 1953. The reader may judge, from exposure to his own alumni bulletin, how far the good intentions of all concerned have carried.

I BEGIN, as the title suggests, with a crucial assumption: that our colleges and universities educate the whole man. That is, these institutions teach him something and train his mind, as well as carry through the rest of the program of character molding, body building, and personality polishing that has been assumed by or foisted upon our system of higher education during the past few decades. In other words, we are going to agree for the sake of argument that your readers have intellects to which you might appeal.

I have taken care to make this assumption explicit because I suspect the notion that college alumni have intellects is not widely shared among alumni editors. This is certainly the impression gathered by an occasional student of your bulletins. You are engaged, of course, in conducting a private line of communication which is not intended for the untuned ears of listeners-in, and you have the delicate, ulterior motive of kindling certain tender sentiments between your public and your institutions. It may well be, as your publications suggest, that the alumni relationship is one of the heart and not of the head. Whatever the reason, our alumni press, by and large, promotes a picture of our colleges which excludes the possibility that learning is embraced in the higher educational process.

In bulletin after bulletin, college after college is shown to be possessed of the same ill-assorted cluster of old buildings. The soft-focus frontispiece and the tear that dims the eye of the beholder bathe each hideous detail of Old North or Old South in the same swimming haze of nostalgia. The inhabitants of these islands of refuge and repose come in two varieties. There is, first, a community of elderly gentlemen; we read of their advance to emeritus and then, a little later, of their ascent beyond. These kindly fellows somehow maintain a genial symbiosis with a breed of robust young people who, on playing field and campus walks, are uniformly animated by reverence and devotion to the dear precincts that make possible this last four-year reprieve before they scatter to begin their respective life sentences at hard labor. Turning to the notes, one finds that the alumni present a reasonable cross section of the white-collar class, having little distinction in common, except higher take-home pay.

Of course, this is not a complete picture of the college. The alumni editor would hasten to add that it is not intended to be. On the other hand, it is alleged to be a faithful reflection of the lotus-laden mental image held by the average alumnus. Alumni editors, as other editors, will inevitably plead that they give their readers what they want.

If this is what our alumni really want and all that they want, then we have a clue to a better understanding of some serious aspects of the plight of our system of higher education. The present is an unhappy and dangerous period for American colleges and universities. To point to the most tangible index first, the financial crisis continues and is heading for a showdown. Income lags behind the constant increase in costs, and the gap grows. It ought to be observed, however, that the number of college alumni has doubled during the same period in which costs have doubled. Apparently there is trouble on the income side as well, a relative decline in the flow of alumni contributions. The mental image of college as a combination old folks' home and nursery for the prolongation of adolescence does not give the alumni fund a sufficiently high rating on the schedule of family checkbook priorities.

But money is not the only problem. There is a touch of suffocation in that haze which pervades the old quadrangle. It does not stifle only scholars in the humanities, where some thoughts have always been considered dangerous on this side of the Atlantic. Scientists need fresh air, too; the advance of science cannot be sustained on the exclusive grounds of its utility to business or national defense. Our college presidents and professors have not shown the requisite courage and clarity in meeting the current tide of anti-intellectualism that menaces our culture and our freedoms. In almost every case, they have let the vandals through the campus gate. But even the middle-ditch positions of compromise with thought control prepared by our college officialdom need battalions of volunteers to maintain them. There have been few forthcoming from the alumni, who are supposed to provide the constituency of our colleges. Those graduates whose careers in the big, real world make such impressive reading in the notes section of every bulletin find it difficult to take their kindly old professors and their troubles seriously.

The discomfort of professors and of intellectuals in general is, of course, not a new thing in our culture. Their status has always been junior to the man of action. The eighteenth-century idea of the perfectibility of man by education, however, argues for an improvement in the professors' situation. Statistics show that a change for the better is overdue. Today we have more than five million college alumni at large in our social system. They ought to provide the public opinion and the public action that is so urgently needed on so many fronts in higher education.

In this situation, your magazines, as the principal channel of communication between our beleaguered colleges and their alumni, are challenged to render a decisive service. That service is to provide our colleges, as well as our alumni, with a press. By this I do not propose that you should take up press-agentry, propaganda, or psychological warfare. The service I have in mind represents one of the major assignments outstanding on the list of those neglected by the rest of the American press. This assignment is to cover teaching and learning as thoroughly as you cover the other, ancillary and subsidiary aspects of the educational process in your college communities.

The distinction drawn here between journalism and press-agentry is, I feel, a critical one. It reflects my own conviction about the assumption that your readers have intellects. Actually, there are not many editors who can address themselves to audiences composed exclusively of college alumni. The contempt for readers implied by the "give them what they want" excuse for less than 100 per cent honesty and performance surely has no standing here. Those boarded-up motion picture theaters across the country are appropriately hollow monuments to the principle of the least common denominator. Everybody in a group is superior most of the time to the group's average. Sooner or later they find the pitchman out. It is much safer to address yourself to the sharpest critics and most interested readers in your audience. One of the best reasons for doing so is that this policy opens up a wider range and scope of interest to your paper. You will enjoy reading it yourself.

There is no doubt about the range and scope of the subject matter posed by this assignment of covering the educational part of college education. Teaching and research constitute a major portion of the sum total of our country's intellectual life. Close to two million people are directly involved in the processes of higher education. The advance of knowledge and the preparation of our brightest young people for leadership are matters of high public interest. When all goes well, both processes seethe with vitality and controversy on a national scale. The same issues and ideas engage the energies of scholars and students at Bowdoin and at Reed. Most often the story to be told will be that journalistic ideal, a national story with a strong local angle.

For example: Under the heading of teaching there is presently a major controversy to be covered in every alumni bulletin surrounding the ultimate aims and objectives of education in a democracy.

Next come questions of educational method; the central issue today is argued under the title of general education, with a dash of great books. This is another national development that most certainly has a locus in your college.

Then there are particular courses to be reported on. Stories about these make interesting reading even for the cursory reader outside of education. Getting back closer to the prevailing mood of alumni journalism, why not appreciative essays on favorite courses given by great teachers?

Examples of the handling of each of these topics are to be found in the alumni bulletins of one or another college. Such stories are interesting enough when they turn up as random items from issue to issue. They would be much more interesting and intelligible to their readers if they were presented as a part of a consistent program of journalistic coverage.

If you succeeded in developing the appeal to the intellect of your alumni which is inherent in the subject of teaching, you would accomplish a good deal more than the mere improvement of your readership. You might start building the public interest and discussion that promote the health of every enterprise in a democracy.

When it comes to reporting the advance as distinguished from the dissemination of knowledge, the problem is where to stop. We are here concerned with work that is interesting and important enough to engage the life energies of some of our most able and energetic citizens, even though most of the rest of us never hear about it. Scholars and scientists in America have almost no means of communication with their fellow citizens. Their own press, comprising some hundreds of learned journals, serves principally to wall them off from one another, compartmenting the community of learning into specialties. Their books tend to find similarly restricted circulation on the lists of university presses. Yet there is no labor performed by any other element in our society which has more profound or universal meaning than the advance of knowledge. This, of course, should go without saying. The fact that it needs to be said suggests the degree to which the scholar and scientist are isolated from the community as a whole.

Here we are at the source of the troubles that beset our colleges today. Our exploration of the public domain of knowledge depends increasingly upon public support. That support will not be forthcoming unless the public is brought into possession of the riches that are found. The contribution that the alumni bulletin can make to this end is necessarily small. But our college alumni constitute the decisive sector of the broad public, the one that our colleges can't do without.

Many alumni bulletins have already discovered that the output of their faculties does indeed make interesting copy, and regularly publish really significant contributions to the popularization of knowledge. Unfortunately this holds truer for the sciences than the humanities, and more so for applied than for pure science. With a few pictures and some reasonably straightforward English, it is easy to tell an exciting laboratory story. The underlying objectives and ideas are somewhat more difficult to cope with. At Caltech and M.I.T. alumni editors have developed a model system of collaboration with their authors that places their journals among the best-read scientific publications in the world. Though one would think that researches in history and literature would hold more universal appeal than most undertakings in science, we have yet to see a comparable collaboration of editor and scholar on the popularization of the humanities.

The scholar suffers from the same handicaps as the scientist when it comes to talking to his fellow men, and needs the same kind of help. His essential problem is that he is conditioned to addressing only the captive audience of his colleagues. To tell his story to the rest of us, he needs primarily a clearer picture of what it is the layman wants to know about his work. The principal contribution of the editor to the collaboration, therefore, is his story sense. There is always a story to be found. No matter how specialized or narrow the field of investigation, the scholar always enters it out of concern for a general question that is of interest to all of us.

About 80 per cent of the time, the first manuscript that you are likely to get in undertaking such a collaboration is one on which you will want to do a complete rewrite job. You will almost certainly have to do it once over lightly. Principally you will need to give the story a structure, to give it backbone, to develop the logic and the connectedness of what it is your author has to say. The practice of clarity is neglected in our technical press, because it may be assumed by the author that his readers know what he is talking about and, if they don't, are under an occupational obligation to figure it out for themselves.

As to the devices for bringing this material into your pages —they range from the feature article to the news item, the book review and the editorial. It might be added that a good lecture is a fine intermediate for the production of a good article. Some of the most interesting reading in the Dartmouth alumni magazine, for example, has been provided by the Great Issues course.

In sum, if your colleges have equipped your readers with intellects, then there is much that is of interest to those intellects waiting to be reported from those same colleges. If you were to do the job thoroughly, it would be hard to find place for the alumni notes columns. The vision of our alumni bulletins blossoming into highbrow "little" magazines, generating new centers of ferment and excitement in the life of our culture, is an appealing one. But I would be the first to object and to demand that you reinstate the *Weltschmerz* portrait of the chapel belfry and the items about the class of '37. Your readers and the needs of the times will be served by a rounding out of your coverage to include the content as well as the trappings of higher education.

3

Scientists and Other Citizens

THE AMERICAN ASSOCIATION for the Advancement of Science is the peak organization of science in the United States, a holding company to which all other scientific societies and some 40,000 individual members adhere. When the A.A.A.S. was founded in 1848, it was the forum to which scientists reported their work. Over the century, as scientists became biologists, physicists, chemists, anthropologists, and specialists in the ever narrower subdisciplines of these fields, the A.A.A.S. has yielded this substantive function to its member societies. It still assembles 5,000 to 7,000 scientists at its annual convention in Christmas week. As these meetings have been emptied of formal scientific content, they have become increasingly preoccupied with the relations of science and society.

In 1953, when the A.A.A.S. gathered in Boston, the question of academic freedom, the subject of this essay, was at the top of the agenda. The subcommittee of the Committee on Government Operations of the U. S. Senate, headed by Joseph McCarthy, had joined the Un-American Activities Committee of the House in disturbing the peace on the campus and especially in the laboratories of the universities. The A.A.A.S. had responded to attacks upon a succession of its distinguished members by electing them to its presidency. The chairman of our symposium on the evening of December 29, 1953, was Edward U. Condon, then president of the

A.A.A.S. and a scientist who had endured the attentions of the committees for nearly a decade.

Curiously, my holding on this occasion that "academic freedom is not a different kind of freedom, nor a special privilege for a pressure group," was to be overruled by Mr. Justice Frankfurter. In *Sweezey* v. *Wyman*, he wrote pages of eloquent dicta in praise of academic freedom as distinguished from the ordinary elector's freedom and as a special privilege of scholars.

But neither the weight nor the grace of his prose was to hold down the scales for academic or any other kind of freedom when the U.S. Supreme Court, in later opinions with Frankfurter concurring, proceeded to apply the Frankfurter "balancing" doctrine (see "Founding Fathers as Social Scientists") and sent college professors off to jail impartially with other citizens convicted of contempt of Congress. In his dissent in the Wilkinson case, Mr. Justice Black declares:

"The result of all this is that from now on anyone who takes a public position contrary to that being urged by the House Un-American Activities Committee should realize that he runs the risk of being subpoenaed to appear at a hearing in some far-off place, of being questioned with regard to every minute detail of his past life, of being asked to repeat all the gossip he may have heard about any of his friends and acquaintances, of being accused by the Committee of membership in the Communist Party, of being held up to the public as a subversive and a traitor, of being jailed for contempt if he refuses to cooperate with the Committee in its probe of his mind and associations, and of being branded by his neighbors, employer and erstwhile friends as a menace to society *regardless of the outcome of that hearing.*"

The universities have been less troubled by congressional visiting committees during the past few years. One must, however, await the next cycle of campus hearings with trepidation. Academic freedom, having now, for sure, no reality inscribed on fading parchment, will exist only to the degree that it is asserted by the action of men.

Wᴇ ᴍᴀʏ ᴛᴀᴋᴇ heart in the fact that almost every recent meeting of the A.A.A.S. has featured a symposium on the double heading of science and society. One heavy price we have had to pay for the advancement of science is specialization. Scientists and other citizens have hitherto been content to live in separate worlds, almost in separate societies, to the detriment and hazard of both. It may not be too late now to discover that science is a social activity which involves other citizens as well as scientists. The fact is, science today in America is a largely socialized activity that is bringing scientists into new and not always comfortable association with their fellow citizens.

American science was never really demobilized at the end of the Second World War. This year expenditures on research in our universities will exceed $500 million, more than twelve times prewar expenditures. Nearly nine tenths of this money comes from government and industry. The bulk of it is for military research, and almost all of it, no matter how pious the protestations of the sponsors and the scientists involved, must be credited to the support of applied, as contrasted with basic, research.

This flood of money has profoundly altered the conditions of scientific work and the lives of scientists in our country. As Curt Richter, of The Johns Hopkins University, said in a recent issue of *Science:* "Large funds encourage great enterprises, great experimental designs. They encourage 'great teams of workers'; they take good research men away from their workbenches to direct many technicians." Worse yet, they set up pressures that divert scientists from their own work to devote their energies to the projects of others. Especially in war-motivated grants, says Professor Richter, "it is the project, the design that counts. Who does the work is often relatively unimportant."

This subordination of the scientist to the status of employee, even in an executive capacity, heavily conditions his independence. All too often it means loss of independence from within as well as from without. Unquestionably it has a role in encouraging the preoccupation with little questions and the soft-pedaling of fruitful controversy about which scientists in every field may be heard complaining. One wonders what effect it must have upon the quality of teaching, since students traditionally take aspiration from their masters.

Their new and closer relationship to their fellow citizens thus faces scientists with a host of problems. But there is none more serious, because it compromises the possibility of action on all others, than that which confronts scientists in the realm of civil liberties. The present erosion of their academic and personal freedoms is in itself a measure of the decline of the scientist's traditional status as an independent scholar. The public record shows an increasing frequency of affronts to the integrity of scientists as citizens. In secret proceedings, many more scientists have suffered humiliation and jeopardy as the result of invasion of their freedom and privacy.

The situation must be deeply disturbing to anyone who senses the crucial relationship between the ethics and law of a free society and the conditions that are essential to the work of science. Freedom of conscience, speech, publication, and assembly are required alike by the advancement of science and the self-government of a democracy. Due process in the law has its analogue in the tests of logic and evidence observed in research, and both have the purpose of arriving at the truth by induction. No scientist can surrender his freedom as a citizen without resigning his independence as a scientist. No society that muzzles political dissent will long delay the clamping of restraints upon science. In any discussion of the relationship between science and society today, these issues must come to the top of the agenda. They are the topic of legitimate professional concern, not only because they affect colleagues who have been wronged but because they ultimately involve the freedom of every scientist to carry on his work.

Taking a broader view of this situation, two observations force themselves upon us. The first is that scientists are not alone in their plight. The constriction of the freedom of scientists is part of a general pattern that involves the freedom of people in every department of intellectual activity. The same indignities have been visited upon writers, actors, scholars, government administrators, teachers, lawyers, and ministers. The present movement differs from similar episodes in the American past in that it favors intellectuals as its target.

The second observation is that this movement has its origins deep in the structure and condition of American society today. It is no mere case of democracy fumbling, as has been said, with the difficult reconciliation of security and freedom in a dangerous world. Espionage, sabotage, and treason are familiar perils to the existence of national states. Our people long ago equipped the federal government to deal with them by methods that accord with the institutions and ideals we want to protect. The spectacle we have been witnessing is not only repugnant to the spirit of our society but largely irrelevant to national security. In fact, according to Senator Herbert H. Lehman, this "full-scale assault on the Government service, the schools, the stage, the publishing world and even the churches has done more harm to the national security than disclosure of all the nation's defense secrets could have done."

Nor is this the first time that conscienceless politicians have undertaken to exploit popular apprehension in a time of world unrest. They have ample precedent in our history from the XYZ papers to the Palmer raids. But the present crop of demagogues and their ignoble collaborators have been spared for too long the wrath that should spring from the sense of fair play innate in the American tradition. That is why we are moved to see these events as symptomatic of some serious malaise in our culture, of grave disturbance in our social order.

Though they are not really looking for the causes of these deeper troubles, our contemporary inquisitors seem to sense that the hunt is warmer when they have a scientist in the dock. It is, after all, quite widely understood that science does have something to do with the amenities and the troubles of living in our time.

In an address before a similar gathering of the British Association for the Advancement of Science last year, Alexander Macbeath, professor of logic and metaphysics at The Queen's University in Belfast, described the situation thus: ". . . it is to the power over his environment which it placed at man's disposal, that science mainly owes its present prestige. The miracles of the modern world—motor cars and airplanes, radio and television—all derive from science; and for the mass of mankind, they constitute its justification. . . . But the dangers and discomforts which have come in their train have been equally great—high explosives and atom bombs, the squalor of urbanization, the exploitation of man by man— and it is of these that men have become painfully conscious during the 20th century. . . . After learning by bitter experience that [the knowledge and power that science brings] are not always used wisely, men have reacted not only against freedom to misuse them, but against freedom in general."

In fear and insecurity, the people seek the reassurance of conformity and thereby create the market for our latter-day revivalists and promoters of authoritarianism. The intellectual who disturbs their uneasy peace with doubting questions comes to be regarded as a heretic, a revolutionary, and worse. Hence the apathy, if not the approbation, with which the public has thus far permitted the stifling of our civil liberties to advance.

That advance is already considerable. There is not enough time here to catalogue the grievances. Suffice it to say that

3 4

they include practices which recall the obnoxious test oath, bills of attainder, search and seizure without warrant, Star Chamber prosecutions, and other abuses to the relief of which our Declaration of Independence and Constitution were addressed.

Many of these practices have unfortunately been found to be, as Supreme Court Justice William O. Douglas recently observed, "within the letter of the law." "But," says Justice Douglas, "even when lawyers and judges justify them, they violate the ideals of freedom we profess." In formal opinions from the bench, he and other judges have observed that the courts, too, may be swayed by the tides of emotional majority-ism that have swamped the executive and legislative departments.

With great wisdom Alexander Meiklejohn has observed that our Constitution provides for a fourth independent branch of the government, co-equal with the executive, legislative, and judicial. This fourth branch in the division of power is the sovereign citizenry, acting in its capacity as the electorate. Clearly, if our system is to work, each elector must be protected from intimidation and coercion, especially with regard to his political action, by public officials who become infected with the insolence of office. That protection is provided by the secrecy of the ballot box and by the right of privacy that shelters the freedom of conscience, speech, and association.

Now, as we have been told so often in the past few years, a citizen has no right to a job on the public payroll. But he is nonetheless entitled to protection against harassment and deprivation of livelihood by executive department loyalty procedures that violate the essence of his constitutional rights. The independence of the elector draws the same clear boundary around the matters that may be legitimately inquired into by legislative committees. Officials and legislators who overstep this boundary are guilty of invading the integrity of the fourth branch of our government and stand in contempt of the electorate.

There is a disturbing tendency for these inquisitorial procedures to spread outside the government into private business, labor unions, and civic organizations. Pressures in this regard are especially heavy upon educational institutions. The president of Harvard, for example, was recently reminded that only a legal fiction insulates privately endowed institutions from supervision by a congressional committee. They could be stripped of their tax exemption for failing to meet some congressional standard in faculty appointments.

In view of the pronounced tendency of this movement to persist and increase in intensity, the following description by Leo Szilard of parallel events in Germany may be taken as a warning of where we might go from here: "The German learned societies did not raise their voices in protest against these early dismissals. . . . It seemed much more important at that moment to fight for the established rights of those who had tenure, and this could be done much more successfully, so they thought, if they made concessions on minor points. In a sense, the German government kept its word with respect to those who had tenure. It is true that before long most professors who were considered 'undesirable' were retired; but they were given pensions adequate for their maintenances. And these pensions were faithfully paid to them until the very day they were put into concentration camps, beyond which time it did not seem practicable to pay them pensions. Later many of these professors were put to death, but this was no longer, strictly speaking, an academic matter with which the learned societies needed to concern themselves."

Fortunately, there are signs of a willingness and a resolve on the part of the academic community to get defensive counteraction going before it is too late. Not all these efforts, however, are wisely conceived. Many betray an utter failure to understand the nature of the challenge. Among them are resolutions and declarations that speak on the topic of civil liberties with great warmth and erudition. But they have a common flaw that vitiates their impact. This is the plea of "not guilty." The plea is entered, of course, against the charge of communism. By now it should be clear that no person or institution can be completely cleared of the stigma attaching to this charge. This is because it relates not to acts but to the private realm of conviction and belief.

By its very nature, therefore, the charge tends inevitably to become ever more vague and meaningless. In this condition, it serves even more admirably the purposes of those who use it as a weapon. The less precise and meaningful it is, the less does it need to be proved and the more impossible does it become to disprove. For the objectives of the demagogue, it must be capable of infinite expansion, ultimately to compromise every position and every conformity except the demagogue's own. The label of communism has served this purpose well; it embraces not only all shades of Marxism and socialism but New Dealers, Fair Dealers, and Democrats, and now includes even Republicans.

The real charge here, of course, is not communism at all, but heresy. This is an imaginary crime in the most literal sense of the term, since it is one that a man is supposed to commit inside his own head. To plead "not guilty" to such a charge is to permit it to be lodged and thereby to resign the dignity of citizenship that rules such inquiry out of order in the first place. This is the point on which the American Association of University Professors has stood fast since 1915. It is the point that the Association of American Universities regrettably failed to make in its declaration early this year on the problems raised by the self-appointed visiting committees from Congress.

The issue is complicated by the fuzzing out of the legal concept of conspiracy to comprise another new crime—crime by association. Like heresy, this chimera, too, is dissipated by the clear test of action. It is basic to our sense of justice that a man can be charged only for his own personal acts and cannot be held responsible for the behavior of associates. The charge of guilt by association must be met on the same grounds as that of guilt by thinking: its admissibility as a charge must be denied at the outset.

The charge of heresy is a hoax. But it takes a party of the second part to bring it off. Like the emperor's new clothes, the crime of heresy derives its principal substance from the consent of those who are willing to be hoaxed.

No defense of academic freedom can compromise on this issue of the admission of the crime of heresy to our law and ethics. To do so is to surrender the day to the demagogues and to lend the sanction of scholarship and science to the promotion of fraud. On the contrary, it is what Robert Redfield has called "the dangerous duty of our universities" to defend the heretic and provide sanctuary where heresies may thrive.

It is not only that freedom for somebody else's wrong idea secures my freedom to advance my right idea. Error is essential to the determination of truth itself. Heresy has the same role in scholarly inquiry and in politics as "noise" in communication theory. The theory adapts the powerful concept of entropy, from thermodynamics, to permit us to measure information quantitatively. In information theory noise plays the role of entropy and is equated with maximum disorder. Noise thus assumes a critical relationship to information. As Warren Weaver has explained: "Information . . . is a measure of one's freedom in selecting a message. The greater this freedom of choice, the greater is the uncertainty . . . Thus greater freedom of choice, greater uncertainty and greater information go hand in hand." In the context of a concern with human freedom, this idea takes on a significance transcending its importance in communications engineering.

It states, in effect, that what we know depends equally upon knowing what *is* the case and what is *not* the case.

Hence the paradox and the futility of enforced orthodoxy. It is not only that the received view of any subject whatsoever may be in error. It may be in the right. But we can know this with assurance only to the extent that we are informed on all the known alternative views. To the degree that alternative views are either not recognized or are suppressed, our information and, hence, our capacity for rational thought and action are reduced. To our peril, we expose ourselves to an increased risk of believing and acting mistakenly.

In the end, civil liberties cannot merely be defended. They must be exercised. They have no reality inscribed on fading parchment; they are sustained by no brooding omnipresence in the sky. They exist only to the degree that they are asserted by the action of men. Academic freedom is the most vital area of human freedom because it comprises the frontier. It is not a different kind of freedom, nor a special privilege for a pressure group. It includes and is continuous with the freedom of other citizens. The scholar and the scientist, however, require the widest range of freedom. When they exploit their liberty and advance its boundaries, they enrich and increase the liberty of all.

Here is the connection between the narrowing freedom of American scientists and the condition of our scientific enterprise as a whole. If the objectives of science in America have been subordinated to the demands of technology, this is in part because American scientists have failed to advance to their fellow citizens the case for science in its true role in our culture. Now that the taxpayer has assumed the burden of the financing of science, his well-known enthusiasm for its mere utility must be offset by a deeper understanding of what science is. The people must be shown that science is concerned with the ends as well as with the means of human life; that through increased understanding of himself and the

world around him, man may expect to set himself free from the residues of superstition and ignorance which still darken his existence; that in the expanding horizons of knowledge he will find motivations and objectives for his actions which are worthy of his natural endowment.

Such an undertaking is essential if the National Science Foundation is not to become a poorhouse for American science, a catch basin for the overflow of design and development projects from other departments of the federal government. We may hope that the public education campaign projected for the A.A.A.S. at Arden House will be directed to this end and that it will secure the backing of all who have the welfare of science at heart.

The same considerations give added force to the recent statement issued by the Society for Social Responsibility in Science, calling on scientists to "maintain and strengthen the spirit of free enquiry by clear and courageous public expression of considered opinions concerning the relation of science and society." The statement declares: ". . . each person has the individual and moral responsibility to consider the end results of his work as far as he can see them. This is a responsibility to society and implies a strong insistence on public expression of opinion."

Finally, the present situation calls upon scientists to take an unequivocal and unbudging stand on civil liberties. That stand is simple to define: There shall be no compromise whatever with the freedom of the mind. But it is a position that is difficult and dangerous to maintain in practice. It means professors must often be braver than their universities. It means defending persons and ideas that may be obnoxious as well as unpopular. It means individual risk that no man can ask of another. But this is the example of tolerance and courage that distinguishes the contribution of scientists to the history of liberty. It is the example of freedom that our country needs in this hour of danger.

4

The Planet Earth

IT TURNS OUT that our planet is somewhat pear-shaped and not quite round at the Equator. The atmosphere, which exerts a pressure of fifteen pounds on each square inch of our skin, reaches out to the distance of the moon, where it engages the somewhat sooty and foggy atmosphere of the sun. Submarine ribbons of water flowing eastward in the oceans at the Equator return the waters carried westward by the equatorial surface currents. A great rifted mountain chain runs twice or more around the earth on the bottom of the seas.

These are some of the major features of the earth that are beginning to be recognized as the scientists of the world sort out the results of their collaboration during the International Geophysical Year. The year was extended for an extra year. And the collaboration will continue under an international committee of scientific societies presently chaired by V. V. Beloussov, director of the Institute of the Physics of the Earth in Moscow.

In a period when national states could not decide to confer with one another even about the problems that united them, scientists all around the world were making precisely timed, simultaneous observations of the diverse events of nature. Their international community now claims the entire continent of Antarctica as its first geographic province.

A half century separated the first International Geophysical Year

41

in 1882 and the second in 1932; only twenty-five years intervened between the second and the third in 1957. Hopefully, the third is to be continued without adjournment.

I presented this preview of the third International Geophysical Year and reflections it suggested on man's adaptation to his planet at the Town Hall in Los Angeles in April 1955.

WE HAVE LEARNED a great deal, in recent times, about the world around us. From all that we know one grand conclusion now comes clear. It would be hard to discover or design, anywhere else in the universe, a more comfortable or pleasant place for mankind than this planet Earth.

By some lucky chance, the earth spins through the black vacuum of space at exactly the right distance from the sun. It is not, like Mercury, too hot; nor, like Pluto, too cold. The thin film of atmosphere that clings to the earth's surface has just the right depth and composition to admit those wave lengths of solar energy that activate and sustain the processes of life and to filter out those that would destroy it. The atmosphere is admirably compounded for breathing, moreover, with nitrogen and oxygen mixed in nicely proportioned amounts, as contrasted with the suffocating blanket of carbon dioxide that gives the planet Venus its brilliant silver light.

Besides air, the earth is abundantly supplied with water. The oceans cover more than two thirds of its surface. By the combined force of sunlight and the planet's rotation, the waters of the ocean are picked up in the atmosphere and distributed generously upon the land. Only about a third of the land is what you might call dry, as it is here in the environs of Los Angeles at the edge of the Great American Desert. The rest is pleasantly furnished with lakes, springs, brooks, and rivers.

The Planet Earth

After perhaps five billion years of turning in the sunlight, the planet Earth teems everywhere with life in a still un-catalogued variety of form, size, color, and activity. In the oceans, the streams, and on the land, man finds an abundance of plants and humbler animals ready at hand to support his higher order of existence.

No wonder, then, that early men lifted up their faces to the sun and praised the Almighty for so wisely arranging their abode. It is true that the earth at times confronted human life with menace and calamity. But men were ready to under-stand that earthquakes, storms, drought, and pestilence were also a part of the grand design. They looked into their own hearts for the wickedness that brought evil forth abroad.

Today, of course, we have a different view. We know the earth was not designed to accommodate the life of man. We comprehend, on the contrary, that man was designed for the earth; that he is its child. He was adapted to his existence on this planet by the same insensate evolutionary pressures that fashioned all the other species, living and extinct.

We know that we are much more like other creatures on earth than we are different. The twenty-odd amino acids that go to make our tissues compose the tissues of all animals and plants. In the blood of the daphnia, the tiny water flea that swarms in stagnant pools, we find the same hemoglobin that carries oxygen in our blood streams. The same marvelously complicated kind of molecule coiled up in the nucleus of a living cell is capable of encoding the information required to construct either an amoeba or a man.

But there is a difference. It is not only that the genes of human heredity encode a more elaborate plan. At some time in the distant past, men learned to carry a major portion of their heredity forward from generation to generation outside the nucleus of the cell. They learned to select and to reject, to combine and enlarge upon the experience of living, and to teach their children what experience taught them.

43

This adaptation proved speedily to be the most successful invention in the two-billion-year history of life. In a mere million years, the human species proceeded to adapt its existence to the full range of habitats offered by the earth. Men had occupied the margins of the arctic ice, the desert, the prairies and mountains and lonely islands in the ocean long before the memory of civilization began. No other creature, except the ant, is to be found so widely settled on the face of the earth. There may be some significance in the fact that ants, too, are social animals.

Now, in our lifetime, a new phase has opened in the story of our species. The faculty of learning which proved so successful in man's adaptation to the earth has assumed an immense new scope and power. Modern man is able to reverse the order of adaptation. He has acquired a high degree of control over the processes of nature and has begun to make the earth adapt to the demands of his existence.

Our new understanding forces us to concede that this planet was not designed with us in mind. Yet we have it in our power today to make the earth at last our home.

It is of the nature of the search for understanding that it has always taken the whole earth as its province. No man ever posed a significant question to nature without serving the interests of all mankind. The value of new understanding leaps over the gulf of generations as well as the barriers of nation and culture. The immense body of accumulated knowledge that is modern science rests upon foundations laid in the first days of civilization and earlier. As the common heritage of all mankind, it incorporates the thought and work of all the world's great cultures.

In our culture, from Newton to Einstein, science has always been an international enterprise. The giants upon whose shoulders the giant Newton stood were a German, Kepler; a Pole, Copernicus; and an Italian, Galileo. So our modern understanding of the nature of matter is the collaborative triumph

44

of Frenchmen, Lavoisier, Pierre and Marie Curie, and De Broglie; Englishmen, Dalton, Thomson, and Rutherford; a Russian, Mendeleyev; an Italian. Enrico Fermi; a Dane, Niels Bohr; Germans, Einstein, Planck, and Heisenberg; Americans, Gibbs, Michelson, and Millikan. This is why men of different nations, so often in the history of science, have made the same discovery simultaneously. Such coincidence is almost inevitable in the case of great discoveries. Within the same half decade, Newton and Leibniz fashioned the powerful instrument of the calculus. Joseph Henry, an obscure schoolteacher in Troy, New York, anticipated almost every one of the basic experiments that won Michael Faraday his fame as the founder of electrical technology.

Science has always given its workers a sense of citizenship in the world. The first national academies of science in the seventeenth century invariably provided for the election of foreign members. Franklin was a member of the French academy; Benjamin Thompson, of Massachusetts, the soldier, diplomat, confidence man, and scientist, later styled Count Rumford, was elected to a half dozen European academies.

The academies of science were devoted principally to the all-important function of communication. Then, as now, new research had no significance and, almost literally, no existence until it was communicated to other scientists. The academies, therefore, sought the widest distribution for their publications. Their proceedings and transactions circulated far beyond the borders of their own countries.

Even more important, perhaps, were their meetings. No published paper can accomplish the intense interchange of idea and opinion that is effected by personal discussion. The academies brought scientists together from all over Europe for colloquy and debate. Even in war, when other communication was suspended between enemy nations, scientists maintained contact with one another by correspondence and publication. In 1813, when England and France were fighting each other, Sir Humphry Davy was invited to Paris, where he was awarded the gold medal of the Academy of Science and elected to membership.

In the second half of the nineteenth century, with the advance of science accelerating, it became necessary to provide formal organization for this international enterprise. International unions and congresses were constituted in each of the major disciplines of science. These unions promoted collaboration of a more active kind. They set up the international standards of measurement that give science and technology a common world language today. Especially in the geological sciences and astronomy, they organized co-operative researches that co-ordinated the work of laboratories and observatories the world over.

The international spirit of science finds an especially deep source of strength in the education of scientists. It is an old tradition that young scientists should spend at least part of their graduate years abroad. The great teachers of science in each country attract students from all over the world. Among the leading figures of American science today—men such as Rabi, Urey, Oppenheimer, Pauling, Beadle, and Muller—it is hard to find one who did not have graduate training at Copenhagen, Zurich, Göttingen, or Cambridge. Now these men in turn have graduate students in their laboratories from these same universities and from the Orient.

At the outbreak of the Second World War science was a kind of world republic. The scientific community was an international community. It was the only truly international community in an epoch that was to see nationalism and the narrower concerns of national power rise again to ascendancy in world politics.

Statesmen discovered early in the war that science is an essential element of national strength. Today they rank it as equal in importance to their industrial and military establishments. Accordingly, each major power has sought to monopolize the talents of its scientists and to put them to work in the name of national security. This suppression of international motives in favor of national ends has now had serious consequences upon the life of science. The situation in our own country provides an extreme case of what, to a greater or lesser degree, has been happening in other nations.

Scientists are agreed, in the first place, that there has been a dangerous diversion of resources and talent from the really significant long-range concerns of science to the narrower short-range objectives of practical results. Nearly half of our expenditure for research and development each year goes to weaponeering. Economic and social pressures have moved a disproportionate percentage of our inadequate supply of scientists from universities to industrial and government laboratories. Even in our universities, the work of science has become dependent upon income from outside contracts and subject to the outside motivations that such contracts imply. As a result, the careers of an alarming number of our younger generation of scientists are now permanently lost to science. The education of the next generation is jeopardized by the breakdown of science teaching in our high schools and colleges. In short, we have mortgaged the future of science in our eagerness to exploit its past.

Science has come under another kind of duress through our preoccupation with national security in the narrow and negative technical sense of the term. Military secrecy seriously hampers publication and communication in a number of major fields of work. Direct contact between scientists has been disrupted by restriction on the travel of American scientists abroad and the admission of foreign scientists to our country. Scientists have been among the most notable victims of the invasion and abuse of personal privacy and dignity which characterizes the loyalty and security program of the federal government. In areas with no conceivable connection with national security, the attendant obsession with loyalty has created an atmosphere of fear and conformity which is as obnoxious and stifling to science as to any other branch of free inquiry.

It is impossible to calculate the damage that has been done to the integrity and vitality of our scientific establishment. Without doubt we shall pay for it in the future. It will show up in the loss of the advances in technology which should have come from the progress in science we have set aside today.

There is a lesson in this recital. The scientific enterprise cannot be successfully subordinated to merely national ends. Without the long view, the world view, the advance of science must falter and come at last to a halt.

The international tradition runs too deep in the life of science, however, to have been throttled in fifteen years. Among scientists in every field, their personal and professional associations with colleagues abroad, their mutual respect for one another, and the sharing of achievement in significant work establish bonds that outreach the divisive movements of this period. The international community of science still provides us with our most hopeful example of a world polity, in which statesmen and citizens as well as scientists may someday participate.

The newspaper stories about the Antarctic adventures of the icebreaker *Atka*, for example, have introduced us to the plans for a great scientific undertaking called the International Geophysical Year, to be carried through in 1957–8. Actually, this is the third venture of its kind. The first International Geophysical Year was in 1882; the second in 1932. To these efforts we owe a great deal of our present understanding of the physics of the earth. The third International Geophysical Year is designed to get the answers to a large number of new questions about our planet that have accumulated in the past quarter century. Scientists of thirty-eight nations, including the Soviet Union, are enlisted in the work. The elaborate and highly co-ordinated plans they have now made reflect the intimate personal relationships that prevail in the international democracy of science and prove that there are no real obstacles to such co-operation when men have common objectives.

Geophysics is concerned with the larger and more universal aspects of the earth which it holds in common with other planets and with the stars. The geophysical earth is a huge, spinning, electromechanical rotor, intimately engaged in its immediate cosmic environment. Immense tides and currents flow through its interior, its crust, its oceans, and its atmosphere. Each is interlocked in its dynamics with the others.

It is thought, for example, that the difference in temperature between the earth's hot core and its cooler crust must set the semi-plastic rock and metal of the interior to turning over in age-long, slow convection currents. These currents would account for the generation of the earth's magnetic field. Reaching far out into space, the magnetic field engages the flux of high-energy cosmic-ray particles that rain upon the earth from the sun and elsewhere in the depths of space. The interaction between the field and the cosmic showers sets up the electromagnetic storms of the ionosphere, the far, outer shell of our atmosphere. We "hear" such storms when they blank out our radio and telephone communications. These storms, in turn, are somehow linked to those that constitute our weather at the bottom of the atmosphere. Both are affected by the raging turmoil on the face of the sun, which we see as sunspots and as great clouds of fire in the solar atmosphere.

When the International Geophysical Year opens, a great network of observatories will embrace the entire earth. Three chains of weather stations, strung out on three meridian lines from the Arctic to the Antarctic, will chart the circulation of the atmosphere. A corresponding grid of delicately instrumented laboratories will monitor the ionosphere, taking simultaneous observations at hourly intervals throughout the year and at quarter-hour intervals during scheduled World Days and periods of unusual disturbance. On the World Days, rockets and rockoons (rockoons are ballons that carry lighter rockets upward for launching at high altitudes) will explore the upper regions of the atmosphere and take readings on outer space near by. Outposts in the Arctic and Antarctic will record the intense electromagnetic activity that centers around the earth's magnetic poles and generates the beautiful displays of the aurora borealis and australis.

Years of analysis, speculation, and debate will follow the work of the International Geophysical Year before the record can be reduced to conclusive findings. The work will have immense practical bearing upon many departments of human life. For example, improved understanding of the general circulation of the atmosphere will provide a sound basis for long-range weather forecasting. The work on the ionosphere will similarly secure the world's communication system from the disturbances of this region.

The International Geophysical Year suggest that men can increase their understanding of the earth only by investigation of the planet as a whole. Such investigation today requires international collaboration of a high order. But the collaboration is international only because men have divided the earth into their separate and transitory worlds. The earth itself remains one planet and the only one the next few generations of men are likely to know.

Let us now take a closer look at this planet, close enough to see what men have made of it. We do not find a happy picture. It is clear, at once, that the life of man is at odds with his apparent understanding and command of the mighty order of his world.

For some people, it is true, conditions are better. In twenty nations with a population of about 400 million, the masses of people are comparatively well off. They are better off, in fact, than masses of people have ever been before in history. Take just one index of well-being. During the past half century, they have succeeded in increasing their average length of life from thirty-five years to sixty or seventy years. They have added a full generation to their life span and are living about as long as people can expect to live. This must mean that they have achieved control of infectious disease, and their nutrition is equal to the needs of life, and that they are reasonably well clothed and housed.

For the rest of mankind, however, for the overwhelming majority of more than two billion people, life is a different and grim story. Their average length of life is still around thirty years. This means that most of them die in childhood, with the death rate highest among infants and mothers.

They have been making some progress in their control of epidemic disease. But this has confronted them with an alarming population growth and a widening of the gap between the supply of and the demand for food. They live already in a chronic state of malnutrition, with a calorie intake 500 units below the minimum required to sustain the vigor of life. In all other respects their existence may be fairly described as correspondingly intolerable. It is clear that people in this condition are physically unable to experience what it can mean to be alive.

Discouraging as this picture is, we may count as progress the fact that we have today a true measure of the condition of man. For the first time, we have world statistics and a reliable estimate of human want. We have also in hand, for the first time, the world statistics that tell us that the earth's resources are equal to the needs of mankind.

For this first world balance sheet of supply and demand, we are indebted to the all too little known technical agencies of the United Nations. During the first ten years of the UN, it has been the Security Council and the Assembly that have attracted the attention of the public. But the debates in these forums are by no means the whole story. History will show that in this period, in the achievements of its technical agencies, the UN has made significant progress toward realizing the hopes in which it was launched. And when the story is told, it will be seen that it was the international community of science that gave these agencies their leadership and the model for organization and action.

The two principal UN technical agencies, the Food and Agriculture Organization and the World Health Organization, were organized in the first place by members of the world scientific community. They are headed by scientists. The success of their operations depends primarily upon the voluntary effort of the men of science in all their member nations.

Beyond the balance sheet, the UN technical agencies have managed to set in motion the work that will ultimately bring food and hunger into balance. Measured in dollars, the effort has been pitifully small. But, as citizens of the world, the scientists engaged in this work comprehend that people are desperately eager to help themselves. What the people want to know is how to go about it.

As with the first academies of science, the principal function of the UN technical agencies has been communication. The funds have been spent not on brick and mortar, machinery or tools, but upon the exchange of information. Under the UN technical assistance program four thousand experts, mobilized by FAO, WHO, and UNESCO, have gone into the field to work with their colleagues on some three thousand technical assistance projects. The build-up even to this modest scale of enterprise has been slow. But already the results are visible.

Most impressive are the gains scored in the control of epidemic deasease. The ancient scourges of plague, cholera, and malaria have yielded easily to a minimum of technique. Spirochetes, mosquitoes, and rats are highly susceptible to penicillin, DDT, and Warfarin. There have been no major plague or cholera epidemics since 1950.

Bombay, a focal point of plague, is now plague-free. An

estimated 240 million of the 550 million people in the malarious regions of the world are now protected by the dousing of their homes and countryside with DDT. In Greece, the rate of new infection has dropped to one fortieth of what it was before. Concurrently, family income in the malarious districts has climbed from $200 to $400 per year and the land under cultivation has increased by 67 per cent. In Haiti, five years ago one third of the rural population was infected with yaws, a spirochete disease resembling syphilis in its symptoms. Last year the rate of infection was down to a fraction of 1 per cent.

As contrasted with the low birth rate and low death rate of the United States, the populations of the underdeveloped regions are characterized by a high birth rate and a high death rate. The reduction of the death rate, which can be achieved so easily, portends an explosive increase in population. But we should not pull long Malthusian noses at these people. Our own population is presently increasing at an even faster rate. In America, with capital and labor going unemployed, the population increase is the most hopeful single drive in sustaining the expansion of our economy. In the lower-income half of the world, for the present, more people means less to go around. The world's increasing hunger sets up a bigger challenge than disease.

There are some who say we cannot meet this challenge. Here in America we have a school of especially vocal disciples of Thomas Malthus among our soil and wildlife conservationists. According to their calculations, we can never produce enough food. They have popularized the notion that the world needs 2.5 acres per person, as we do in our own country, to produce an adequate diet. By this standard, there is not enough farm land to sustain the present world population, let alone the 1.5 billion additional mouths that will have to be fed before the end of the century.

Happily, the facts about the world food problem, now that

we have them, give a different and more hopeful face to the future. The wealth of international statistics available through FAO shows that our provincial standard of 2.5 acres has no significance beyond our own shores. In the first place, more than two of each of our 2.5 acres are devoted to producing the animal protein that makes up such a disproportionately large part of our diet. Being rich in land, we are extravagant with land. The Danes manage to achieve a comparable level of nutrition on less than half the acreage. Similar disparities in land use are to be found among the underfed peoples. The frugal and intensive agriculture of Japan feeds its people on less than half an acre per person. In India, it takes twice as much land to produce a less adequate nutrition than that of the Japanese. The FAO estimates that, if the best techniques available were practiced wherever they are applicable, the world's food supply could be increased by more than half on the land now under cultivation.

Actually, since the Second World War food production has caught up with the growth of population. But this is due largely to the gains achieved in the advanced countries. In the underdeveloped countries, food production is lagging behind the increasing number of people. Not only has their calorie count fallen since the war; the quality of their nutrition has declined even more sharply. This is reflected in an increase in the incidence of protein-deficiency diseases, which must soon be reckoned as the world's principal public health problem. The bloated bellies of the native children in travel-magazine pictures are a symptom of such diseases; if those children survive, they may never be physiologically whole adults.

There is no one big bulldozer solution to the food problem. Neither dollars, if they could be had, nor tractors, nor fertilizers can achieve the necessary expansion of output everywhere and all at once. The measures taken must be carefully adjusted to local conditions, to soil and water supply, to culture and tradition, to farming practice, and to the way people cook their food and raise their children. The gains must be sought in little steps, country by country and village by village.

Since a 50 per cent increase can be attained by applying the best techniques wherever they are appropriate, this is obviously the place to start. Here, as FAO has now demonstrated, is fertile ground for the genius of international co-operation. No one nation can provide the answers for all other nations. Through FAO, by exchange of expert assistance, all of its seventy-two member nations have been cross-fertilizing the techniques and practices of one another. The result is not one big agricultural revolution, but hundreds of little revolutions that are changing the lives of villages and nations all over the world.

Through FAO, for example, farmers in Europe were supplied with the newest strains of United States hybrid corn, at a total cost to FAO of $40,000 for seed and expert consultation. Five years later, with less than 5 per cent of the European corn acreage planted with hybrid seed, the increased yield paid a return of $24 million. Similarly, FAO technicians are crossbreeding the rice strain *Japonica*—which gives the farmers of Japan such a high yield per acre—with the native *Indica* species of Southeast Asia and India. In Egypt, farmers are learning to use Japanese tools and techniques to cultivate, harvest, and thresh their rice; they not only are improving the yield of grain but are converting the straw they used to waste into valuable by-products. Turkish sheep have been crossed with the hardy native stock of the Barbary coast of Africa to yield more meat and wool per acre; New Mexican sheep are making similar gains in Ecuador, and Australian sheep in India. In Afghanistan, the American-style scythe is replacing the ancient sickle. A species of carp from Israel is now harvested in the farm fishponds of Haiti; an African fish called tilapia is thriving in the rice paddies of Thailand and giving the farmers a yield of protein in addition to carbohydrates.

The effort is as yet on far too modest a scale to be reflected in world food statistics. But the FAO technical assistance experts can measure their achievements in big as well as little figures. There are tens of thousands of acres coming into irrigation and cultivation under FAO engineering in India, Pakistan, and Iran. In the Near East, a seven-nation commission was organized to fight the last plague of locusts and now, apparently, has this recurring menace under reasonable control. Rinderpest, a costly disease of cattle, has been eliminated in a half dozen countries, with 16 million inoculations administered in India alone.

Even in advance of achieving an adequate calorie count, FAO experts have pushed improvement in the quality of nutrition. With the oceans as a major, neglected source of protein, they have helped the fisheries of Chile, India, Pakistan, and Ceylon to improve their catch and to establish fish in the local diet. With the installation of modern dairy plants, they have secured an increase in the milk consumption, particularly by infants, in a dozen countries.

On undertakings of this kind, the UN laid out a mere $18 million in 1953. But this was only a minority interest in the total effort. The work couldn't have been done if the assisted nations had not laid out more than $50 million in the same period. When the UN experts go home, moreover, the people they have advised go right on spending at the same rate. In every case, local experts have been trained to carry on the work. Under FAO and UNESCO guidance, agricultural colleges and extension services, mechanics' training schools, institutes of technology, and applied research establishments have been organized on a permanent basis in nearly two dozen of the underdeveloped countries. It will not be long before the investment in technical assistance does make itself felt in the world nutrition balance sheet.

At this hopeful juncture, it is too bad that the United States should be deciding to curtail its own technical assistance pro-

gram and to terminate its annual contribution in support of the
UN technical agencies. It is unfortunate for our national
interest at a period when we are seeking friends abroad. It is
more than unfortunate for the people, the world over, who
are making such good use of what we offered.

As a people and as a government, we must learn that technical assistance projects are not charitable enterprises to indulge our wish to feel good about ourselves. They are an
economic and political necessity. They are the beginning of a
movement that will engage the principal energies of mankind
in the second half of this century.

Consider the economic aspect for a moment and from the
point of view of our self-interest. To the north of us live 14
million Canadians, who enjoy a standard of living roughly
equivalent to our own. Our exports to Canada amount to
nearly $500 million each year. To the south are 156 million
Latin Americans, who must be counted among the submerged
two billion members of the human race. Our exports south-
ward to these people, eleven times the number of Canadians,
barely exceed our $500 million annual exports to Canada. If
they lived on the Canadian scale, we would be shipping them
$5,500 million in goods and services.

If the economic aspects are not compelling, then the political pressures soon will be. It is not yet too late for us to learn
that the revolt against hunger is the primary dynamic force
in the world's unrest.

We have been mesmerized by our contemporary clash of
ideologies. But history shows that great powers have always
found one or another ideology to clothe the nakedness of
power. The theater of the contest for power today is the
vacuum of revolution in what we used to call the colonial
regions of the world. The issue there is not ideological; it is
the hard, practical question: When do we eat?

It is true that starvation and disease have not been positive
political forces in the history of man. Most of the fifty billion

human beings who have ever been born, died early of hunger and infection. Most of them expected to and accepted their lot as the misfortune of birth. But now the word has got around that malnutrition, disease, and early death are not necessary conditions of existence. And just because they are human, people are determined to do something about it.

They are doing it without assistance when no assistance is forthcoming. But to build up production requires capital. To create capital, savings must be taken out of current consumption. When there is not enough to go around in the first place, saving means that someone must starve to death. To decide who will starve requires compulsion. Some people have followed this logic to its conclusion. They have accepted compulsion and the revolutionary dictatorships that supply it, in the expectation that they will get somewhere with the main task.

Other people, with more or less exposure to the political traditions of Europe and America, are still trying to avoid the agony of going it alone and are seeking assistance from outside. They would rather get the help they need through the UN. In the UN, along with other nations that share their problems, they have a voice and a vote in the making of policy. If necessary, however, they will take help on a bilateral basis, from the United States, Great Britain, or France, along with what they regard as political and imperial strings attached. Through their embassies in Washington and their delegations to the UN, they are asserting their hopes and needs with a diplomatic pressure which it will be dangerous for us to ignore.

With help, they hope to improve their lot and simultaneously be able to maintain as much of their identity with our kind of political tradition as they have managed so far to enjoy. Since, in each of the needful countries, the people who prize this identity are a tiny minority, they can be easily displaced if they fail in their mission. Behind them are impatient people who will find ways to do it themselves.

The measure of our ability to help is to be found in the principal anxiety that haunts our economy. This is the overhanging threat of overproduction. The record of the past two decades suggests that we must throw off an increasing percentage of our product as surplus. The $4 billion public works budgets of the New Deal have been succeeded by the $40 billion arms budgets of the cold war. Yet when the federal government reduced its expenditures for armament ever so slightly and briefly in the summer and autumn of 1953, the American economy was seized by a rolling readjustment.

We are accustomed then, if not compelled, to produce surpluses. It should not, therefore, be out of order to raise the question whether we are getting the most out of our surplus capacity. We have, perhaps, an even more pressing question: whether war or the expectation of war provides a dependable foundation upon which to rest our economic prosperity.

There are indications that governments as well as people are concluding that war is no longer a practical method of resolving international differences or achieving national ends. With thermonuclear weapons at hand, it is beginning to be clear that no nation ever again can win or even survive a war.

Fortunately, there are alternatives to war for the employment of our surplus capacity. The industries that produce armaments are the very same industries that produce capital goods—the machines that make the hard and soft goods of industry, the rolling stock of transportation systems, and the agricultural machinery that gives our farms the highest output per man-hour in the world. Our surplus capacity, in other words, precisely offsets the deficit capacity of the underfed peoples of the world.

Since it would require not even a rolling readjustment to do so, it is easy and even attractive to consider the possibility that we might divert a part of our surplus from armaments to the production of capital goods for export abroad. We might begin by increasing instead of decreasing our appropriations this year to the United States and UN technical assistance programs. If we made a start in this direction, we would assuredly see our surplus capacity to create capital yield dividends of another kind.

The arms race is a symptom of the world's affliction. Capital goods are the cure for its underlying cause—the hunger and destitution against which even the most underfed and underdeveloped people have at last risen in rebellion. We might ultimately find little surplus capacity available for weapons. This would be all to the good. For men will have less need for weapons as they proceed to make themselves at home on this most bountiful of all known planets.

PART **II**

Science in America

Science in America

In his Farewell Address on January 18, 1961, President Eisenhower enjoined his fellow citizens to beware the "conjunction of an immense military establishment and a large arms industry."

"The total influence," he said, "economic, political, even spiritual—is felt in every city, every state house, every office of the Federal Government. . . . In the councils of Government, we must guard against the acquisition of unwarranted influence, whether sought or unsought, by the military-industrial complex. The potential for the disastrous rise of misplaced power exists and will persist. We must never let the weight of this combination endanger our liberties or democratic processes."

To this hazard he coupled the "prospect of domination of the nation's scholars by Federal employment, project allocations and the power of money . . . [and] the equal and opposite danger that public policy could itself become the captive of a scientific-technological elite."

We have come five years closer to 1984 since I delivered the Walgreen Lectures in the first semester of the 1955–6 academic year at the University of Chicago. The five lectures follow.

As the reader will himself conclude, the welfare of our science, taken as an index of the health of our society, continues to give an uncertain reading. The economic gradient that works against the independence of the scholar remains as steep as ever—about 20 to 1 in terms of dollars. There has been no *cause célèbre* like the Oppenheimer case, but the federal personnel loyalty and security system still counts most of the scientific community among the six million persons on its rolls. The arms budget is bigger, and the investment in world development has grown smaller than it was.

To one development in the past five years, however, we may cling with hope. This is the continued suspension of nuclear weapons tests by the two great nuclear powers. The first step toward this first step was the Einstein-Russell Manifesto in 1955, reported as a current event in the last of these lectures. In direct response to their challenge, scientists from the two sides of the world met with one another as individuals in the cycle of Pugwash conferences. From their agreement that a cessation of tests could be policed came the official diplomatic effort to write an agreement and the concurrent tacit suspension of tests.

If an agreement has not yet been concluded, the cause is to be traced at least in part to President Eisenhower's "scientific-technological elite." An elite only in the self-selecting sense of that term, its members are the scientists and technicians who have found new careers as intellectual *condottieri* in the employ of the military services and their suppliers. They figure also in the story I have to tell here about how the hydrogen bomb was made. But President Eisenhower could tell better than anyone how national policy on test cessation and the questions of disarmament to which it leads became for a critical period the captive of this elite. Their monopoly was broken by the appointment of the Science Advisory Committee, which now gives the President clear access to the opinion of the open community of science. As a result, the test-cessation talks were continued and, under the Kennedy administration, may yet yield an agreement.

Thereafter must come the next steps toward disarmament if civilization is not to disappear beneath plains of concrete or vanish in the fire storms of a thermonuclear war. Given disarmament, the community of nations can turn to the realization of the new paradise.

I

The Social Compact

IN THIS CONSIDERATION of the place of science in American life, we shall find ourselves contemplating two Utopias. They stand in strange contrast to each other. One of these Utopias evokes history; the other makes a prophecy. Each is scientific, though in different ways, and both in certain respects are American. But they are divided by the gulf that lies between hope and despair. To that contrast between these only partly imaginary commonwealths we shall find ourselves led by the questions that most concern us about science in America today.

We shall return first to the Utopia of our history. It is the society of the Social Compact. The first paragraph of the Compact proclaims a revolutionary scientific discovery. Governments, it says, are instituted by men and derive their just powers from the consent of the governed. This was an inevitable discovery. It flowed inexorably from the application to society of the same powers of observation and reason that had established Newton's laws of motion. The social order that rested thus upon science was to be, in the dream of its founders, the mistress of science as well as the asylum of liberty. With freedom to think and to speak, the condition of man would proceed always in improvement.

Turning now to the future, we are assured that it holds another vision. In the brave new world, now scheduled for incarnation in 1984, the mission of science has been accomplished. Nature is subdued and the environment of man is man-made. Human nature is subdued as well. No man escapes the thrall of the new order that has found in social science an implement of tyranny far more pervasive than the divine right of kings. History has been brought to a close.

We shall not for the time being look more closely into these Utopias. As visions of hope and despair, they belong to the past and to the future, and are only partly real. We are more concerned with the actual present state of affairs. But as we proceed we shall be able to determine more surely which aspects of these Utopias are real and which may be discounted as the products of mere hope and despair.

We shall see to what degree America has fulfilled her mission as the mistress of science and how well our institutions and culture have provided for its advance. We shall consider in turn the impact of science upon America and the changes it has brought in our way of life and social order. We shall then be able to ask why the change of mood in our Utopias and what of our original buoyant hope science and America sustain for the future.

It is well, at this point, to remind ourselves that America holds no patent on the Social Compact. Science and democracy are international. They are causes that citizens may prize above nations. They are the highest causes of citizenship, as they were to the founders of our nation. For the past three centuries they have provided the central themes and the driving energy of the history of Western civilization.

Wherever they have taken root, the two movements of science and democracy have mutually sustained each other by their close correspondence in motive and objective. As democracy substitutes persuasion for force in the relations of men, so science establishes observation and reason in the place of authority at the foundations of knowledge. In democracy, the government is open at all times to change and improvement by the governed. In science, every hypothesis is provisional, every finding tentative, and no work lays claim on final truth. Science and democracy are open-ended; they set no limits to human knowledge and experience. The autocrat and dogmatist are enemies of both.

An examination of the state of science in a democracy may thus be expected to tell us much about the health of the democracy itself. We may be excused for restricting this inquiry to America out of provincial interest in the welfare of our country. But there is more than provincialism to justify taking America as our model. As the richest and most powerful of all nations, America represents science and democracy in their hour of triumph. Its wealth and abundance are the standard to which other peoples aspire. It is the example of America that today moves the colonial regions to disturb the world with unrest and revolution.

Sometimes the dimensions of America can amaze even us. They are a measure of the enormously fruitful power of science applied to the exploitation of a continent. Each year the American people produce and consume more than half of the world's output of energy. We use more than a third of the world's energy merely to heat the indoor spaces in which we live and work. We constitute a scant one fifteenth, 6 per cent, of the world's population, but we produce and consume more than half of its steel and a corresponding percentage of just about all the other products of technology. We work at tasks that few other people in the world would recognize as work, and we spend fewer hours of the day and fewer years of our lives engaged in work. We consume the fruit of our labors in an abundance and variety of goods that are unknown to the daily existence of most of the rest of mankind. By comparison with other peoples, the well-to-do members of our society make up more than two thirds of our families. Though the poor are still with us, they and their needs have ceased to provide the typical issues of our domestic politics.

This popularization of the abundance that flows from the application of science has been accompanied by the equal popularization of an enthusiastically utilitarian faith in science. There is no problem, in the American view, that science cannot solve, from the control of weather to the cure of cancer. As in the historic case of the atomic bomb, we need only invest a sufficient number of billions of dollars and we shall have the answer. This applies even to our economic problems. Americans expect that the continued advance of science will maintain their industrial system in the state of perpetual flux and expansion that is needed to sustain full employment.

The welfare of science in America would seem to be secured as well by the degree to which its outlook is imbued in our folk culture. We may have occasion to deplore the ignorance of science among a people who are so dependent upon science. But the truth is that dryads, leprechauns, and trolls have long since fled a culture that prizes oil burners, television sets, internal combustion engines, deep freezers, and all the other devices that ease and complicate our existence. These inanimate gadgets, animated only by the mechanic's tools, have generated a powerful antidote to the pathetic fallacy that once populated the universe with the creatures of man's fear and imagination. Almost everybody now has acquiesced in the Copernican revolution and the displacement of our earth and us from the center of the universe. There is general recognition of the idea that the cosmos is a vast impersonal system, ordered by laws of mechanics. The germ theory of disease brings people to their doctors, not to their knees. In our law there is increasing acceptance of the idea of the criminal as a victim of psychological and sociological handicaps, an object for treatment, not for vengeance. In the relationships of man to man, our fellow citizens are agreed that all men are members of the human race, and they expect that we will eventually learn to act like members of the same human family.

It is doubtful that such a universal acceptance of the rational and scientific view can be found among the people of any other nation. Future historians may well conclude that it was in the inculcation of the rational outlook on the world among our citizens in all occupations and professions that science had its greatest impact in our time upon the life of mankind.

This appraisal of the place of science in our culture, however, must be qualified by an admission. The ground still held in men's hearts by fear and superstition is narrowed. But on many of the most important questions of life it seems to remain the decisive ground. Ironically, science itself seems to have fallen heir to much of what remains of the frightened awe formerly accorded to the outer darkness.

Science still occupies the House of Magic in which it was exhibited at the New York World's Fair in 1939. In the popular view science is first of all our most securely established body of knowledge. It is a rich mine of hard facts that have a tougher consistency and more utility than Revelation. How these facts originated and got put together, nobody inquires. The notion that they might go on growing in number is disturbing to an increasing number of people. They raise the question whether there shouldn't be a law or a moratorium or a breathing spell.

Scientists are the workers in this House of Magic. They are qualified by special gifts—today, of course, they must also be cleared—for access to technical information. Their job is to make something useful out of the ready-to-hand facts. Science is thus primarily an important step in the immense technological process that makes our country so rich and strong. The suggestion that science has cultural as well as technological implications is downright suspect and heretical, if not worse.

As we shall now see, this is a critical reservation in America's commitment to the advance of science. It is the symptom of a complex of circumstances that seriously condition the welfare of science in our country.

We must first consider the distinction, with which Americans have recently been impressing themselves, between pure and applied science. The logic of it is simple. Pure science is devoted to the advance of knowledge. Applied science, or technology, is the exploitation of knowledge already established. Thus, it is clear, there must be an advance before there can be an application. It is widely understood, therefore, that the progress of science must be continued in order to maintain the progress of technology.

The word "pure" suggests that this effort must somehow be maintained apart from practical concerns and considerations. This view is warmly sustained by the events of the day. We have seen the most highly theoretical understanding of the nature of matter and energy, backed by only a few isolated experiments, move within a decade from the blackboards of a few ivy-clad laboratories to create the immense new technology of nuclear energy. But this romantic view overlooks a highly important flow of inspiration the other way. Galileo was employed by the Duke of Tuscany as an expert on artillery; it was undoubtedly in the course of this work that he perceived the connection between trajectories of missiles and the orbits of planets. Our technology today lays demands upon materials which pose fundamental questions for investigation by physics; science depends upon industry for the massive instruments that are needed for modern research. Thus, it is clear, the cycle of progress is maintained by an interaction between pure and applied science in which the two enterprises fructify each other. On the standard of more or less practical or more or less pure, it is difficult to find a distinction between them.

What our utilitarian culture overlooks is that science is more than a merely useful activity of men. It has another aspect, which makes the advance of science an end in itself. This is the aspect of science that bears upon man's understanding of himself and the world he lives in and hence upon the ends and purposes to which its achievements may be applied. Seen from this vantage, science ceases to be merely a necessary adjunct of technology. It becomes, what it truly is, a branch of free inquiry.

In these times, science is indeed the main branch of inquiry. It is not concerned exclusively with little questions, though its main day-to-day advance is by small increases in precision of measurement and small new grains of evidence. Underlying this work, however, there is always ultimately a big question. It is through science, in fact, that man now carries on his most fruitful inquiry into the universal questions of human existence. Some of the questions that science asks are old questions —about the nature of matter, of life, and of mind—that are as old as human consciousness. They are asked by science in new and more productive ways. Some of them are new questions that were never dreamed of in the philosophies of the ancients. The new understanding that comes from the asking of questions enriches the value of human life because it is itself the expression of man's noblest capacity. The fact that the advance of science may also have practical consequences is incidental. People will eventually find a practical and a profitable way to use just about everything they know.

The brief history of our country shows that it has been America's role to exploit and apply scientific knowledge rather than to advance it. None of the basic discoveries upon which the growth of our technology in the nineteenth century was based were made in America. They came universally from the great European centers of learning, where the advance of knowledge was a long-established enterprise, cherished by traditions going back a thousand years. The dozens of little colleges that mushroomed across the American landscape were devoted exclusively to teaching. They did not become universities until late in the nineteenth century. It was only then that professors became scholars and scientists and were encouraged to advance learning as well as to teach it.

What America lacked in tradition it soon made up in enterprise. At the turn of the century, the first great fortunes of American industrial expansion began to flow generously to the support of science in our universities. Even greater sums were invested, of course, by the great corporations themselves in industrial research, and America soon led the world in the number and vitality of its industrial laboratories. But by the outbreak of the Second World War pure science had acquired in America a vigorous and flourishing establishment. It reflected the interests of its early patrons in its emphasis upon astronomy and the life sciences. America's comparative deficiency in physics and mathematics was repaired overnight by the rise of Fascism and Nazism, which brought so many of the Old World's great men to continue their work in the freedom of our democracy.

From the very beginning of the Second World War, however, pure science was suspended in America for the duration. The scientists of our country were mobilized, largely on their own initiative, even before Pearl Harbor, and were more fully committed to the fighting of the war than the scientists of any other nation on either side in the conflict. They have never since been completely demobilized.

The disclosure, at the end of the war, of atomic energy, radar, and the host of other wartime scientific and technical triumphs had the effect of elevating our established conviction in the utility of science to a national enthusiasm. The Age of Science was at hand. Everyone—industrialists, congressmen, generals, and taxpayers—had a project and an unlimited budget to back it.

Today our annual expenditure on research and development stands at more than $3 billion, ten times the prewar budget. Nearly all of this huge sum is supplied by government and industry, and nearly half of it goes to weapons development projects sponsored by the Department of Defense and the Atomic Energy Commission. Not more than 3 per cent of the total is supplied by university endowments, philanthropic foundations, and other sources of free funds which have financed basic science in the past. These funds constitute a minor source of support for science even in our university laboratories, where more than $500 million is now spent annually by the government and industry on contract research projects.

The trends in the employment of our scientists tell the same story of the neglect of the long-term values of basic science in favor of the short-run accomplishments of technology. These highly trained professionals number less than one tenth of 1 per cent of our total population; how this precious nucleus of our intellectual resources is employed today will critically affect the life of our nation for years to come. Under the pressure of salary differentials that range from 50 to 100 per cent higher in industry and government, scientists are migrating away from the campus. Where once our universities employed more than half of our scientists, they now employ less than a quarter of them. The pressure is felt especially by the recently articled doctor of philosophy; he finds it difficult to resist an opportunity to begin his career on a salary equal to that of his professors. As a result, a dangerously disproportionate percentage of new talent is being diverted to applied research.

But even with this redistribution of talent, apparently urgent applied research programs are stalled for lack of manpower. The current crop of new scientists falls far below the demands of industrial and government laboratories. The same is true of young engineers; demand exceeds production by an estimated 100 per cent. It is difficult to see how we are going to catch up in the predictable future. Enrollment in science has declined in our colleges, principally because high schools have been losing their science teachers to more lucrative employment elsewhere. But science is, of course, only the most neglected department of our overcrowded, understaffed educational system, now being swamped by the offspring of the wartime baby boom.

We can find some comfort in the indications that the plight of American science is temporary. It is the result in part, at least, of the cold war; it is an emergency created by the half of our expenditures for research and development that goes to weaponeering. With the prospective relief of world tension, we may hope that things will go back to normal. When they do we shall be better able to calculate the damage that has been done to our scientific resources. We need not, however, wait to be convinced that we are not only neglecting the present welfare of science in America but seriously compromising its future.

It was clear at the end of the war that philanthropy and endowment could no longer finance the claims of basic science against the huge budgets available to back the demands for applied research. There was no longer any question that science would have to seek public support. Among the ingenious devices developed for this purpose are the public subscription campaigns that appeal to the public's fear and pity at the mention of certain diseases. The promise of research has helped to swell public contributions, and a few million dollars from these sources has gone to support fundamental work in the life sciences. But the principal financial agency is the National Science Foundation, which was set up in 1950 as a means for investing the taxpayers' money in the advance of pure science. Its budget this year is $15 million. Though pure research projects tend to cost less than applied, we still have many millions of dollars to go before present trends are reversed and the serious imbalance of emphasis is redressed. Meanwhile, government and industrial officials are voicing alarm that the neglect of pure research will soon confront us with a crisis in the progress of technology.

The arrival of the taxpayer as the patron of science is, of course, entirely in keeping with the theory and practice of democracy. But the public support of science raises the serious question of the public's understanding of science. As the present period has shown, it is not the amount of support but the terms on which it is given that counts.

The need for public understanding is, of course, related to larger questions than this special issue of the support of science. Not so long ago most of the processes of production which supported the life of the American people were a matter of common understanding to most of the active members of the community. People were at home in the sciences, too. The advance of science was extending the boundaries of a world that was familiar to everyone. Only a few radical thinkers were then concerned with the possibility that the universe was not everywhere pervaded with Euclidean geometry and the forces of classical mechanics.

Today, in contrast, the technology that sustains our existence is known only to a tiny corps of specialists. They and their collaborating technicians constitute a bare 1 per cent of our population. Even these men know the system only one facet, one narrow branch of science, at a time. At the same time, science has moved on out beyond the world of daily, common-sense experience to open up a universe that, in the words of J. B. S. Haldane, may "not only be queerer than we imagine, but queerer than we can imagine."

Thus, between technology and science, on the one hand, and common understanding, on the other, there has developed a gap. It is a gap in the communications of our society which challenges the underlying assumptions of the democratic process. The public issues that preoccupy the political life of America today are heavily conditioned by purely scientific considerations, involving realms of information and ideas that are unfamiliar and unknown to the vast majority of the American people. One of the new questions in self-government is the support of science. The understanding required is of a special kind. It involves not so much the subject matter of science as the method and spirit of science and the nature of the scientific enterprise as an activity of men. This being the case, we could scarcely find a more unfortunate period in our cultural history in which to qualify science as a ward of the public.

Everyone who prizes freedom and science must be concerned at the present authoritarian drift in our culture. The uncertainty and anxiety of this period in world history have undoubtedly accelerated this drift. But it has deeper springs in the estrangement of the humanities and the sciences that prevails in the traditions of our universities, in our art and literature. The humanist is characteristically ignorant of science and of the insights it offers into his concerns. The scientist, in his insularity, evades the distraction of the larger meanings of his work. A people that regard science as a merely practical enterprise must fail to comprehend its relation to purpose and policy in their public and private affairs.

The past unsettled decade has evoked an intense popular demand for words of reassurance. These have been supplied by a swelling chorus of historians, philosophers, and moralists, of a wide range of eminence and sophistication, who are propounding the solace and security that are to be found in antirational retreat down various pathways to the absolutes of the past. The mood is echoed and amplified in the fiction, nonfiction, and semi-fiction that is served up as entertainment and information by our mass media. Sin is still original; history is circular, and it is safer to stop thinking.

The aggressive promotion of conformity has even become a path to political power and distinction. The attendant erosion of our civil liberties has been as stifling for science as for other departments of free inquiry. Though their work is remote from the political questions presumed to be at issue, scientists have figured prominently in number and eminence among the citizens who have suffered invasion of their rights and dignity. No government agency has attempted to promulgate an official American genetics. But the test oath and the clearance procedure attached to government financing of unclassified as well as classified research hamper work and communication and pall the freedom of contact and controversy that is the life of creative work in any field.

Our country has seen similar storms gather in its past and blow themselves out. It may be that this is another such temporary phase in our history. As the world crisis has tended to subside during the past year, so the tide of conformity has shown signs of receding. But this movement has so undermined the traditional regard for the individual in our culture and politics and so degraded his status in law and custom that we are moved to look deeper for the causes that set it in motion.

These are to be found, no doubt, in the transformation of our society that has attended the growth of our technology. The rural republic has become a city-state. The typical American no longer makes his living by the exploitation and increase of his own property. He has evolved from farmer to factory worker and now to white-collar employee. Technology has everywhere changed the character and condition of his employment. Whether in factory or office, he finds his job reduced to a minimum of craft and skill and so to a minimum of status and satisfaction. As jobs become interchangeable, so do men. Their identity as individuals is merged into the nameless identity of the crowd. With the attendant centralization of initiative and authority in the giant organizations of industry and government, the individual becomes the anonymous creature of decisions and compulsions originating he knows not where. It is easy for twentieth-century medievalists to show that the serf found more happiness in the security of his bondage than modern man in the insecurity of his liberation.

This inquiry into the welfare of science in America has led us into the thick of much wider and deeper problems. It would seem that we are now halfway along the road from the Utopia of the past to that of the future. Technology and the centralized social order which wields the power that technology affords could quite possibly bring an end to freedom and science. History shows that the conditions necessary for the maintenance of free inquiry are by no means the natural state of affairs. They are to be found prevailing only for limited periods in a few golden ages in the past.

To bring the monolithic economy that has grown up around modern technology under democratic control is the central issue of our time. The effort to do so has already failed in other nations where the traditions of liberty were not so securely established as in our own. Success in the effort for us will require the invention of new institutions and methods for encouraging the diffusion of initiative and responsibility among the people, and for vesting with them the control of the ends and purposes to which our society will use the tremendous power now at its command.

One of the more urgent problems on the agenda for the revival of democratic action and control is the support of science. If our present neglect is not to do irreversible damage to our scientific resources, we must soon take active measures to redress the balance of emphasis on pure and applied science.

The very first of these measures must be to develop a wider understanding of the nature of the scientific enterprise among the citizens of our country. If they are to play their role wisely, they must be shown that science is not solely or simply a branch of technology, that mere utility has never provided sufficient motive to inspire its great works. If they are to find other motives for the support of science, then the people, too, must be able to share in those fruits of research that bear on the larger questions of human life. Here we enter a much wider area of concern than the support of science. In the four hundred years since Copernicus, scientific enterprise has brought more than an industrial revolution. It has undermined the ancient absolutes in which men once found the purpose and plan of their lives. Science, so far as general public understanding is concerned, has brought forward no adequate substitutes for the system of values that it has thus destroyed. But the demands of the human spirit cannot be denied. If we are to maintain individual freedom in our crowded world and manage civilization democratically, then each man must have conviction in his own worth as an individual and purpose that fulfills the personal miracle of his existence. It is now too late in the history of science for men to satisfy these demands by retreat to authority. It is, in fact, impossible for the human mind in its integrity to deny for long the inescapable conclusions of its capacity to know and think.

The rational method offers no absolutes and no blueprints prepared in advance to tell us what we want to live for. But science does broaden and secure the ground on which men can make their choice. It has shown in the triumphs of technology that human life is not fated to be nasty, brutish, and short. In our increasingly complete and connected knowledge of the cosmos, we have an ever clearer understanding of ourselves and our place in nature. We see that the perfected man, that ideal of the eighteenth-century enlightenment, is the ultimate product of the cosmic process as it is known to modern science.

2

Founding Fathers as Social Scientists

Fʀᴏᴍ Pᴀʀɪs in 1780, where he was engaged in the campaign of diplomacy that secured the support of France for the American Revolution against the British crown, Benjamin Franklin wrote a letter to his friend Joseph Priestley in England. Franklin was known to Priestley and the scientists of Europe as the man who had brought all of the isolated phenomena of electricity, from the spark at the knuckle to lightning in the sky, together into a consistent and ordered body of theory. Priestley, a clergyman and one of the founders of modern chemistry, was later to emigrate to the new republic in America, hounded from his own country as a heretic and traitor for his support of the French Revolution. To Priestley, Franklin wrote:

"The rapid progress true science now makes occasions my regretting sometimes that I was born so soon. It is impossible to imagine the height to which may be carried, in a thousand years, the power of man over matter. We may perhaps learn to deprive large masses of their gravity, and to give them absolute levity, for the sake of easy transport. Agriculture may diminish its labor and double its produce; all diseases may be by sure means prevented or cured and our lives lengthened at pleasure even beyond the antediluvian standard."

Today we are less than two centuries forward into Ben Franklin's millennium. Yet his vision has already been in a large part accomplished. We have yet "to deprive large masses of their gravity," but the convenience he envisioned in off-the-ground transport has been realized for a substantial fraction of our freight and passenger traffic by aircraft. Medicine has eliminated infectious diseases as a major cause of death; the medical frontier is now the diseases of old age, beyond which lies the longevity of Methuselah. As for agriculture, we have long since forgotten the rural life of our grandfathers.

Within the past half century the United States has become that new kind of society in the history of mankind, an industrial society. We live no longer in the world of nature; the principal forces and events in our lives are the work of the brains and hands of man.

All of this, in the view of the philosophers and engineers of the American Revolution, was to be expected as the inevitable outcome of the release of human energy and capacity in the social order of democracy. In science they found a strategy for the conquest of the unknown—the wilderness that reached into the continent behind their seacoast colonies. They were practical men; as planters, surveyors, printers, physicians, lawyers, and merchants, they were well acquainted with natural law and knew how to turn it to their use. For the advance and application of science liberty was the natural climate.

Science, in their understanding, rendered a like service to liberty. Natural law showed that men are born free and equal and are endowed with certain inalienable rights. This bold extension of science into social questions may seem naïve, perhaps, in retrospect. But with the same boldness they carried their theorems into the realm of practical social invention.

The aim of their Constitution was to make sure no American would ever again be the subject of tyranny by government. They not only provided for constant change of government but divided its power in order that the citizen might rule. As a special protection for the sovereignty of the citizen, they took care, out of their own vivid experience, to mention in the Constitution the crime for which they themselves might have been hanged. They devoted Article III, Section 3, to the crime of treason—specifying that the crime of treason should never be charged except upon proof of an overt act supplied by the testimony of two witnesses to the act—with the aim of making treason the charge that government would find most difficult to bring against its sovereign. Then, lest future generations forget the natural law, they amended the Constitution to say what went without saying. The first Amendment speaks the plainest language. It says that the Congress shall make no law abridging the liberty of speech and assembly. This is the liberty that secures to self-governing citizens the power to organize, control, and change their government.

But no constitution, however eloquent and foresighted, could secure the blessings of liberty. These were to be won by the exertions of men. It was to future generations that the natural lawyers of eighteenth-century America looked for fulfillment of their vision.

The robust environment of America in the first years of its independence encouraged the practical application of science rather than the advance of scientific knowledge. Despite the Yankee brag of ingenuity, Americans made few fundamental contributions even to the applied art of industry. Our industrial revolution was imported from England. The industrial transformation of England had attained such revolutionary tempo by 1776 that the colonial revolution across the Atlantic went largely unnoticed. But Americans proved able at the application of what had been demonstrated in the home country. Paul Revere built the first rolling mill in America, copied from an English prototype. Samuel Slater came here from England carrying in his head the plans for our first power-driven factory, built at Providence, Rhode Island. From England also came Henry Maudslay's machine tools, James Watt's steam engine, and Thomas Newcomen's locomotive. But Americans knew how to use these tools and had the resources of a continent to exploit. By the middle of the nineteenth century, the colonials who had startled Europe with their claim for "separate and equal station among the powers of the Earth" were secure in that station as one of its first industrial powers.

When Alexis de Tocqueville visited America he had this to say of the state of our science: "In America the purely practical part of science is admirably understood, and careful attention is paid to that theoretical portion which is immediately requisite to application. On this head Americans always display a clear, free, original, and inventive power of mind. But hardly anyone in the United States devotes himself to the essentially theoretical and abstract portion of human knowledge."

One American who met De Tocqueville's specifications was Rufus Porter, founder in 1845 of *Scientific American*. He was also the inventor of the camp chair that folds up into a cane and a horse-powered treadmill for ship propulsion. More important, according to the Society for the History of Aeronautics, he was the first man to fly a working model of an "aircraft propelled by its own power plant installed aboard." Porter's "aerial locomotive" was to be floated aloft by a two-hundred-foot-long, hydrogen-filled paper-and-lathe dirigible and propelled by a charcoal-burning steam engine driving an airscrew. He demonstrated this "safe and pleasant way to travel to California in 3 days" in the form of a one-tenth-scale model, which he flew successfully before large crowds in public parks and armories up and down the land from Washington, D.C., to Boston. A fire in his workshop in 1850 burned up his full-scale ship in the early stages of construction and along with it his capital, including the tools and materials he had bought with the proceeds of the sale of *Scientific American*. Porter was also somewhat of a poet. He helped the country to celebrate the invention of the telegraph with this buoyant verse:

> He who created heaven and earth,
> And gave the rolling thunder birth,
> Hath kindly unto Morse revealed
> What heretofore had been concealed.
> He doth the rapid lightning tame—
> A Telegraph he calls its name—
> And with a single vivid flash,
> A dot—a space—a line—a dash—
> Can send around the earth the news,
> Or stop it, just as he may choose.
> What a mysterious mighty power!
> No noise is heard—no cloud doth lower,
> And yet the lightning wings its way,
> And tells whate'er we have to say.

This was the time when the teaching of science came into its own, with the founding of the first institutes of technology and the installation of science curricula in the colleges that dotted the land from Cambridge, Massachusetts, to Danville, Kentucky. But not one of these institutions could be classed as a center for research and the advance of learning. Their function was to teach. They taught a prescribed curriculum of classics, mathematics, and elementary science. Teaching was by drill and rote. If all went well, the wayward, contumacious youth would be chastened by discipline as well as fitted with knowledge.

The life of the American scholar and scientist was in bleak contrast to that of his contemporaries in Europe. There, the great universities were self-governing communities of schol-ars, whose corporate integrity could be traced back a thousand years, to the autonomy of the guilds and the sovereignty of the Church. They jealously protected their independence and cherished the advance of learning. American colleges, in con-trast, were the creatures of their communities. They were governed by lay boards, in this period still composed princi-pally of churchmen, and the professors were employees. The trustees naturally expected the professors they hired to teach what was right and not to disturb the community by seeking after truth. As late as 1869 Charles William Eliot, in his in-augural address as president of Harvard College, had to declare that his institution did not possess, "with the single exception of the endowment of the Observatory . . . a single fund primarily intended to secure the men of learning the leisure and means to prosecute original researches."

The first man of science to hold his position at Harvard, Eliot turned at once to remedy this situation. He took as his model the universities of Germany. With the organization of the faculty of arts and sciences at Harvard, the college became a university, and the advancement of science was established as a recognized function of American institutions of higher learning. All across the land, college presidents set out to make their colleges into universities; at Johns Hopkins, Chicago, and Stanford, Daniel Coit Gilman, William Rainey Harper, and David Starr Jordan built their universities from the level ground. To secure the princely sums required, this remarkable generation of academic entrepreneurs showed captains of in-dustry the way to sunset careers in philanthropy. The method that worked best with these men was an appeal to their interest in the advancement of science. Out of their respect for the demonstrated utility of science, they could be persuaded to endow it and other fields of learning as well.

As science served to encourage the support of scientists and scholars, science in this period also provided a rationale for their freedom. The first assertion in America of academic freedom in its modern sense was occasioned by the controversies over Darwinism that engrossed the public at the end of the Civil War. At a number of colleges, including Columbia, sectarian trustees brought members of their science faculties under inquisition upon charges of atheism. In the scandals that followed, the trustees discovered that Americans had been learning to prize science above Revelation in a substantial sphere of human experience.

While it was difficult to excite public interest in the academic freedom of a historian—and downright hazardous to argue for the economist's right to think his own thoughts—all fields of learning found affirmative grounds for their independence in the moral values of science. The demonstrable and accumulative success of science showed that the test of truth could no longer be whether it was agreeable or orthodox, but whether it was supported by evidence. The test of the scholar was to be his competence, not his opinions or associations. The ultimate ground for arguing the claims of evidence and competence against all other considerations was the pragmatic faith in progress, shared by trustees and public alike and powerfully confirmed by the burgeoning growth and prosperity of the nation.

The inquisitions into Darwinism were only the first skirmishes in the struggle for academic freedom in America. The last battle has by no means been fought. Thanks to the secure independence of the universities in England and France, the dismissal of one of their professors is unthinkable on any but moral or criminal grounds. In America, only a few universities have sufficient prestige to sustain their independence in public controversy involving members of their faculties.

Throughout most of the country, the sole statute protecting academic freedom is a resolution of the American Association of University Professors, first passed in 1915 and amended to its present form in 1940. It sets up standards of appointment,

culminating in life tenure, and a kind of due process to govern
dismissal procedures. These principles have been incorporated
into the bylaws of only a few institutions. But the professors'
resolution carries undoubted weight even with the most insensitive administrators. It is backed by the 40,000 members of
the Association. The resolution establishes the terms of reference that define the issues in the case of a beleaguered col-
league and a ground on which to appeal to public conscience.
Thus, by democratic action and invention, American scientists
and scholars have secured recognition and protection of their
freedom not provided otherwise by our law or tradition.

This recollection of the historical background of academic
freedom in the United States has an important relevance to
current events. No article or section of the Constitution provides for the freedom of the scholar as such. The Constitution
protects the scholar only insofar as he is endowed with the
same rights and dignity as any other individual. The pragmatic
arguments in favor of academic freedom, which carry such
weight in public controversy, find no echo in the Constitution.
There one finds no appeal to utility. The individual's rights
derive from natural law, and they are absolute. Thus, if the
Constitution offers the scholar and scientist any protection at
all in his line of work, it is the same protection that it extends
to all other citizens against infringement of their liberty by the
power of government.

In order to secure their freedom to work for the advancement of knowledge free from the control of trustees and
vigilantes, scholars and scientists in America had to set up their
own system of moral suasion. In doing so, they won for
their professions the esteem of their fellow citizens. It is a
limited esteem, however, qualified by the fact that the advancement of knowledge leads other citizens as well as
scholars and scientists forward into the unknown. What is to
be found there is not always agreeable at first sight. Sometimes
it takes a generation or two before the most recent shock to

received orthodoxy becomes embedded in common sense. The American folk culture has now absorbed the origin of species; presumably it will absorb a continued increase in understanding on many other matters. Eventually, we may hope, the public will come to comprehend and cherish the process by which such increase in understanding is attained. It is fair to say, on the whole, that the American academic community has worked out a reasonable *modus vivendi* with the community at large.

During the past decade, however, a new element has entered the life of scientists and scholars in America. This is their increasingly intimate involvement with the power of the government. The experience is not unique. It is shared by citizens in every occupation. Government has assumed a larger role in the life of everyone in our increasingly complex and centralized society. But science has probably felt the impact of this revision in the relations of government to citizen more than any other profession. There are few scientists in the United States today who are not dependent, directly or indirectly, upon the federal government for support of the work they are doing.

People who find themselves in this situation nowadays soon discover that the citizen's relationship to his government is complicated by a new doctrine. The federal government in recent years has assumed the power to legislate and regulate in a realm of citizenship from which it was excluded by the clearest language in the Constitution. This is the realm of public speech and assembly. The government predicates its power on the constitutional doctrine of "clear and present danger."

This phrase and the fundamental revision in the Constitution which it implies first appeared in one of the relatively few majority opinions of the Supreme Court written by Oliver Wendell Holmes. The case at issue was one that arose out of the concern with individual loyalty that swept the country at the end of the First World War. Where the Constitution made the rights of the sovereign citizen paramount, the Holmes opinion places these rights on a par with the security of the state: clear and present danger to the state may require the curtailment of the individual's liberty of opinion, speech, and association. In the language of Felix Frankfurter, it has now become a question of "balance." Individual freedom and national security, in other words, are two desirable objectives that may, upon occasion, be found to be in conflict. It is then the difficult responsibility of government to balance the claims of the two sides, weighing "risk for risk." The federal government, through its executive, legislative, and judicial agencies, thereupon becomes the (hopefully) evenhanded dispenser or withholder of the rights of citizenship. Unfortunately, when the government is called upon to weigh the security of the nation against the freedom of an individual citizen, it is all too easy to predict on which side the scales will fall.

We have been living in a prolonged period of anxiety and concern for national security. And we have seen a progressive decline in the sovereignty of the citizen. The onset of this erosion came at the end rather than the beginning of the Second World War. It is true that, at the outbreak of the war, the Japanese-American residents of the West Coast were transported from their homes, businesses, and farms to what were politely called relocation centers. Except for this incident, however, our national security met the test of actual warfare with a comparatively minor cost to our heritage. As in the unsettled world situation after the First World War, it is in the cold war that the damage has been done.

The demagogue, playing his traditional role, has given the period most of its headlines and much of its color. But congressional committees have involved comparatively few individuals in their proceedings. A far larger number of citizens —something like one tenth of the labor force—are embroiled in the no less repugnant procedures of the personnel loyalty and security program conducted by the executive department. Moreover, the precedents established by the federal legislature and executive have induced a pandemic of loyalty investigations and security programs on every level of government from state to village, at the furthest remove from any imaginable connection with national security. The infection has spread even into private organizations, in industry and labor, education and the press. The unnatural climate of fear, distrust, and conformity thus engendered among citizens everywhere has prompted Chief Justice Warren to declare that the Bill of Rights might not be adopted if it had to be submitted now to a vote by the American people.

In a review of the policies established by Congress and the executive for the purpose of combating activities held to be inimical to national security, John Lord O'Brian declares that "in reality we have been establishing something like a new system of preventive law applicable to the field of ideas and essentially different from traditional American procedure. Until these new administrative policies were adopted, this nation had adhered firmly to the traditional Anglo-Saxon method of combatting activities of an anti-social character. . . . In the past nothing has more clearly differentiated the basic principles of free government from those of despotism in the police state. In recent years, however, punitive remedies against unorthodox political ideas have been increasingly imposed, on the theory that unless such preventive action is taken the communication of such ideas will be the direct cause of acts which are wrongful in themselves. This of course has long been the practice of those foreign systems of law which failed to give recognition to the presumption of innocence characteristic of Anglo-American jurisprudence."

The blight of conformity which this change in the American climate has laid upon scholarship in the humanities is vividly experienced by scholars in those fields and deplored by the critics of our arts and letters. It is evidenced in the disappearance of significant controversy from our politics and press, and it is reflected in the continued decline in the cultural values represented and promoted by our mass media. But conformity has had its effect also on the life of science in America. This is the case even though the quandaries in which physics finds itself today might seem to be far removed from the realm of political opinion in which national security is said to be engaged.

Science has given a kind of eerie reality to the science-fiction menace of the saboteur and spy. Large areas of science are involved in the weaponeering to which the national security is committed. Although no real scientists have turned up among the atomic spies, all scientists are suspects. Through their dependence upon government subsidy, scientists have been brought into the toils of the personnel loyalty and security program in large numbers and have figured prominently in the public pillories of the free-lance investigators. Communication by publication in important areas of research is inhibited by secrecy. A new criterion of semi-secrecy is now being promoted by an agency of the Department of Defense which is charged with the mission of controlling the publication of non-secret work; papers and reports relating to such work would be circulated in private to pre-selected lists of workers in each case, on the theory that this constriction of the traditionally open channels of scientific communication would inhibit the progress of science in other nations to a greater degree than it would cripple progress in our own country. Communication by direct contact between scientists, which is so often more important than the written word, is hampered by the caprice of the Passport Bureau of the State Department. It has been said that the only place in the United States where an international meeting of scientists can be held is Ellis Island.

Now, each of us holds dear his own right to form judgments and opinions and to speak his mind. For the sake of our right we declare our readiness to defend this right for others. The connection between free speech and good government is also widely recognized. The value of a man's opinions is not to be measured by his capacity to withstand intimidation and coercion. The best test, in the words of Justice Holmes, is "the power of the thought to get itself accepted in the market place of ideas."

The stake each of us has in the integrity of the next man's freedom has been amply demonstrated in this period of conformity. The trials and tribulations of a few unimportant heretics attracted little public sympathy at the time when the doctrine of clear and present danger made it a crime to advocate an opinion held to be inimical to national security. But now we have seen that once one brand of opinion can be suppressed under the authority of law, the way is open to the suppression of others. It is not necessary to pass new statutes. On the contrary, it is an ancient experience, only the more vividly confirmed by our own, that when the label of heresy has been attached to a particular opinion it can be adapted for application to a wide range of opinions, around all points of the compass, even to opinions directly opposed to the one first labeled. In the report of a recent congressional investigation, the entire scientific enterprise was implicated by a finding that subsumed "empiricism" and "materialism" into the heresy of our time.

What gives heresy its gravity as a charge, whether before the courts or in public opinion, is that it is the devil's own work. Historically, and in our times, heresy is the crime of treating with the powers of outer darkness. In one ugly word, it is treason. Through the popularization of heresy in our country today, the crime of treason has escaped from Article III, Section 3, where it was confined by the authors of the Constitution. Heresy is treason by opinion and not by action, a treason strange to our laws but familiar in history. The resulting pollution of political and cultural controversy recalls the words of James Madison: "As new-fangled and artificial treasons have been the great engines by which violent factions . . . have usually wreaked their alternate malignity upon each other, the convention have, with great judgment, opposed a barrier to this peculiar danger, by inserting a constitutional definition of the crime, fixing the proof necessary for conviction of it and restraining Congress, even in the punishing of it . . ."

As in seventeenth-century Salem, responsible and respectable, non-heretical citizens have begun to take countermeasures, because the cows are not being milked and the harvest is beginning to rot for lack of harvesters. It is apparent that the recklessness of congressional inquisitions is to be curbed. Criticism of the executive department's personnel security proceedings has brought reforms that will supposedly make these proceedings fairer to the defendant. Such reforms must fail, however, to get at the heart of the matter; that is, the question whether these proceedings have any place whatever in the American system. To reform them while failing to challenge them on the essential grounds of propriety is to endorse them and install them the more permanently in the machinery of government.

The impropriety of inquiry into men's minds was recognized by the natural lawyers of the eighteenth century. As practical men, they would agree that their moral absolutes could also be regarded as summary statements of the wisdom of experience. The witchcraft trials of sixteenth- and seventeenth-century England had shown that "the Devil himself cannot try the soul of man."

But there is still another aspect to freedom of speech, which transcends the speaker's stake in his own opinion. This is the right of the community to hear what he has to say. John Stuart Mill defined the stake of the community in these plain words: "The peculiar evil of silencing the expression of an opinion is, that it is robbing the human race; posterity as well as the existing generation; those who dissent from the opinion, still more than those who hold it. If the opinion is right, they are deprived of the opportunity of exchanging error for truth; if wrong, they lose, what is almost as great a benefit, the clearer perception and the livelier impression of truth, produced by its collision with error."

The tolerance of error, then, is a need of the community. It is a need each of us tends to overlook in our eagerness to hawk our own wares in Holmes's market place of ideas, a need that Holmes himself overlooked in coining that phrase. The case for the right to hear as well as to speak was stated with great shrewdness and clarity by Alexander Meiklejohn in his Walgreen Lectures in 1948. Within the past month, in an appearance before the U.S. Senate Committee on Constitutional Rights, he put it this way:

"When men govern themselves it is they—and no one else —who must pass judgment upon public policies. And that means that, in our popular discussions, unwise ideas must have a hearing as well as wise ones, dangerous ideas as well as safe, un-American as well as American. Just so far as, at any point, the citizens who are to decide issues are denied acquaintance with information or opinions or doubt or disbelief or criticism which is relevent to those issues, just so far the result must be ill-considered, ill-balanced planning for their general good. It is that mutilation of the thinking process of the community against which the First Amendment is directed."

Perhaps the operation of the principle in the life of science may help to sharpen its meaning for society. In science, error has high pragmatic value. As should be more widely understood, the process of induction which brings the rational method to grips with nature does not consist in mere collection of facts. It begins always with a question. The question necessarily derives from a hypothesis; that is, a preliminary and tentative prediction of what the experiment is going to show. In the history of science wrong hypotheses have, beyond any doubt, outnumbered those that turned out to be right. Only the lucky man makes the right guess the first time in advance. Most often the labor begins with a wrong hypothesis; experiment exposes the fallacy; the question is reframed and confronted with experiment until at last the wisely framed question leads to a new finding supported by secure evidence. Science must thus be regarded as much an error-correcting activity as a truth-finding process. Clearly, any inhibition laid upon the freedom to ask wrong questions—such as might be imposed by some orthodoxy—must mutilate the scientific process.

But error has an even deeper meaning in the progress of science. A discovery gains its primary significance from the new questions that it poses. In other words, no statement about nature can ever be closed or final. Every truly significant statement is correspondingly burdened with potential error. This is the inherent risk of venture into the unknown.

What is more, this entrapping of error at the heart of truth has turned out to be implicit in the very foundations of logic. According to the famous proof of Kurt Gödel, every set of premises must bear within it a contradiction or paradox. The paradox can be resolved only by the addition of another premise to the set, but this stratagem ineluctably generates yet another contradiction.

The moral of this analysis for the conduct of human affairs is plain. Democracy and science are together inherently progressive because each is open to and tolerant of error. The vitality of the scientific enterprise is thus a sensitive measure of the health of a society. It is true that closed societies can carry on effective work in science for periods of time. But they do so only to the extent that they can draw upon the capital of work already accomplished. In the not very long run, the stifling of individual liberty must extinguish the search for truth. However much our contemporary utopians may lay their despair to science they cannot claim science for their polities. Science belongs to the society of the Social Compact and endures and grows only where men are free.

3

Our Industrial Culture

ONE OF OUR national assets at a critical hour in the Second
World War was four thick volumes containing nothing but
pages and pages of numbers. These pages of numbers had the
same forbidding opacity as the logarithm tables with which
most of us terminated our unhappy exposure to mathematics
in our second year of high school. But they were significant,
because, like those in the logarithm tables, these numbers expressed functions; that is, the numerical relationships between variables in a system of equations. The functions in this
case, called Bessel functions, after the nineteenth-century
astronomer Friedrich Wilhelm Bessel, expressed relationships
between variables at a somewhat more advanced stage than
trigonometry. The possession of these tables saved precious
hours of computation at many centers engaged in the urgent
business of developing new weapons for the fighting of the
Second World War. In the laboratory at Los Alamos, for example, the Bessel functions helped to facilitate calculations involved in the development of the most horrendous weapon
of all.

For the existence of these tables, the war effort was indebted to a less enthralling period of our nation's history.

They were, in fact, a boondoggle of the Works Progress Administration. They recalled a time when the nation had too many engineers and too many scientists and when even some of our 1,100 Ph.D.'s in the field of mathematics were to be found on W.P.A. In those days, before the giant mechanical brains had put in their appearance, the forbidding labor of computation blocked the application of advanced mathematical methods in many fields of engineering. With a surplus of ordinary human brains available—unemployed clerks and accountants and the like—the mathematicians on W.P.A. put them to work compiling tables of Bessel functions and many other much needed numbers.

Today, with billions of dollars in public and private funds available each year for research and development, all kinds of urgent projects go begging for lack of engineers and scientists. The shortage of talent is advertised in all of our major cities by pages of display copy in the help-wanted sections of the Sunday newspapers. One corporation president has declared his readiness to hire the entire class of 1955, from engineers on up through Ph.D.'s in physics. Today there are no unemployed mathematicians. Nearly a fourth of them have left the campus to go to work for industry, where they command a median salary of $9,100 a year.

It may seem surprising then, in this seller's market for their talents, that there are scientists and mathematicians who sigh for the old days. Physicists recall the times when "sealing wax and string and love" were all they needed to do their work. Some mathematicians have even been heard to say that they wish they were back on W.P.A.

The discontent among the scientists arises from their feeling that the work for which they are now so well paid is not the work of science. The billions available for expenditure on research and development, in the view of many scientists, are not going toward the improvement of the situation of science in America. On the contrary, these expenditures are using up irreplaceable resources. The money and the talent that it buys are going not into the advance of science and the lofty, long-range goals it sets for human capacity, but the lowly, short-term gains of practical advantage in weapons, productive machinery, and consumer goods. For the future welfare of our technology and our science alike, they fear that irreversible damage is being done to our scientific resources.

It is a confession often made by American engineers and scientists that the United States has made less than its proportionate contribution to the advance of basic scientific knowledge. In the words of one distinguished chemical engineer, Crawford Greenewalt, president of the Du Pont Company, "We have been fortunate in the past in having available to us the results of basic science from the world at large. This has permitted us to indulge our industrial genius without at the same time contributing our fair share to the world's fund of basic knowledge."

Among the few Americans who are credited with major achievements in the advance of basic understanding is Benjamin Franklin. His investigations of the nature of lightning—according to the Latin inscription on a famous portrait: "He snatched lightning from the sky and the scepter from the hand of the tyrant"—establish him as an experimenter of the first rank; it is less well known that Franklin made fundamental contributions to the theory of electricity—represented by such terms as "charge," "plus" and "minus," "current," and "pressure"—which are still used in the textbooks of today. We have to skip more than a century of American history before we come to Josiah Willard Gibbs, whose contributions to the theory of thermodynamics pervade all of the disciplines in industry and in science that deal with the behavior of matter.

It is difficult, of course, to measure a nation's attainments in any branch of culture, even science, by objective standards. If we take the admittedly special record of the annual award of Nobel Prizes for such a standard, however, we see that it is not until the present generation that American scientists begin to win these prizes in proportion to our possession of the world's wealth and technological power.

Our industrial system rests upon discoveries of fundamental new knowledge and basic scientific principles which were made in Europe. It was there that scientists formulated the laws governing the play of natural forces, the transformations of energy and the nature and behavior of matter and energy, the chemical behavior of matter, that underlie the giant achievements of American industry. Even in our own day, we have seen the technology of nuclear energy arise from the work of scientists who came to our country from abroad.

In the realm of applied science as well, we must credit Europe with such basic developments as the machine tool, the steam engine, the steam turbine, the dynamo, and the internal combustion engine. Like the Soviet Union today, America was able to import a largely full-grown and mature technology from abroad to accomplish its industrial revolution. As recently as the First World War, the American economy was dependent upon Germany for its supply of critical organic chemicals. Only with the seizure of the German patents did American industrial enterprise enter this field.

Thus, the primary technological distinction of the United States lies neither in fundamental science nor even in engineering. America's pre-eminence rests upon the national capacity to organize technology on a grand scale. For the evocation of this capacity, Americans have been fortunate in the possession of the resources of a continent and a political system that made the continent the market for its own abundance. American industry could take advantage, as could no other national industrial establishment, of the efficiencies made possible by capital investment. The result is the giantism that characterizes American technology. The efficient unit of production in America is larger than in any other country. Our steel industry can build an entire plant around a high-speed, continuous-strip mill that rolls a ribbon of steel ten feet wide. The only reason for rolling such a wide strip is the convenience and economy of the one-piece automobile roof, drawn with one stroke of a giant press; the widest sheet rolled abroad is eighty inches. Similarly, it is only in the United States that an automobile manufacturer can tool an engine plant for the production of ten million identical units and thereby achieve a degree of automatization that is the envy of engineers abroad. The resultant reduction in the labor cost of American manufactured products prices them within the means of the mass market.

Science did not begin to receive the encouragement of significant patronage in this country until the turn of the century. It was then that the first giant fortunes accumulated in the American industrial revolution became available for such nonutilitarian enterprises as the advancement of learning. In testimony to the patrons' aspiration to disassociate their philanthropy from the harsh world of industry and commerce, the largest sums went to astronomy and medical research. Consequently, it was in these fields that American science first established claim to world eminence. No other nation's scientific establishment approaches the American in the magnificence of its observatories, and the United States excels all other nations in the number of first-rate medical research institutions per unit of population.

Other departments of science in our universities came in for their share of funds during the first half of this century, through the swelling of university endowments. A decisive role in the broadening and diversification of support was played by the Rockefeller fortune. It financed the reconstruction of the entire system of medical education and set the system on the path of self-sustained progress, with teaching fructified by research. The list of Rockefeller fellows contains, among others, the names of the first generation of

American nuclear physicists—Rabi, Oppenheimer, Lawrence, Allison, Smyth, and others—whose fellowships took them to the great centers in Europe for their training in this new field. In big sums, Rockefeller money went to the creation of new centers of scientific enterprise, at the Rockefeller Institute in New York City, at Vanderbilt University, and at Washington University in St. Louis. In smaller sums, in accord with the strategy devised by Warren Weaver, the Rockefeller Foundation laid "greatly increasing emphasis on biology and psychology, and on those special developments in mathematics, physics and chemistry which are themselves fundamental to biology." There is no doubt that this strategy contributed heavily to the great distinction of American science in genetics, biochemistry, biophysics, and the other growing points in the life sciences where physics and chemistry have been brought to bear. When the first generation of American nuclear physicists was ready with original work of its own, it was Rockefeller money that staked them in the building of the first giant accelerator, the Berkeley cyclotron, completed in 1940, just in time to make its contribution to the Manhattan Project. That the Rockefeller influence was considerable may be judged from the calculation that the total Rockefeller outlay at least equaled the total endowment income available to science in our universities through the first four decades of this century.

On a dollar basis, however, the most impressive development in this period was the initiation and the expansion of industrial research, starting in those industries that were dependent upon the most recent advances in science, first the communications and electrical industries and then, after the First World War, the chemical industry. By 1940 the nation's total annual investment in research and development had climbed to $350 million. This was a little less than 0.5 per cent of our gross national product and compared unfavorably with the 1 per cent or more that was maintained in England

and Germany. Characteristically, the bulk of these funds, $240 million, came from industry. Some $70 million was provided by the federal treasury, and only $35 million, a tenth of the total, came from other sources, including university endowments.

It is a commonplace that money has strings tied to it. Given the fact that most of the money for science was supplied by taxpayers and stockholders, we must conclude that the bulk of it was directed to applied science—or science as means to an end—rather than science as an end in itself. On the most favorable basis, it has been calculated that not more than one dollar out of every six was then going to the support of basic research.

Of course, the dollar figure may not be the most reliable index of the division of effort. It costs a great deal more to do industrial research than to equip a pure mathematician with his blackboard and chalk. But in England, where the development of industrial research was admittedly retarded, the corresponding ratio of support for applied research was estimated to be about fifty-fifty.

It was at the outbreak of the Second World War that the United States first came to recognize science as an essential element of national strength, to be ranked equal in importance to the industrial and military establishments. From the outset, the scientific community was the most thoroughly mobilized of all of the elements in our population. Thanks to the indiscriminate policies of our draft act, teaching as well as basic research was suspended for the duration. The nation's scientists became engineers for the duration, engineers in the all-embracing discipline of scientific warfare.

The mobilization of science for the Second World War makes a memorable chapter in our history. Whereas the industrial might and the manpower of the nation were mobilized under draft, the scientists of the country came forward on their own initiative to press their services upon the government. Long before Pearl Harbor, the "uranium committee" assembled the few score workers in the new science of nuclear physics. They rounded up their own funds, set up their own security system, and conducted the first fateful and conclusive experiments before they persuaded the federal government to back them in the Manhattan Project. Less well known is the story of the research in biological warfare, which originated in a masterful two-hundred-page monograph prepared by two Columbia University biologists and submitted by them in secret to the War Department.

These and other volunteer efforts were co-ordinated by the organization of the Office of Scientific Research and Development as a formal government agency. Headed by leaders of the scientific community, this agency not only deployed its own substantial budget but guided the expenditure of a tenfold increase in the annual federal outlay for research. The concerting of money and talent reduced years of development to months and brought such spectacular new arts and devices as radar and sonar, the proximity fuse, and servomechanism control of gunfire from the laboratory to the battlefield in time to play a decisive part in victory. With equal dispatch, it brought penicillin and blood plasma into mass production to reduce battlefield deaths to less than 2 per cent of the wounded delivered to battalion aid stations on the battlefield. The Applied Mathematics Panel of the O.S.R.D. brought radically new and powerful methods to the task of quality control in the factories and to the rationalization of the technology and tactics of aerial warfare. But no development so completely symbolizes the role that science played in the fighting of the war as the double thunderclap at Hiroshima and Nagasaki.

In the demobilization, there was no cutting of expenditures for research and development comparable to the slashing of budgets in other departments of the federal government. Government and industry were now committed to support science on the same grand scale to which it had become so uncomfortably accustomed in the war. The nation's annual outlay for science has mounted from $350 million in 1940 to more than $3 billion in 1955.

In the universal euphoria the one note of dissent was sounded by the scientists themselves. Their mood is best expressed in a mournful ballad sung by the atomic scientists at one of their first professional meetings at the end of the war. The last verse goes:

Take away your billion dollars, take away your tainted
  gold,
You can keep your damn ten billion volts, my soul will
  not be sold.
Take away your Army generals; their kiss is death, I'm
  sure.
Everything I build is mine, and every volt I make is pure.
Oh, dammit! Engineering isn't physics, is that plain?
Take, oh take, your billion dollars, let's be physicists again.

The sentiments of the atomic scientists were shared by the scientific community at large. With equal eloquence, in prose, other scientists urged all who would listen to take account of the important distinction between engineering and science. They presented their brief to the public in an impressive series of hearings before the Kilgore Committee of the U.S. Senate and in the Bush and the Steelman reports, prepared at the direction of Presidents Roosevelt and Truman.

Things like atomic bombs and penicillin, they said, show us what we can do with knowledge we have already won. This application of existing knowledge to practical ends is the business of applied science, or engineering. Science, in contrast, is concerned with increasing our knowledge through the investigation of the unknown. The continued progress of applied science requires sustained advance in pure science. As the Bush Report declared: "Basic research leads to new knowledge. It provides scientific capital. It creates the fund from which the practical applications of knowledge must be drawn. New products and new processes do not appear full-grown. They are founded on new principles and new conceptions, which in turn are painstakingly developed by research in the purest realms of science."

With pure science suspended for the duration, the wartime developments had eaten heavily into the accumulated capital of scientific knowledge. Vannevar Bush said: "We have been living on our fat." The Steelman Report pointed out that "our country has made less than its proportionate contribution to basic science" and that, in such projects as the atomic bomb, our scientists were merely exploiting basic knowledge that had been established abroad, by German, French, English, Russian, and Italian investigators. The destruction of the ancient centers of learning abroad portended the drying up of the traditional springs of new knowledge. With the continued neglect of science threatening to bring the advance of engineering to a halt, our industrial system faced the prospect of intellectual bankruptcy.

The reports were unanimous in prescription as well as diagnosis. It was clear that pure science could no longer depend on private philanthropy to offset the overriding demand by government and industry for applied science. The future of science was now dependent upon the taxpayer. Through their government citizens must now open up the endless frontier of science. Just as, in the past, the opening of the public domain had fostered the rise of our industrial prosperity, so the expanding public domain of scientific knowledge would guarantee its future.

Specifically, the reports urged the establishment of a National Science Foundation. This agency would be devoted exclusively to the financing of pure research. It would become the agency through which public funds, in tens of millions of dollars, could redress the balance in emphasis between pure and applied science.

Today, after a decade, the vision of an expanding public domain of pure science financed by the taxpayer is far short of realization. For lack of public interest, it took five years to get the National Science Foundation through Congress. In the interim, thanks to statesmanlike management, the Office of Naval Research served as a kind of under-the-table National Science Foundation, finding seagoing justification for such un-naval studies as the behavior of army ants and the navigation of bats. This year the National Science Foundation has $15 million to spend. But this outlay must support its entire program, including the financing of scholarships and fellowships as well as the backing of research. Meanwhile the total research and development budget of the federal government has mounted to $2 billion. The weight with which these huge expenditures fall upon the side of applied science is indicated by the fact that 75 per cent of the total is laid out by the Department of Defense and another 10 per cent by the Atomic Energy Commission.

Industry has meanwhile increased its expenditures nearly five times to more than $1 billion a year. The current directory of industrial research laboratories lists nearly 30,000 of these institutions. Their glass-brick façades and green lawns have become a familiar feature of the suburban landscape and the four-color covers of corporate annual reports.

As against the total $3 billion expenditure by industry and government, the income from endowments and philanthropy adds up to no more than $90 million, compared with $35 million before the war. If we enter the inflation discount, the free funds available to science for research in our universities are not much greater than in 1940. They constitute a minority interest even in the financing of the work of scientists within our universities. More than $500 million of the outlays of the federal government and industry is expended through contracts in universities and other non-profit laboratories. To put themselves in the way of these funds, our universities have been developing a new corporate device. This is the off-campus research institute, which undertakes applied research and development projects under contract to industry and government. By means of this device some insulation is provided for the university's own research laboratories against the stigma of commercialism and the nuisance of the security system surrounding military research. On the other hand, many institutions are conducting these extracurricular activities under their own roof.

It is difficult, of course, to determine in any exact way what proportion of the total national budget of somewhat more than $3 billion is expended on applied as against pure research. In the laboratory itself, there can be no hard and fast distinction. The most hopeful estimate of the National Science Foundation is that one out of every fifteen dollars of the government's expenditures goes to pure science. Given the even stronger practical bias that corporate management must lay upon the expenditure of its stockholders' funds, the emphasis in industrial expenditures must go more heavily to applied science. The truth, therefore, is that we are spending about one dollar on pure science for every twenty dollars available for applied science, as against the ratio of one to six which prevailed before the war.

The important point is that both kinds of money seek the time and talent of the same finite number of qualified investigators who constitute our country's primary scientific capital. A ratio of twenty to one in favor of applied science sets up a powerful and all-pervading pressure that subtly modifies the aims of a career in science, brings competing and inappropriate values into the university laboratory, and subverts the character of the scientific enterprise. The scientist who stays on the campus does so at the personal cost of a large differential in income and under the professional hazard of having to promote the largest portion of support for his work from external sources. In weaker institutions a professorship has come to be little more than a "hunting license," and even in strong institutions the standard of performance is to multiply "hard" money three times over in "soft," or short-term support. Industrial consultantships and research salaries attached to government contracts help to ease the personal-income differential; soft money comes most easily from sources interested in the project rather than the man. Quick solutions and the heady sense of participation in large events carry more immediate satisfactions than the lonely gamble on a lifelong work. These are the poignant circumstances expressed by the gross statistics of expenditure on science. They have prompted more than one honorable scientist to cry out for peace and quiet on the campus.

Meanwhile, in the big world outside of the academy, science continues to ascend in influence and prestige. Along with 400,000 engineers, industry now employs nearly 100,000 scientists. On the average, the technical personnel of industry represent one out of every forty employees. Some industries employ as few as ten workers for every engineer or scientist, and some companies, including some very big ones, have as few as five. The office of director of research has attained top-managerial status, and Ph.D.'s are moving thence with ease into full command—three of the seven largest chemical companies are headed by Ph.D.'s.

The arrival of the scientist in industry has had an almost equally remarkable effect upon the strategy of industrial management. With industry spending $30 billion a year on new plant and equipment, it is the initiative and judgment of the director of research that heavily determine what business his company will be in five years from now. The Du Pont Company reports that half of its sales and more than 75 per cent of its profits come from products that were in the research laboratory only ten years ago. The security analyst of today must consult the scientific journals as well as the balance sheet in forecasting the growth of corporations.

The acceleration in the tempo of technological progress continues itself to accelerate. Whereas it took one hundred years for the steam engine to make its arrival felt in economic and social history, and fifty years for electricity to have its impact, the present interval between a discovery in the basic sciences and its application in technology seems to have shrunk to a decade. Applied science has been brought into the closest liaison with current progress in the pure sciences. The gigantic industrial installations of nuclear technology embody ideas and concepts that existed in the heads of only a few physicists just a few years ago. In some industries, notably communications, electronics, aircraft, and chemicals, the progress of technology presses on the limits of knowledge. The prospect of power from the fusion reactions has brought the even more remote discipline of astrophysics into engineering. It is for assistance in these realms that industry and government now bring their hundreds of millions of dollars to the university laboratories and the off-campus research institutes.

There is much, therefore, to support the view that the continued progress of technology is confronted with an impasse. In our eagerness to exploit the possibilities of applied science, we have neglected the claims of pure science. As we use up the accumulated capital of basic knowledge, the progress of technology must slow down and come eventually to a halt.

Some of the questions confronting applied research are fundamental in the deepest sense and open new pathways in basic research. They would never have occurred to an investigator working in isolation from technology; they are generated by the high complexity of the industrial system. But the problems raised by technology tend to become the only fundamental ones, because they are advanced with the most compelling insistence by the system itself. Increasingly, the existing order of technology tends to assert the priorities of research and give direction to the work of science. Progress may therefore continue. But, as in organic evolution, the increasing intricacy and specialization of the system must set corresponding restrictions upon the possibilities for further growth.

It may be that we are already surfeited with technology—although that is a statement one hears only from citizens of the world's more fortunate nations. It may even be argued that existing technology is adequate to the satisfaction of the material wants of mankind, even with allowance for the present steep increase in world population. If the advance of technology supplied the sole motive for work in science, then the book might be closed without regret.

But, of course, this is not the case, and the work of science is not yet done. To bring the work to a stop, men must be made to stop asking questions. The brave new world that takes up this task will need all of the crushing and insidious power that a highly advanced technology can place in willful hands.

We still have many questions to ask; we have just begun, in fact, to ask the right ones. Our concern to be answered engages larger aspects of our existence than the utilitarian ends, vital as these are, that are served by technology. The appeal to utility, which helped to sell Congress on the National Science Foundation, must not be permitted to obscure the public's true interest in the public domain of science. That interest is identical with the true interest of the scientist; it is the need to understand. Paul Sears, a botanist and student of human ecology, has defined this interest: "It is the great destiny of science not to ease man's labors or prolong his life, noble as these aims may be, nor to serve the ends of power, but to enable man to walk upright without fear in a world which he at length will understand and which is his home."

If the scientific enterprise is to flourish under public

patronage, it must be supported for the right reasons. The taxpayer, who has succeeded the philanthropist as the patron of science, must advance those reasons. He must do so against the claims of special interests in government and industry that press forward with the wrong motives today.

What this implies is public support of higher education as well as of research, for the two functions of the university are inextricably involved with each other. Curiously, while university presidents set up new departments in their cabinets to solicit public funds, they continue to debate the propriety of public support. The bogey of political control of our universities fades, however, by comparison with the consequences of the present traffic with selfish interests. Peace and quiet must be restored to the campus. Our universities must be reconstituted as autonomous centers of initiative, independent of their sources of income and beyond intimidation in their service as primary springs of innovation and change in the life of society.

4

Security and Heresy

ORDINARILY history is a comforting study. In times of
trouble, we consult the record of the past for the guidance and
wisdom it has to offer. We are reassured, almost always, to
find that history has gone on.

Recently, many Americans have been consulting the
story of the times of the Alien and Sedition Acts, during
the early years of our republic, and of the Palmer raids at the
close of the First World War. We find ourselves living in an
ebb tide of the tradition of liberty that distinguishes the
history of our country. But the tide has been running out
longer and seemingly farther than in the past. History shows
us nothing quite like it. To understand what is going on, it
seems, we must look more closely into the present.

The stage was set by the Second World War. It is not only
that the battlefield casualties exceeded those of all wars of the
past. This was a war directed at the extermination of civil
populations. Millions of people were killed, not only in the
newly legitimized action of assault on great cities but in cold
blood behind the lines. Man's capacity for violence was
brought to its most savage expression in all of history. It re-

mained for this record of violence to be climaxed by a new kind of Apocalypse made in the U.S.A.

The American people were only a little less prepared than their President for the advent of atomic weapons. He first learned of the existence of the Manhattan Project after he had taken his oath of office and within eighteen weeks of the hour in which he ordered their use. The decision was made on strictly military grounds. The record indicates that almost no one, except the scientists who had fashioned the weapon, anticipated its political consequences. The killing of nearly 150,000 Japanese in two instants of annihilation sealed for the American people their complicity in the violence of war. The theaters of action up to this time had seemed far away in the immense domestic prosperity the war had brought to the nation. Peace came with fear at the end of a war that had found the people unafraid.

To fear there must be added another potent element—ignorance.

Nuclear fission was a discovery proceeding directly from the main line of research that had engaged the international fraternity of physicists for the previous two generations. The atom was nonetheless a secret to those outside of physics who had not before been aware of the enormous force that binds its nucleus. Despite the emergency public information campaign staged by the atomic scientists—despite the careful exposition of the truly open state of nuclear science and technology presented in the official Smyth Report—the myth of the secret quickly gathered overwhelming vested interests of its own. The illusory monopoly of atomic weapons became a keystone of national policy in the cold war that shortly got under way. For unscrupulous politicians and newspapers eager for circulation, the secret was an unexampled way to public notoriety. Nor could the pamphleteering and lecturing of a few scientists prevail when, in Canada, England,

and America, spies were arrested, tried, sentenced, and even executed for the betrayal of the secret.

Fear and ignorance must thus be reckoned as major elements in the climate of the last decade. It was in this climate that Americans convinced themselves they faced a choice of security or liberty, that security and liberty are the opposite horns of a dilemma. In the atomic age, the argument goes, it is not enough to catch the spy, the saboteur, and traitor after he has done his work. He must be caught in advance. New and unusual methods are needed to ferret out the intentions of those who may expose the security of the nation to harm. Such measures may infringe upon the dignity and privacy of the citizen, especially in the area of his opinions and associations. But these are measures to which any good American will submit in order to preserve the safety of the nation.

This view of the relativity of liberty is now firmly embedded in our law. It is a view advanced by conscientious and responsible public officials. At the same time, it has served well the purposes of the irresponsible and the unscrupulous.

During most of this period, it has been the legislative departments of our state and federal governments that have held the center of the stage. Under their powers of investigation, they have established a new kind of quasi-judicial proceeding which responsible lawyers and judges deplore as making conviction a mere matter of accusation.

We have recognized only more recently what an important role the executive department of the government has played in the increasing disregard for the traditional liberties of the citizen. It is, in fact, the personnel loyalty and security program of the federal government which has provided the major grist for the congressional mill.

The program was established by a President who professed himself as " 'hipped' on the question of civil liberties."

Executive Order 9835, issued on March 21, 1947, nonetheless, set up political opinion and association as criteria of an individual's fitness for employment by the federal government. The genuineness of the President's sentiments in regard to civil liberties is reflected in the character of the procedures set up under the program. They were intended to offer the employee fair play and the protection of a kind of due process of law, with the right to written charges, hearing, and appeal. It is these arrangements, as we shall see, that have most confounded the President's good intentions.

The record shows that the personnel loyalty and security program had significant political motivation. The investigative power of Congress had been turned upon the Administration. It is clear that the loyalty program was instituted in an effort to outflank the congressional committees on their inquisitorial right. Since the government was already well equipped by statute and procedure to ensure the reliability of personnel in its sensitive agencies, there is no other explanation for the blanket coverage that Executive Order 9835 laid upon the entire federal payroll of nearly three million men and women.

Today the program reaches far beyond the original three million. It has expanded outside of the federal payroll into the working force of private industry engaged on government contracts. It takes in the seamen and officers of our entire Merchant Marine. It involves, in ominous fashion, the more than two hundred institutions of higher learning that have government research contracts. Altogether, some six million citizens now find themselves living under the sanctions of the federal loyalty program.

It is important to consider the nature of these sanctions. Disloyalty by action is treason. Disloyalty by opinion carries the taint of treason. The charge of disloyalty—or its euphemism, "security risk"—threatens not only employment but employability, not only the tenure of a public servant but his membership in the community itself. This explains the gravity of the charge and the anxiety, heartache, and tragedy which the loyalty and security program has brought to thousands of citizens. But we are here not concerned with these matters that, in the words of Chief Justice Warren, "haunt our courts." It is our purpose to consider the program in its relationship to national security.

The personnel loyalty and security program is concerned with an undoubtedly real and proper responsibility of government officials. It is not too much to say it is their heaviest responsibility. The choice of personnel, more than any other decision, conditions the character of an organization and determines its efficiency and fiber. Like any other employer, the government is entitled to choose the people it determines are fit for the job that has to be done. No less than private employers, it has the right to expect competence, good moral character, sobriety, and loyalty of its employees. In the vast organization of the government, moreover, there are certain jobs involving responsibility for high policy and the custody of secrets of state. There are analogous positions in private employment. In filling these positions, the government and the private employer must take extra precautions.

We have had such sensitive agencies in our government since its beginning. The ordnance laboratories of the armed forces, the foreign service, the cryptographic bureaus of the military, and the Department of State were hiring people long before the laboratory at Los Alamos came into being. In the choice of such personnel, the question of loyalty comes up as a special one. Customarily, we have gone beyond the usual interview and checking of references to subject the prospective employee to the scrutiny of confidential investigation by intelligence agents. When the returns are in, however, the decision to hire has always, in the past, been made by the official in responsible charge of the agency.

In these cases, as in any other when a man is hired, it has always been his boss who had to take the risk. It is a risk that people must take every day; it is the largest one in life: the risk on the competence, integrity, and loyalty of other people. Against what he has learned about the man, from his own acquaintance with him and from the reports of his intelligence officers, the boss has to make the decision that the value of the man in the job will make good the risk that is involved in hiring him.

On this question of risk, we have some enlightening testimony from John J. McCloy. In positions ranging from Assistant Secretary of War to chairman of the board of the Chase National Bank, McCloy has hired cashiers as well as civil servants. In the record of a recent loyalty and security proceeding, his testimony was recorded as follows:

"One of my tasks in Germany was to pick up Nazi scientists and send them over to the United States. These Nazi scientists a few years before were doing their utmost to overthrow the United States Government by violence. They had a very suspicious background. They are being used now, I assume—whether they are still I don't know, because I am not in contact with it—on very sensitive projects in spite of their background. The Defense Department has been certainly to some extent dependent upon German scientists in connection with guided missiles. I suppose, other things being equal, you would like to have a perfectly pure, uncontaminated chap, with no background, to deal with these things, but it is not possible in this world. I think you do have to take risks in regard to the security of the country. Even if they put, say, Mr. Stimson or anybody in charge of the innermost secrets of our defense system, there is a risk there. . . . It is too bad you have to calculate sometimes. But in the last analysis you have to calculate what is best for the United States."

Let us take one instance of the normal operation of this risk-taking procedure. It was just such a calculation that made it possible to hire J. Robert Oppenheimer to head the Los Alamos laboratories of the Manhattan District during the

Second World War. This decision was made by a highly security-minded general officer of the United States Army, Leslie Groves. He made it despite the grave misgivings of his security officers, who had found many things to disturb them in what they had learned about Oppenheimer's political sympathies, opinions, and associations. One of these security officers had even come to the extreme conclusion that Oppenheimer was secretly an agent for a foreign power. General Groves hired Oppenheimer nonetheless. He did so in exercise of his responsibility as the officer in charge of an urgent military project. He weighed the risk of what had been reported to him by his subordinate intelligence officers against his own estimate of the man's character and fitness for the job at hand, and took the risk.

Other scientists about whom the security officers had grave doubts were also hired to work at Los Alamos. Some others were refused employment on the grounds of their prior associations and opinions and were kept on jobs at other stations in the project or were detached from civilian positions and drafted into the Army. The wisdom of each of these decisions might be subject to review and second guess. But the record shows that, on balance, the general's judgment was good. The project was a success.

The personnel loyalty and security program has brought some essential changes in this sensible procedure. The program first of all formally establishes standards of political opinion and association as the test of loyalty. More important, the program interposes between the responsible official and the prospective employee an impersonal quasi-judicial proceeding which is charged with the primary determination as to loyalty. The official is thus relieved of his personal responsibility for making this judgment of the fitness of the man for the job.

In successive "reforms" of the original Truman order, the burden of proof in the proceedings has been laid upon the employee with increasing weight. The employee, it is true, is furnished with a statement of the charges against him, but these may or may not disclose all of the charges on the docket before his judges. He has no right to cross-examine his accusers, and their identity may be concealed entirely from him. Nor does he have access to all the documents that may be in evidence before his judges.

The subordination of the rights of the employee built into this procedure is apparent. But there is another aspect to the procedure which is too often overlooked. This is the subordination of the resposible official and of his loyalty review board to the terms of the proceeding. They, as well as the prospective employee, are denied access to the secret files in which the charges originate. They, too, must arrive at their determination without being able to question the employee's accusers or to see all of the evidence that may be in the files. In military organizations, when a subordinate officer disputes an intelligence report but is not cleared for access to secret information, he can always appeal to a superior officer who is upstream from intelligence and empowered to review the entire record. But no one today stands upstream from the Federal Bureau of Investigation. On grounds of national security, this agency jealously protects the secrecy of its files and the identity of its informers. The effect of this arrangement is to make the country's secret police the ultimate authority on the fitness of people for employment by the government. The F.B.I. and its director, J. Edgar Hoover, have often enough disavowed any ambitions to acquire the authority that the proceeding willy-nilly lays at their door. They insist that the information which the F.B.I. provides to the security officers is unevaluated and that they make no judgment of the fitness of the employee. But such is the awe-inspiring volume of the contents of the agency's secret files that officials high and low are intimidated at the mention of the F.B.I. In fact, the public record shows that the President himself may be subjected to such intimidation. And a former President has been accused of willful or unwitting disregard for national security in exercising his own judgment of the value of an employee in the face of what the F.B.I. files contained.

The loyalty and security procedures have now been in force for some eight years. By this time, all of the approximately three million federal employees, plus an additional one million who have been on and off the payroll meanwhile, have gone through the mill. Just what has been accomplished is not clear. Some two or three thousand employees, it seems, have been separated from their jobs. This is a tiny fraction of the normal turnover and includes those found to be undesirable for such reasons as habitual intoxication. Some indefinite fraction is made up of those judged to be security risks. Among these, however, there was not one spy or saboteur. In fact, the program failed to uncover the single government employee who is now held for disclosing state papers to a foreign power. This man had passed the test of loyalty and security with flying colors.

If it has proved anything at all, the loyalty and security program has proved what we always have assumed, that Americans take pride in their citizenship and are imbued with a loyalty that is affronted when it is questioned. There is no assurance that we are better off for having fired two or three thousand public servants. The program has given us no surer or more objective measure of an employee's reliability than the individual, personal judgment of the cabinet members, commissioners, bureau chiefs, superintendents, postmasters, and straw bosses upon whom we have relied in the past.

Let us consider the operation of the system in one case in detail. It will show us why we can place no confidence in the loyalty and security proceeding as a way of proving anything. We shall see why concern for the sources of our national security requires that the program be abolished.

It is fitting that the principal prize of the program should have been J. Robert Oppenheimer. He was an architect of the atomic weapon that has given obsession with loyalty its major impetus. At the time this obsession took over, he was one of those who showed most eloquently how the pall of secrecy would menace the atomic energy program. In testimony before Congress, in his writings and speeches, he urged wider understanding of the fact that people are made of isotopes. The atom, he said, was "a gold brick."

As a respected spokesman of the scientific community, Oppenheimer served the government during the postwar period in the important task of mobilizing the talent of our scientists for the work of the Atomic Energy Commission and for the weapons program of the Defense Department. In the innermost councils of the government he functioned as a valued adviser on the technological revolution in warfare. The loyalty and security program would have had to reach into the Cabinet itself to find a bigger prize. When Oppenheimer appeared before the personnel security board convened by the Atomic Energy Commission to hear his case, the chairman, Gordon Gray, declared: "The security system itself is on trial."

We are fortunate in having a public record of the entire proceeding in the matter of J. Robert Oppenheimer. The transcript of the hearings runs nearly a thousand pages in Government Printing Office 8-point type; the principal briefs, documents, and letters run to several hundred more.

They tell us first of all that the proceeding in this case was not quite typical. Out of deference to the man, a more than usual effort was expended on a more than usually elaborate proceeding. The Gray Board testified in its report: "The Board worked long and arduously. It has heard 40 witnesses, including J. Robert Oppenheimer, and compiled over three thousand pages of testimony in addition to having read the same amount of file material. Dr. Oppenheimer has been represented by counsel, usually four in number, at all times in the course of the proceeding. He has confronted every witness appearing before the Board, with the privilege of cross-examination. He is familiar with the contents of every relevant document which was made available to the Board, except those which under government necessity cannot be disclosed, such as reports of the Federal Bureau of Investigation. He has, in his own words, received patient and courteous consideration at the hands of the Board. The Board has, in the words of his chief counsel, displayed fairness in the conduct of the hearings. And, finally, perhaps it should be said that the investigation has been conducted under the auspices of a responsible agency which has the obligation of decision."

If any such proceeding could prove anything about a man's loyalty and security, this one should have.

The proceeding began with a letter from Major General K. D. Nichols, general manager of the Atomic Energy Commission, to J. Robert Oppenheimer dated December 23, 1953. Such letters in the loyalty and security proceeding are equivalent to a bill of particulars in a case at law. They are supposed to tell the subject what his case is about. General Nichols's letter specified some twenty-four allegations about the opinions, associations, and activities of J. Robert Oppenheimer. Of these, twenty-three were concerned with his life antedating and up through the first years of the Second World War. The twenty-fourth was concerned with his role as adviser to the Atomic Energy Commission in the postwar period.

In the proceeding, these allegations were referred to as "charges." But upon analysis, it is not at all clear what the charges were charging. Some were evidentiary statements, to be taken as evidence of something, but of what, General Nichols did not specify. Other statements suggested conclusions, but these were not specified either. For example, charge No. 18—reading, in part: "It was further reported, however, that: . . . During the period 1942–1945 various officials of the Communist party . . . are reported to have made statements that you were then a member of the Communist party . . . that you had talked the atomic bomb question over with party members during the period . . ."—might appear to have been the most serious of all. What this third-hand hearsay implied was that the Los Alamos Laboratory had been directed throughout the war by a man who was secretly a member of the Communist party.

But all of the charges 1 through 23 had been considered before, and when one read them in the newspapers at the time of their release in April 1954, they seemed to have no specific gravity whatever. They had been known to General Groves back in 1942 when he had weighed the intelligence reports in his calculated risk. They had again been reviewed by the Atomic Energy Commission itself in 1947 when the loyalty and security order first came into force and J. Robert Oppenheimer was "processed" along with other federal employees. The first twenty-three charges, therefore, had no meaning in themselves.

If they had meaning in the context of the Nichols letter, and General Nichols did not say so, it was in connection with charge No. 24. This last charge was addressed to Oppenheimer's opinions and activities in connection with the hydrogen bomb. It said that he had "strongly opposed the development of the hydrogen bomb: (1) on moral grounds, (2) by claiming that it was not feasible, (3) by claiming that there were insufficient facilities and scientific personnel to carry on the development, and (4) that it was not politically desirable"; that Oppenheimer "had continued to oppose the project and declined to cooperate fully in the project" after it was determined to go ahead with it, and that he had been "instrumental in persuading other outstanding scientists not to work on the hydrogen bomb project, and that the opposition to the hydrogen bomb, of which [he] was the most experienced, the most powerful and most effective member, has definitely slowed down its development."

Apart from Oppenheimer's opinions in the matter, this charge specified one action in support of what it was implying. Oppenheimer was said to have "departed his role as advisor to the Commission and caused the distribution of the report to the General Advisory Committee opposing the hydrogen bomb to top personnel at Los Alamos for the purpose of trying to turn such top personnel against the development of the hydrogen bomb." It turned out on later examination that this specification was the result of bad intelligence work. The report had in fact been distributed at Los Alamos by General Nichols's own predecessor in the office of general manager, and with quite different objectives in mind. But the charge about Oppenheimer's opinions stood.

What did that charge mean? Was a recommendation on a matter of high policy to be adjudged evidence of disloyalty when decision was made against it? Was General Nichols trying to say, with charge No. 24 coming after charges 1 through 23, that Oppenheimer had treasonable motives in making the recommendation? General Nichols did not say so. But something like this is what the letter clearly implied. That is what James Bryant Conant deduced; he testified at the hearing: "It seems to me that clearly the question before you here is the question, rather is the implied indictment, I submit, namely, because of the information in the first part of this letter—Dr. Oppenheimer's association with alleged Communist sympathizers in early days in his youth—that that somehow created a state of mind in Dr. Oppenheimer so that he opposed the development of the hydrogen bomb for what might be said reasons which were detrimental to the best interests of the United States, because they were interests of the

Soviet Union which he had one way or another had at heart. That, I take it, is the issue which I take it is before you in part in considering this letter."

Vannevar Bush had no doubt on this score at all: "I feel that this Board has made a mistake and that it is a serious one. I feel that the letter of General Nichols which I read, this bill of particulars, is quite capable of being interpreted as placing a man on trial because he held opinions, which is quite contrary to the American system, which is a terrible thing. And as I move about I find that discussed today very energetically, that here is a man who is being pilloried because he had strong opinions, and the courage to express them. If this country ever gets to the point where we come that near to the Russian system, we are certainly not in any condition to attempt to lead the free world toward the benefits of democracy."

In response to anxious questioning by Gray and his colleagues, Bush declared further: "I think the moment you were confronted with that letter, you should have returned the letter, and asked that it be redrafted so that you have before you a clear-cut issue which would not by implication put you in the position of trying a man for his opinions."

The members of the Gray Board were greatly distressed at the suggestion that they were trying a man for his opinions. In their report, at the conclusion of the hearings, they took pains to disclaim any such intention. They went even further and rejected General Nichols's entire bill of particulars. They not only rejected the single conclusion that it implied; they rejected the evidentiary statements themselves as grounds for any adverse finding on Oppenheimer's fitness. Although they found that charges 1 through 23 were "substantially true," they were able to explain them away to their own satisfaction and conclude that they cast no reflection upon Oppenheimer's present integrity and loyalty as a citizen. Similarly, with regard to charge 24, the Board found that Oppenheimer's opposition to the hydrogen bomb, which he himself had acknowledged, involved no lack of loyalty to the United States and no attachment to the Soviet Union.

Having thus set aside the charges on which Oppenheimer was brought before it, the Gray Board had to develop a bill of particulars of its own in order to find him to be a security risk. They accordingly developed four brand-new charges from the transcript of the hearings itself.

The first, reflecting on Dr. Oppenheimer's more recent "conduct and association," held that he had a serious disregard for the requirements of the security system which Gordon Gray had said at the outset was itself "on trial." The second found that he had a susceptibility to influence by others—in diametric opposition to General Nichols's charge 24, which had pictured Oppenheimer as having a suspiciously undue influence upon others. The fourth declared the Board's sentiment that Oppenheimer had been "less than candid" in his testimony; this charge developed out of the country-courthouse tactics of the Board's counsel in his cross-examination on the question of Oppenheimer's motives for opposing the crash-program approach to the hydrogen bomb. The third charge fell with the greatest gravity of all. While the Board had held Oppenheimer blameless in his opinions on the hydrogen bomb, it concluded that he did not "show the enthusiastic support for the program which might have been expected of the chief atomic adviser to the government under the circumstances."

On the basis of this new bill of particulars, the Gray Board decided it was "unable to arrive at the conclusion that it would be clearly consistent with the security interests of the United States to reinstate Dr. Oppenheimer's clearance" and therefore did not so recommend. The verdict, in plain talk, was: Guilty!

But, guilty of what? No fair-minded observer can conclude that the weeks of proceedings and the thousands of pages of documents and testimony had proved anything whatever about General Nichols's original charges. On the new bill of particulars stated in the Gray Board findings, Oppenheimer's lawyers promptly asked for a hearing before the Atomic Energy Commission itself. The A.E.C. denied their request, permitting them only to file a written brief.

Meanwhile, despite the solemn treatment given by the press to the whole affair, something in the Gray Board findings had touched the risibility of the American people. The charge of lack of enthusiasm became the butt of satirical essays and cartoons on editorial pages not otherwise noted for a sense of humor or a concern for civil liberties. It appeared that the entire proceeding might be laughed out of court.

This crisis in A.E.C. public relations was met by the lodging of a third bill of particulars. In the letter that escorted the Gray Board findings to the commissioners, General Nichols reinstated the charges in his original letter that had been rejected by the Gray Board, with an amendment that transformed one of those charges into an entirely new charge of perjury.

On June 29, the day before Dr. Oppenheimer's appointment was to have expired in any case, the members of the A.E.C. completed their review in the matter of J. Robert Oppenheimer and issued their conclusion. They dismissed the Gray Board's deliberations in a paragraph and presented still another bill of particulars. To develop the new set of charges, the commissioners searched the transcript of the hearings. "The important result of these hearings," they said, "was to bring out significant information bearing upon Dr. Oppenheimer's character and association hitherto unknown to the Commission and presumably unknown also to those who testified as character witnesses on his behalf." They cited six episodes of conflict in testimony which had developed in Oppenheimer's responses to cross-examination about events in the past, including the one that occasioned the charge of perjury by the Commission's general manager. With the gratuitous statement that "the catalog does not end with these six examples," they declared them to be "proof of fundamental defects in his 'character.'" They also made a second, somewhat supererogatory, finding that "his associations with persons known to him to be Communists have extended far beyond the tolerable limits of prudence and self-restraint." The sole "association" cited in support of this charge involved a person about whom the record shows no clear evidence that he was ever a Communist, much less still a Communist in the 1950's, when Oppenheimer was so lacking in self-restraint and prudence as to extend his association with him.

With this fourth and last bill of particulars the case of J. Robert Oppenheimer was closed in the books of the A.E.C. Since the new set of charges was incorporated in the final judgment, Oppenheimer and his attorneys had no opportunity to respond to them by brief or hearing. J. Robert Oppenheimer stood convicted by accusation.

Although Oppenheimer and his lawyers could not respond to this last set of accusations, the conclusive answer to them was provided by the dissenting opinion of Henry DeWolf Smyth. The author of the Smyth Report gave the question at issue in these massive proceedings its first clear definition. The question, he said, was "whether there is a possibility that Dr. Oppenheimer will intentionally or unintentionally reveal secret information to persons who should not have it." To this question he found a plain answer: "There is no indication in the entire record that Dr. Oppenheimer had ever divulged any secret information." In the light of Smyth's clear logic, the accusations of his brother commissioners withered to the contrived, synthetic things they were. If fundamental defects of character were to be found, they were in the judgment not in the judged.

After eighteen months, it would seem that the judgment on

Oppenheimer has been reversed by public opinion. His luster in the public eye appears undimmed, as indicated, for example, by his appearance as the valedictorian of the bicentennial celebration of Columbia University. He has even retained his employment as president of the Institute for Advanced Study at Princeton, over which his erstwhile employer at the A.E.C., Lewis Strauss, presides as chairman; plainly, fundamental defects of character are more tolerable in scholarship than in public life.

Oppenheimer is a casualty of politics. As Norbert Wiener has observed: "Any scientist, participating in what has become a moving crap game, must expect to get slugged occasionally."

The injured party in this proceeding is the national security. It is not only that the government is deprived of the services of J. Robert Oppenheimer. Vannevar Bush spoke for many scientists when he testified before a congressional committee that "the way in which our security system is working at the present time is driving a wedge between the military and the scientific people of the country, and is doing great harm." Such estrangement of science and government, during this period of revolution in warfare, can only place in jeopardy the national security which the security system is supposed to protect.

But the effects of the Oppenheimer proceeding are not all bad. It has had the good result of helping to bring about the re-examination of the security system that is now under way. In this process, we may hope that people will not merely tinker and seek minor improvements, no matter how well intentioned. Reform must start with fundamentals. We have in the Oppenheimer case a voluminous record that demonstrates once again the futility of trial of opinion. It should remind us that the earliest victories in the struggle for liberty were won against such trials not only because they aroused public indignation at the grave injustice they did to individuals, but because manifestly they could prove nothing. The Gray Board echoed the dim forgotten past when it declared that it was its duty to "search the soul" of Oppenheimer. This, it was well said by the London *Economist*, "was a shocking claim to make on behalf of the State. A claim of divine prescience which even totalitarians do not bother to put forward."

Now, as we have been told often enough during the past ten years, a citizen has no right to a job on the public payroll. But if government service is not a right, then to many it comes as a public duty. Manifestly, employment by the government ought not to be conditioned on subjection to the workings of a system that tries to prove what cannot be proved. The citizen's good name is safer at the mercy of the caprice of a bureau chief. His security in his job is surely a matter of less moment than his security in his rights.

In those few positions in government service where questions of loyalty are matters of moment, it would be better if we set aside civil service regulations and let the precedents of our normal political life come into play. There are many ways in which an official can protect the national security from an employee in whom he has lost confidence. Short of firing, personnel can be shuffled and transferred to other work in the time-honored ways of bureaucracy. If the employee, in the judgment of one official, is not fit for government service, he should not be dismissed with a stigma that keeps other officials from exercising their independent judgment. When Charles E. Wilson found the employment of J. Robert Oppenheimer politically embarrassing to the Department of Defense, he simply abolished the Research and Development Board. Compared with what the A.E.C. found it necessary to do, Mr. Wilson was right when he said of his own action: "That was a pretty smooth way to handle that one."

There is another concern here, however, besides the question of justice to individuals. It comprises what John J. McCloy, in his testimony before the Gray Board, defined as "the security risk in reverse." It is the failure of the security program to take account of the true springs of our national security.

When the slurs on Oppenheimer's "character, association, and loyalty" are set aside, it can be seen that his dismissal from government service turned on disagreement over policy. As the Gray Board said, a scientist presuming to advise officials on policy matters must have "a genuine conviction that this country cannot in the interest of security have less than the strongest possible offensive capabilities in a time of national danger."

J. Robert Oppenheimer is not the only informed and thoughtful citizen who may be found from time to time advancing equally genuine convictions on the moral, financial, and diplomatic considerations, not to mention the considerations of defensive capability, which enter into national security and which may dilute the fervor of one's convictions about offensive capability. For Oppenheimer and the others it is a matter of concern that their opinions might be excluded from the councils of the government. But it is a matter of even deeper concern to the public that they be heard. Long before the hydrogen bomb, it was observed that war is too serious a matter to be left to the generals. Now, under the unlimited menace of hydrogen bombs, public safety requires that all views on national security be available to those to whom fateful decisions are delegated.

The discomfortingly intimate look at the federal personnel loyalty and security system provided by the Oppenheimer case explains not only why the system has failed of its objectives but why it has worked such demonstrable harm to the security of the nation. We can see that we have been mistaken in finding a dilemma between security and liberty. Experience now shows that compromise of freedom is itself a compromise of security.

"Republics," Machiavelli said, "have a longer life and enjoy better fortune than principalities, because they can profit by their greater internal diversity." If the nation is to find security, it can find it only in the cultivation of the liberties that shelter our diversity and make it possible for an Oppenheimer to be heard.

5

The New Paradise

W HATEVER may have been its reputation before, the University of Chicago is now firmly established in the public mind as one of the world's great centers of science. It was here, they say, that the atomic bomb was invented. Inscribed on the roster of the university faculty are such distinguished names as Harold Urey and the late Enrico Fermi. Fermi is the "Italian navigator" who discovered the principle of the uranium, or fission, bomb. And Harold Urey laid the groundwork for the hydrogen, or fusion, bomb.

There is just enough truth in this public image of the university to sustain a totally false picture of the institution and the men who have won for it this new fame. But the fact is that Enrico Fermi received the Nobel Prize for certain fruitful experiments involving the bombardment of atomic nuclei with particles called neutrons. Systematically he proceeded to expose each element in the table of elements to a flux of slow neutrons. These experiments yielded valuable understanding of the forces that hold the atomic particles, including neutrons, together in the atomic nucleus. When he received the Nobel Prize, neither he nor the judges in Stockholm were aware that, in one of his experiments, his neutron beam had caused the nuclei of the uranium atoms to split in a process which we now know as the fission reaction. It was only after his emigration to the United States, a political refugee from Fascism, that he learned the real significance of his experiment with uranium.

Harold Urey's fame equally distorts the significance of his work. He received the Nobel Prize for experiments in which he separated heavy water from ordinary water and thereby made possible the isolation of heavy hydrogen. The nucleus of the heavy-hydrogen isotope, called deuterium, contains one proton bound to a single neutron; it gives us the simplest instance of the nuclear binding force. Its separation in quantity opened up new ways to explore the properties of the nuclear force and the part that it plays in the structure of all matter. At the time, Urey could not have conceived of the possibility that the discovery of uranium fission would make heavy water a valuable industrial and military commodity.

These two scientists stayed on at the University of Chicago after the war because here they found an environment in which they could continue their fundamental studies. For both of them, their wartime experience in the fashioning of weapons of mass destruction was a deeply disturbing distraction from their work. It is for the increase in man's understanding of the universe and his own place in it that great universities exist and scientists carry on their investigations—not for the creation of atomic bombs or hydrogen bombs.

We can easily see, in principle, that such misunderstanding of science in our society presents serious hazards to both science and society. Let us now go from the general to the particular. By examining an actual instance of the effects of ignorance on public policy, we may take the real measure of the peril in which ignorance places scientists and citizens in our country today. I would like to explore the murky and largely secret process by which our federal government arrived at the military policy which so plainly marks the face that our country turns to the world today.

The making of this policy began with the decision to use the atomic bomb in the last days of the Second World War. And the policy reflects all the weird elements in the circumstances surrounding that decision. Neither generals nor privates in the ranks, neither cabinet ministers nor defense plant workers—no one was prepared to comprehend the instant annihilation of two Japanese cities. Here was a discontinuity in the steadily increasing horror of war, an abrupt ascent in man's capacity for destructive action.

The atomic bomb was, of course, a straightforward and logical extension of two generations' work in modern physics. Scientists of all of the nations that had scientific establishments had contributed to this work. But nobody had paid any attention to what the physicists were doing. All of the fundamental knowledge required to fashion not only a fission but a fusion bomb was in the public record before 1940. But nobody except physicists had read the literature.

The openness and completeness of the literature available deserves emphasis. Until the scientists of the Allied nations imposed their own voluntary blackout late in 1939, there had been no occasion and no effort to conceal this work, even that concerning the unexpected discovery of nuclear fission. The January 1940 issue of *Reviews of Modern Physics* carried a survey article by Louis Turner, of Princeton University, that rounded up the papers on uranium fission then already in print. The bibliography listed contributions from the laboratories of a dozen nations, beginning with Fermi's first communication in 1934 and on through the Hahn-Strassmann-Meitner work in 1939 which disclosed the true import of Fermi's work. Out of a total of 133 papers cited, incidentally, a scant half dozen bear the names of American authors, none of them dated earlier than 1939.

Turner's review article was reviewed in turn in a chapter on nuclear fission incorporated in a standard college physics textbook written by Ernest Pollard, of Yale University, and published in 1940. With the aim of stimulating student interest, Pollard went beyond the formal presentation of the scholarly journal to speculate on the prospect of nuclear reactors that might generate electrical power or detonate as immensely destructive bombs, that might produce radioactive substances for research and industrial processes or for an appalling new kind of physico-chemical warfare.

When Fermi and John R. Dunning confirmed the Meitner work at the Columbia University cyclotron in 1939, even the metropolitan press carried journalistic accounts that developed the spectacular implications of the work. But, again, nobody was the wiser. It was not only the celebrated man in the street who missed the point, but people who should have known better. At about this time, for example, a chemical journal was featuring a series of fanciful letters from its readers satirizing the quantum theory. It was essentially a jurisdictional dispute: a few physicists had presumed to apply quantum notions to a reinterpretation of the chemical bond. Physics, in truth, seemed to have gone out of this world, far out of touch with the other sciences, which were still living in the comfortable and familiar Newtonian world.

As a direct consequence of this void in communication, the atom made its debut in our culture and in our politics as a military secret. The Atomic Energy Act of 1946 gives a measure of the ignorance, and hence the fear, that has engulfed the whole subject ever since. In its section on secrecy, the act gives atomic secrets a peculiar definition. Literally and quite unrealistically, the act says that the entire literature of modern physics, including the 133 papers published before 1940, is secret and shall remain secret until such time as the Atomic Energy Commission might decide to declassify it.

This is not secrecy; it is statutory taboo. Like the taboo of the Polynesian cultures, it derives its sweeping sanctions from popular ignorance.

Herbert Marks, the first general counsel of the A.E.C., observed in the *Yale Law Journal* in 1948 that the administration of the atom from the outset was walled off from the normal processes of "public scrutiny and protest" that are "the chief protections of society against incompetence, unfairness and corruption in government." Today, seven years later, the taboo still throws its pall over all the immense questions of policy that are involved in the atomic energy enterprise. Among these, the most immediately decisive for the national security and welfare is the role of atomic weapons in our national defense program.

It is only during the last few months that the public has been given a chance to comprehend the extent to which our armament is committed to big bombs. The *Schrecklichkeit* theory of modern war, which rests upon the long-range aerial annihilation of civil populations, did not work in the Second World War. The hydrogen bomb may well have made it the strategy of choice for the Third. But there has been no adequate public discussion of its soundness as a policy for our country. Certainly the debate on the question has fallen far short of our traditional standards of controversy on questions of such political, ethical, and military magnitude.

There was one brief moment, away back in 1948, when the possibility of an alternative military policy was actually debated in the public record. It was occasioned by interservice rivalry and the Navy's effort to preserve its independence within the unified military establishment. According to our native custom, the issue was the popular one of corruption —the question whether the first contract for intercontinental bombers had been properly negotiated by the Air Force. The transcripts of the congressional hearings that followed are worth reading today. It is the last time that the public record rehearses the arguments in favor of a balanced military establishment designed to destroy enemy military forces and to take and to hold enemy territory.

Quite apart from the dubious wisdom of our commitment to the hydrogen bomb, what seems important to me and worth careful consideration by all responsible citizens is the fact that the commitment was made in secret. It was made by a very few men. In making it, they did not have the advantages of the guidance—nor the disadvantage of the pressures—under which our public officials normally make such decisions. Since this is a procedure diametrically at odds with our custom and tradition, we are fortunate now in having at least part of the story in the public record. It is told in the current best seller of the Government Printing Office, entitled *In the Matter of J. Robert Oppenheimer, Transcript of Hearing Before the Personnel Security Board of the United States Atomic Energy Commission*. The hydrogen-bomb controversy takes up roughly one third of the million words. It should be widely read for the lesson in elementary civics which it holds.

Here you will find a story of palace intrigue that affronts the traditions of our self-government. It is late August 1949, and the detonation of the first Soviet atomic bomb has just exposed our atomic monopoly for the illusion and the fraud that it always was. How can the United States recapture the illusion of absolute security sheltered by an absolute weapon? There is one more step to the absolute. This is the remote possibility that the fusion reaction can be made to work.

Should we set out to make it go, committing all our resources to the effort? The cast of characters who are to make this fateful decision includes one small group of scientists, technicians, and associated military men who are convinced that the bomb can be made to work and are determined to make it do so. The dramatis personae otherwise comprise scientists, lawyers, businessmen, and politicians—a representative sample of the new American officialdom. For all of them the immense burden of decision is many times multiplied by the fact that they must work in secret. It is clear from the record that no one is immune to the dread anxiety that his choice, whichever way it goes, may later be regarded as wrong. From the scientists on the General Advisory Committee to the politicians, however, you find an increasing tendency to play it safe, to decide that right will be on the side of the biggest bang. It is at this point, of course, that the public would normally be consulted and the responsibility for the decision, right or wrong, laid where it belongs.

We are assured that this was not possible here. Accordingly, those who oppose the headlong rush into a crash program to make the bomb find themselves the prisoners of those who are committed to it. In the secret struggle, what should have been questions of merit become questions of motive. Honorable men are charged with new-fangled and artificial treasons in the secret reports of intelligence agencies. There is a poison-pen letter. One imagination, made fertile by fear, invented a tale of a secret conspiracy of scientists, with a cabalistic code name: ZORC—Z for (Jerrold R.) Zacharias, O for (J. Robert) Oppenheimer, R for (I. I.) Rabi, and C for Charles (C. Lauritsen)! Pathology in some of the personalities involved had brought on derangement of faculties.

But pathology was inherent in the nature of the decision. Even the most insensitive spirit must be warped in the fashioning of a weapon that can serve only the function of genocide. Not only the proponents but the opponents of the decision to proceed with the making of the hydrogen bomb must suffer the same stress of spirit. And not only those directly involved but all of us have suffered the same diminution in our humanity, the same corruption of our thinking processes. It does not save us to say that the other side was going to do it and thereby transfer the burden of guilt to them. For that is their story as well. The world's two most powerful nations thus stand together arraigned as the prospective murderers of civilization and of mankind.

There was no doubt that the decision to proceed with the hydrogen bomb would commit us to the ultimate arms race. We could not enjoy even the momentary illusion of a monopoly on a secret weapon, for the fusion reaction, which generates the light of the stars, antedates the fission reaction in the international literature of science. In the hydrogen-bomb race neither side can win, for neither side can fashion a weapon more absolute than absolute. Nor can either side gain anything by making more weapons than the other, for each can make more than enough to kill the other. Nor can either side develop a better delivery system than the other, for the techniques, from rockets to saboteur's suitcases, are open to both.

For the disaster that now hangs over the world, our democracy has a special responsibility. If our democratic processes had been in better working order, this decision need not have been made in secret by frightened and sick men. We cannot get off by saying that *they* have a dictatorship that decides things for them. We could have confronted them with our power of free decision and asked them to join us in the effort to spare us all.

This at least was the kind of counsel that was urged by scientists on the General Advisory Committee of the A.E.C. Their pleas found no echo among the laymen, military and civilian, involved in the decision.

Perhaps one must be trained to think quantitatively in order to recognize a difference in quality. The hydrogen bomb is not just a bigger bomb. One fission bomb can be made bigger (that is, more destructive) than another up to a finite limit (set by the speed of the fission reaction and the amount of fissionable material that can be engaged in the reaction before the whole assembly flies apart). But there is no limit to the destructive power that can be built into a fusion bomb (it will burn up all the hydrogen that can be made available to the fusion reaction). The megatons in which the power of these weapons is stated do not begin to measure or express the nature of their violence. They are essentially incendiary bombs, miniature suns with surface temperatures hotter than any star. Given a suitable delivery system, a single hydrogen bomb can be made big enough to burn up not merely cities but whole territorial regions. The first vaporizing flash will set everything in line of sight afire over a radius of from thirty out to hundreds of miles. In the firestorm that may rage for days thereafter, those who have found refuge in shelters will die as surely as those who have been caught in the open, though they may die by suffocation for lack of oxygen and not by the direct action of heat and fire. And the fall-out of radioactive poisons will carry death far beyond the region of immediate destruction in both space and time. Clearly, to bring this weapon into being was to put the existence of mankind on probation.

Now we are in the fifth year of the hydrogen-bomb race. We set off the first one in 1952, and our technicians were impressed and somewhat frightened by a "yield" that exceeded their carefully computed expectations. The Soviet Union came in second, but not much later. What is more, their first bomb was a real production model, employing cheap and easy-to-handle materials that are now apparently incorporated in ours. The race has settled down into the neck-and-neck draw that it always must be, right down to the finish that may be the end of everything.

There is, however, still another kind of uncertainty to the outcome. The United States and the U.S.S.R. are now confronted with a consequence of their folly that mocks the claim of either nation to responsibility for the welfare or the freedom of man. Britain already has atomic weapons; France will be next. Then Sweden perhaps; surely not much later, China. Then such stragglers as Franco and Salazar;

eventually Batista. And once there are enough of these weapons in the world, poised on the noses of intercontinental rockets, carted about by aircraft and submarines on picket duty, and carried into the field to furnish realism on maneuvers, they are going to start to explode. It is well to bear in mind also that any nation that has acquired the capability of making an old-fashioned Hiroshima bomb already has most of what it needs to make a hydrogen bomb. The statesmen of the United States and the U.S.S.R. have surely not secured the safety of their countries. Between them they have set the stage for the incineration of all of the marvelous inventions of the last 500 million years of evolution.

Meanwhile, we are just at the beginning of the dehumanization and decerebration of our society that must inevitably attend the build-up to a forty-eight- or twenty-four-hour war. The logic of massive deterrence requires that possession of the weapons be implemented by the will to use them, for the logic implies the preventive as well as the retaliatory attack. People must, therefore, be inured to wholesale violence. This is not so difficult; 60 million casualties stir not much more dismay than 10 million, whether they are our own or someone else's. The acceptance of violence will become more personal when the shelter building starts and people decide that they are ready to survive their cities and their neighbors.

As the danger becomes more clear and ever present, the time will come to suspend public speech. In the conformity of terror, "peace" and "disarmament" must become terms of dissension, heresy, and treason. If the arms race lasts until 1984, civilization will have already begun to move, in J. B. Priestley's phrase, "underground beneath plains of concrete where no bird sings."

In accord with the classical laws of nemesis, it appears that the coeval history of democracy and science is on its way to termination in tyranny and race suicide. Must we accept this prospect as our settled fate? Must each of us submit and turn to the building of the prison in which we are to live out our numbered days?

Surely the scientist must have something to say in response to these questions. He ought to respond in view of his complicity in this threat to the human species. In 1950, Albert Einstein wrote a letter to the scientists of Italy gathered in one of their first assemblies after the Second World War. His words are responsive:

> What then is the position of today's man in science as a member of society? He is obviously proud of the fact that the work of scientists has helped to change radically the economic life of men by almost completely eliminating muscular work. And he is distressed by the fact that the results of his scientific work have fallen into the hands of morally blind exponents of political power, creating a threat to mankind.
>
> He is conscious of the fact that technological methods made possible by his work have led to a concentration of economic and also of political power in the hands of small minorities which have come to dominate completely the lives of the apparently more and more amorphous masses of people. But even worse, the concentration of economic and political power in the hands of a few has not only made the man of science dependent economically, it also threatens his independence from within—the shrewd methods of intellectual and psychic influences which it brings to bear will prevent the development of the independent personality that has distinguished the history of science.
>
> Thus the man of science, as we can observe with our own eyes, suffers a truly tragic fate—striving in great sincerity for clarity and inner independence, he himself through his sheer superhuman effort has fashioned the tools which are being used to make him a slave and to destroy him also from within. He cannot escape being muzzled by those who have political power in their hands. As a soldier, he is forced to sacrifice his own life and to de-

stroy the lives of others, even when he is convinced of the absurdity of such sacrifices.

He is fully aware of the fact that universal destruction may be unavoidable since historical development has led to the concentration of all economic, political and military power in the hands of national states. He also realizes that mankind can only be saved if a supernational system based on law would be created to eliminate for all time the method of brute force. However, the man of science has slipped so much that he accepts the slavery inflicted upon him by national states as his inevitable fate. He even degrades himself to such an extent that he helps obediently in the perfection of the means for the general destruction of mankind.

Is there really no escape for the man of science? Must he really tolerate and suffer all these indignities? Has the time gone by forever when, aroused by his inner freedom and the independence of his thinking and his work, he had a chance of enlightening and enriching the lives of his fellow men? In placing his work too much on an intellectual basis, has he not forgotten his responsibility and dignity?

The answer is—while it is true that an inherently free and scrupulous individual may be destroyed, such an individual can never be enslaved or used as a blind tool. If the man of science of our day could find the time and the courage to think honestly and critically over his situation and the paths before him, and if he would act accordingly, the possibilities for a sensible and satisfactory solution of the present dangerous international situation would be considerably improved.

Einstein was qualified to speak for the troubled conscience of scientists. He was a lifelong pacifist; from his post at the Kaiser Wilhelm Institute in Berlin he had denounced Kaiser Wilhelm's war in 1914, and he had spent the next four years under virtual house arrest. Yet, early in 1940, it was Einstein's immense prestige that won President Roosevelt's backing for the "uranium committee" and launched the Manhattan Project. His motives at the time were clear: the Nazis, already overrunning Europe, must not achieve this weapon first.

A decade later the sum of his counsel is "to think honestly and critically." That is not a very direct route out of the dead end of history. It is necessary to recall, however, that science deals with origins, causes, and antecedents, not ends, purposes, and ideals. Science can tell us why we seek a particular end, but it does not tell us which end to chose. The question of our fate is up to each of us.

Scientists other than Einstein have been doing some hard and critical thinking about their obligations at this juncture. What they have to say, as a result, may suggest at least the hazards of the choice that confronts the rest of us.

One doughty Englishman, Lord Adrian, Master of Trinity College at Cambridge, said in his presidential address to the British Association for the Advancement of Science: "Unless we are ready to give up some of our old loyalties, we may be forced into a fight which might end the human race."

Another Englishman, known as well for his doughtiness, has enlarged on Adrian's theme. Bertrand Russell writes: "This matter of loyalty is the crux. Hitherto, in the East and West alike, most scientists, like most other people, have felt that loyalty to their own state is paramount. They no longer have a right to feel this. Loyalty to the human race must take its place. Everyone in the West will at once admit this as regards Soviet scientists. We are shocked that Peter Kapitza, who was Rutherford's favorite pupil, was willing, when the Soviet government refused him permission to return to Cambridge, to place his scientific skill at the disposal of those who wished to spread Communism by way of H-bombs. We do not so readily apprehend a similar failure of duty on our own side. I do not wish to be thought to suggest treachery, since that is only a transference of loyalty to another national state. I am suggesting a very different thing: that scientists the world over should join in enlightening mankind as to the perils of a

great war and in devising methods for its prevention. I
urge with all the emphasis at my disposal that this is the duty
of scientists in East and West alike. It is a difficult duty, and
one likely to entail penalties for those who perform it. But,
after all, it is the labours of scientists which have caused the
danger, and on this account, if on no other, scientists must do
everything in their power to save mankind from the madness which they have made possible."

Russell rightly defines the scientist's role: to act as the expert consultant on the facts that are needed to implement the
choice of ends. It must also be admitted, however, that he has
here "departed his role as advisor" to make and to advocate a
value judgment. But this is a right the scientist may assert
along with other men. It is, moreover, an obligation that each
individual must face today. National states can no longer secure the public safety; citizens must make their own choices
as to ends.

Early this year Einstein and Russell began a correspond-
ence on the question of the continued existence of our species.
From their collaboration came a manifesto, published after
Einstein's death, in which they were joined by six other
scientists. One of the six is the Polish physicist Leopold Infeld.
The eight scientists said:

> We are speaking on this occasion, not as members of
> this or that nation, continent or creed, but as human
> beings, members of the species man, whose continued ex-
> istence is in doubt. The world is full of conflicts, the ti-
> tanic struggle between communism and anti-communism.
> Almost everybody who is politically conscious has
> strong feelings about one or more of these conflicts that
> divide mankind, but we want you, if you can, to set aside
> such feelings and consider yourselves only as members of
> a biological species which has had a remarkable history,
> and whose disappearance none of us can desire.
> We shall try to say no single word which would appeal
> to one group rather than to another. All, equally, are in

peril, and, if the peril is understood, there is hope that they may collectively avert it.

They then detailed the stark facts of physics underlying the prospect of the Third World War, and continued:

> We have not yet found that the views of experts on this question depend in any degree upon their politics or prejudices. They depend only, so far as our researches have revealed, upon the extent of the particular expert's knowledge. We have found that the men who know most are the most gloomy.
>
> Most of us are not neutral in feeling, but, as human beings, we have to remember that, if the issues between East and West are to be decided in any manner that can give any possible satisfaction to anybody, whether Communist or anti-Communist, whether Asian or European or American, whether white or black, then these issues must not be decided by war. We should wish this to be understood, both in the East and in the West.
>
> There lies before us, if we choose, continual progress in happiness, knowledge and wisdom. Shall we, instead, choose death because we cannot forget our quarrels? We appeal as human beings to human beings: remember your humanity and forget the rest. If you can do so, the way lies open to a new paradise; if you cannot there lies before you the risk of universal death.

They concluded by calling upon other scientists to add their names to this statement and to join them in the task of implementing its objectives. It appears that their call is to be answered and that scientists from the two sides of the divided world will indeed meet to explore the common ground that their expert knowledge may afford.

The Einstein-Russell Manifesto makes a plain decision about ends. The two old gentlemen and their co-signers declare that they would rather live and let live. In this connection they hold out a novel alternative to the great war; this is the "new paradise."

The New Paradise

Since the paradise they speak of is for the living, here on earth, they do not advance the prospect carelessly. Their vision is predicated upon expert knowledge. It is as real and solidly grounded upon science and technology as their forecast of the irreparable destruction that would attend the Third World War. They know—and not enough men know—that the inseparable movements of democracy and science in the four centuries since they emerged together in history have brought a fundamental change in man's relationship to his planet. Want is no longer a necessary condition of human existence. A truly human existence is now possible for every member of the species.

Here in this declaration, then, we discover a new relationship between science and value, between means and ends. The comprehending of causes, origins, and antecedents, which are the things of science, widens and secures the choice of ends, purposes, and ideals, which are the things of value. The choice that is made here and extended to all men was not available to any previous generation.

We forget how recently slavery was abolished in our own country. Nor was slavery an institution peculiar to our southern states. A century ago civilization rested upon slavery— slavery throughout the colonial world, serfdom in Imperial Russia and Eastern Europe, the wage servitude of a proletarianized yeomanry in Black England. Slavery had been the underpinning of civilization ever since civilization began—in Sumer, in the Indus Valley, in China, and in Mexico. Slavery became immoral and was at last abolished only after the progress of technology had made it obsolete. The first powerdriven factory in the United States, built in Providence, Rhode Island, in the first decade of the nineteenth century, was powered by a treadmill. It was not until mid-century that mechanical energy, generated by the wind, falling water, and finally steam, displaced the biologically generated energy of men and beasts.

Human want has now become as immoral as slavery, for the reason that want also is technologically obsolete. Want has been disappearing, in fact, throughout Western civilization over the past century. The mechanization of labor has amplified every year the energy available to sustain and nurture each inhabitant of Europe and North America. The poverty that still blights the lives of people in the West represents the failure of politics and economics. There is no technological reason why the capacity of the industrial system should not already be equal to meeting the real needs of all the people. For there is no limit to the rate at which the plant can be expanded and there is no natural ceiling on its ultimate capacity.

The sources of energy open to nuclear physics—the oceans and the crust of the continents—are essentially infinite. The supply of materials, through the permutations and combinations of organic chemistry, may now be sought in the perpetually renewable resource of the soil. For those end uses that require metals, technology can turn again to the oceans should it ever exhaust the accessible minerals of the continents.

Meanwhile, the techniques of production have been acquiring a correspondingly limitless virtuosity. As the Industrial Revolution in its first phase mechanized the function of muscle, so in its present phase it is mechanizing the function of the brain. The human beings still employed in industry are machine tenders. Their work is being taken over by automatic control systems. The virtue of these robots is that they can perform—and are already performing—tasks that exceed human capacity, tasks that are too complex, too fast, or too dangerous for control by human beings except through the mediation of automatic control systems. In essence, the control system makes the machine and the production process self-regulating. The mechanization of energy freed technology from the frailty of human muscle. The mechanization of the control function now frees technology from the limitations of the human nervous system. With human limitations removed, vast new areas of fundamental knowledge are opened up to exploitation by technology. Thereby vast new resources of nature are made accessible for the satisfaction of human want and desire.

Such is the real substance of the vision of the new paradise. That vision is already a political fact. It is the compelling drive behind the social and political upheaval that is overturning the former colonial—the now hopefully "underdeveloped"—regions of the world. Americans, of all people, should comprehend this. It is the revolutionary example of our own dynamic technology that has convinced the Chinese, the Indians, the Arabians, and the Africans that want is no longer a necessary condition of their existence.

Here is the alternative to the ignorant and frightened choice that has committed our national security to the export of blind violence. Our country is in possession of unexampled power of another kind. The blessings of liberty, to which the underdeveloped nations aspire, were never meant to be a monopoly of the American republic. If we would comprehend the true sources of our security, the productive capacity of the world's most advanced industrial system can be mobilized to secure the abolition of want and the peace of the world before the end of this century.

PART III

I

Secrets of Nature

THE MOSS COMMITTEE—that is, the Subcommittee on Government Information Policy of the House Committee on Government Operations, John E. Moss, of Sacramento, California, chairman—has spent some five years exploring the murky region bounded by military security, executive privilege, personal privacy, and the sovereignty of the citizen. In the Eighty-seventh Congress it has reported out a bill designed to improve the public access to the increasingly secretive activities of the federal government. In March 1956, in the course of the Committee's extensive hearings on governmental secrecy in science, I presented the testimony that follows.

THESE HEARINGS have been concerned with measures taken by the federal government to inhibit communication. By an unhappy confusion in our semantics we have come to think of security as secrecy. We think of security—that is, secrecy—as an end in itself and not as the means to the larger end of national security. Under the security policies of the federal

155

government, we have seen procedures and practices adopted by the government which are foreign and even repugnant to our traditions. You have had in the last three days testimony from scientists who have personally experienced what this means, and you see that they don't like it. That should indicate, from the negative side, that principles like freedom in communication have a practical value.

By examples, I would like to try to show you today how the principle of freedom of communication in science is itself the summary wisdom of hard practical experience, and that we cannot tamper with it without hampering the advance of science.

The problem of dealing with secrets is an old one in government. It existed long before we had democratic governments. The concern of governments is with state secrets, which are close to what are really true secrets—the kind of secret that you won't know unless I tell you. They are concerned with codes, with wave lengths, caliber, horsepower, range, rate, and scale. But the disclosure even of this kind of secret in the contest between states is only a matter of time. Ultimately they become known to the enemy through use—as, for example, in the use of a code over a sufficient length of time— or through interception and capture by the enemy.

But these are different from the secrets of nature, with which science is concerned. The secrets of nature are open to discovery by scientists all over the world. One nation cannot keep a scientific secret that another nation's scientists are capable of discovering. And if they are not capable of discovering it on their own, you couldn't do them very much good by handing it to them all spelled out. As Harold Urey said in his appearance here, to understand and to originate require approximately the same competence.

The truth of this statement is sustained by the history of science, in which we see, time and again, the classic situation of the simultaneous discovery of fundamental knowledge by scientists working in entire independence of one another and in ignorance of one another's work.

The classic story is that of Newton and Leibniz, who simultaneously within the same half decade discovered the calculus; of Priestley, an Englishman, and Scheele, a Swede, who simultaneously made the discovery of oxygen; of Joseph Henry here in America, Michael Faraday in England, and Lenz in Russia, who simultaneously came upon the principle of induction, upon which the dynamo is based—the machine that converts mechanical energy into electrical energy—the event in science in the nineteenth century which had as large an effect on human affairs as the penetration of the nucleus of the atom in this century.

Simultaneity of invention was the rule when there were fewer scientists than today, working on fewer questions and narrower frontiers of research. Today simultaneity is even more frequent, despite the increase in the efficiency and volume of communication in science. In fundamental research, you see, scientists all over the world are concerned with investigation of the same fundamental problems.

In America, our physicists refer to something called the Compton effect. The Compton effect is known abroad as the Debye effect, because Debye discovered the effect at the same time that Compton did. Again, the reason why you so often see two and three names attached to Nobel Prizes is that the same work was done by the recipients independently of one another. For example, Ed Purcell at Harvard and Felix Bloch at Stanford, working on opposite sides of the country, both developed the field of nuclear magnetic resonance, for which they received the Nobel Prize.

This goes on despite all measures that can be taken to maintain secrecy. At the Geneva conference on the peaceful uses of atomic energy last summer, the scientists of the world who had been working in secrecy and in ignorance of one another's work came together and compared notes. They plotted their figures on curves and put the curves on top of one another, and found that they matched perfectly. The matching curves were the symbol of the fact that science is engaged in investigating the same universe on both sides of the Iron Curtain and on both sides of all national boundaries.

Simultaneity of discovery occurs not only in fundamental research but in advances in technology. Back in the time of Henry, Faraday, and Lenz, a man named Thomas Davenport, a Yankee mechanic, knowing of Henry's work, invented the electric motor. Simultaneously, Jacobi in Russia, working with the background established by Faraday and Lenz, invented the electric motor. Within the same year, in 1839, a printing press in New York City was being driven by one of Davenport's electric motors, and a river boat on the river Lena in Russia was being driven by Jacobi's electric motor. It should be added that neither motor worked very well.

Again, despite secrecy and censorship, during the Second World War the technology of radar was developed independently by the United States, England, France, Germany, and Japan. Radar functioned on both sides of the fronts. Development was parallel even down to the details. The cavity magnetron, an oscillator, was produced in the United Kingdom and in the Soviet Union; the "Rising Sun" oscillator was developed in Japan and independently in the United States.

More recently, despite the security system under which our atomic technology and research have been conducted for the past decade, we have the story of the development of the synchrotron. This is a nuclear accelerator, an atom smasher. It was invented by an American, McMillan. McMillan's invention was kept secret until, quite independently, the synchrotron principle was published by Veksler in Russia in 1945. Thereupon the secret on which we had been sitting was released, and the synchrotron came into general use in nuclear physics, available to those not working on secret projects.

It is quite apparent that scientists in every nation working on fundamental research will come to the same views about nature's laws. Ultimately they are going to make the same discoveries. It is only a matter of time. By concealing what we know we may delay the discovery of new work by others. But they will ultimately discover it no matter what we do. By concealing and by frustrating communications within science, however, we will surely slow up ourselves—not only in the making of discoveries but in bringing new work into application.

Communication is a vital part of research. It is inseparable from research. It is not too much to say that research is communication. New scientific work does not have any existence in this world until it has been comunicated from one scientist to another.

Communication goes on at many levels. It is highly subject to disruption, and to frustration, and to tampering. Among human beings it is a difficult thing to achieve at any time.

The most intense and close level of communication in science is that between teacher and pupil. Here is where communication is achieved by the captive-audience process. For example, back in 1919 Lord Rutherford, who headed the Cavendish Laboratory at Cambridge University, postulated in the hearing of one of his pupils, Chadwick, the possibility of a neutral atomic particle. Chadwick carried this in his head; the notion was never published by Rutherford. Then, in 1930, two German scientists, Bothe and Becker, discovered a peculiar kind of radiation they could not account for. It was a non-ionizing radiation. They were not able to explain its behavior; they developed a theory to the effect that this was a new and special kind of electromagnetic radiation. Their work was followed up by the Curies. The Curies came forth with the same sort of hypothesis and undertook to support it by their work. But Chadwick, who remembered, after thirteen years, what Rutherford had said to him, made the assumption that this radiation was a beam of neutral particles. Proceeding with his research on that assumption, he discovered the neutron.

At the next level of communication we have the interpersonal contacts between scientists working in common fields, at their formal sessions and meetings. Here, as among people in other trades and crafts, they do their most important communicating in the bar and grill, and not in the formal sessions. There has been testimony before this committee as to the disruption of this sort of communication by the regulation of travel.

Finally, there is communication by publication and writing. A scientist never publishes until he has argued and discussed and circulated his work among other scientists who work closely with him and threshed out the points with those in his own field whom he knows personally. Through publication he undertakes to reach others whom he doesn't know personally, who are outside of his camp.

I would like to show you an example of what publication means. What I have here is a bibliography from a paper by Louis Turner published in the American journal *Reviews of Modern Physics* in January 1940. The paper, back in 1940, when presumably the atom was a big secret, was entitled "Nuclear Fission." This paper undertook to round up all the work that had been published in this new field.

You will note that the first paper there is that of Enrico Fermi, published in the British magazine *Nature* in 1934. Fermi and his colleagues published two more papers that year. Their work attracted attention, and the next year saw the publication of seven papers by other workers. In 1936 five papers went into the record, in 1937 five more, and in 1938 nine papers.

The point here is that Fermi did not make a single discrete discovery that got published in one place. What he did was set in motion a chain reaction of investigation and effort. It is important to know about this work, too, that Fermi and his colleagues were mistaken in their original assumption about what it was they had found. In exposing the atom of uranium to a beam of slow neutrons they had actually caused the first man-controlled fission reaction. However, they weren't looking for a fission reaction; they thought they had created a new element heavier than uranium by adding a neutron to its weight.

But somehow this interpretation didn't jibe with the evidence; hence the work that Fermi and others continued to put into the question. Then, in 1939, came the Hahn Strassmann-Meitner work that developed the true import of Fermi's original experiment. And now you see an indication of the speed of communication in the then tiny community of nuclear physics. The year 1939 saw 104 papers published in follow-up, confirmation, and extension of the discovery of nuclear fission. You will note, incidentally, that there are very few contributions by Americans, and none before 1939. Also incidentally, the bibliography shows what a hollow "secret" the atom was. There was enough information here to set any of the world's advanced nations on the way to making its own atomic bomb.

For the purposes of this discussion, however, Professor Turner's bibliography demonstrates the essential part publication plays in getting work done, in making a new discovery; it shows, in short, the integral relationship between research and communication.

It is hard to prove the negative of this—that work may be lost through non-publication. But experience gives us no guarantee that publication will always accomplish its purpose. The printed word is a frail medium of communication, as anyone knows who is involved in publishing.

Scientific publishing is better organized today, however, than it was in the last century. Here it is appropriate to recall the story of Gregor Mendel. In 1865 he laid down the fundamental notions of genetics, the rules of nature by which hereditary characteristics are transmitted from generation to generation. And he published it. But the work was lost for thirty-five years, until 1900, when it was simultaneously rediscovered, independently, by three different scientists, Correns in Germany De Vries in Holland, and Tschermak in Austria.

In our own country, one of our two or three greatest scientists, Josiah Willard Gibbs, a professor at Yale, working quietly and obscurely, published his work on thermodynamics in a series of historic papers in, of all things, *The Proceedings of the Connecticut Academy of Science*. It went unread by his American contemporaries. By some accident, Boltzmann, in Europe, read these papers, and thus twenty years after Josiah Willard Gibbs had got his great work under way it came to the notice and recognition of his colleagues.

Today, with our vast number of journals, and even with punch cards and mechanized methods for searching the literature, the communication problem in science is the reverse of that of the nineteenth century. It is the enormous volume of work that must be carried by the channels of communication in science.

An example of this is the story of W. H. Bennett, now with the Naval Research Laboratory. In 1939 he secured a patent on a device for improving the output of the electrostatic generator, another atom smasher. His device today is known among scientists as the "swindletron," because it deceives the atomic particle, so to speak, and makes it move twice as fast as it ought to. Bennett patented his device. Then, fifteen years later, with the patent close to expiration, Luis Alvarez, at Berkeley, independently discovered the "swindletron." The High Voltage Engineering Company, which is engaged in manufacturing this kind of equipment, proceeded to put it on the market. Their patent department made the usual thorough search of patent literature, and they didn't come across Mr. Bennett's patent. So, even with our formal and established procedures, work can be missed.

We ought to consider also the need to keep abreast of work going on abroad. American scientists are notably behind their brothers in Europe in keeping track of work on an international basis. For example, in 1950, in the journal of the U.S.S.R. Academy of Sciences, A. G. Lunts published a paper on the application of Boolean algebra, or symbolic logic, to the design of computer circuits. For five years, from 1950 until 1955, American scientists working in corporations engaged in making computers labored toward the same result; they spent five fruitless years and $200,000, it is estimated, of research money doing work that they wouldn't have had to do had they read that paper.

Just as scientists cannot always tell where to look for work, so we cannot possibly tell to whom it ought to be communicated. I have in mind here the recent proposal from an agency in the Department of Defense, I believe, that publication of non-secret work should be limited, and that new work should be circulated only to select lists of interested investigators in each case. The idea is, of course, to make it hard for scientists in countries whose progress we don't want to encourage.

The fallacy in this approach is that you cannot predict who is going to be interested in a new piece of work. Most of the really historic advances come by cross-fertilization; that is, someone in an entirely different field is able to apply the new understanding to the solution of an apparently unrelated problem. Our magazine, *Scientific American*, has turned up instances of cross-fertilization. One of our favorite stories is that of a University of Illinois geneticist who was trying to figure out how the genetic material in the living cell reproduces itself, as it must in the process of cell reproduction. This material, it is fairly well established, is a complicated molecule that is shaped like two coiled springs intertwined with each other. The geneticist was trying to determine how the two springs could get disentangled from each other. He made drawings and even little models, but he could not get anywhere with the problem, until the January 1950 *Scientific American* arrived in his mailbox. He discovered in this issue a new branch of mathematics—an old one actually, but a new one to him—called topology, which deals exactly with problems of this kind. He looked in the college catalogue and learned that there was a topologist in the house! They thereupon entered into a fruitful collaboration with each other.

Progress often comes from the oddest and most unpredictable places. At Brookhaven, for example, a group of scientists developed a new improvement on the synchrotron, known as the "strong focusing" principle. No sooner had they got the word of their work into print when one Nicholas Christofilos turned up as the prior inventor of this development. Christofilos was not a Doctor of Philosophy, but an electrical engineer. He was engaged in the business of installing elevators, and not in the United States but in Athens, Greece. When he came up with his idea of the strong-focusing principle he sent it in a letter to Berkeley. When Berkeley heard about Nicholas Christofilos later, they looked up his correspondence, and found it in the crank file.

Communication in science is all too easy to tamper with. When we tamper with it we tamper with research itself.

Commercial secrecy, for example, is an old story. A fine story out of that realm is the story of Gerhard Domagk, a biochemist with the I. G. Farben Company. In the early 1920's he made the accidental discovery that a certain family of azo dyes had bactericidal action. The company promptly clamped down its secrecy rules on this promising discovery. For five or six years Domagk and his staff tried to figure out how the azo dye worked, in order to establish a solid patent claim. When they thought they had it, they patented the drug under the name of Prontosil. But as soon as publi-

cation brought this work to public notice and common understanding among scientists—within eighteen months—the
patent was broken by scientific work that went on in France,
England, and America. From the improvements on Domagk's
work came the family of sulfa drugs. The fact that
I. G. Farben felt it necessary to conduct this work in secret
delayed this historic advance in medicine for five years.

Peril of another kind is created when we try to wrap national security in secrecy. There is a terrible tendency,
inside secret projects, to incest.

In the atomic bomb project there was at the outset the
important problem of separating and concentrating the fissionable isotope of uranium—that is, uranium 235—from the
more abundant non-fissionable uranium 238. Three main
lines of attack were developed: thermal diffusion, electromagnetic separation, and the conversion of U-238 to plutonium in a pile. There was a fourth attack, known as gaseous
diffusion, which was set aside in programing the development
campaign. But one stubborn group of men, working outside
the project, proceeded to push the gaseous-diffusion possibility. They pushed it without support from the project,
without support from the government, until late in 1942,
when the Du Pont Corporation came into the picture as the
contractor for the building of the giant plants. The Du Pont
people surveyed the work that was going on and, making a
chemical engineer's, not a physicist's, judgment, concluded
that gaseous diffusion was the closest to a straightforward
industrial process. They insisted that the gaseous-diffusion
program be picked up and pushed, practically as a condition
of their taking on their assignments.

It turned out, when the gaseous-diffusion plant went on
stream early in 1945, that it was by far the most productive
and efficient method for concentrating fissionable materials.
The 40,000 kilograms of U-235 that our government has
recently been able to present to the international atomic

energy authority in order to encourage the advance of atomic power elsewhere, is a measure of the efficiency and enormous output achieved by this process, and of the importance of the independent stubborn group of men at Columbia University who carried on their own work outside the secret formal program.

Under our constitutional principle of separation of powers, Congress has long opposed the human tendency in the executive department to make government a private affair. It is an old experience in the administration of our country that secrecy can be a shield for incompetence and corruption. Now we have a new reason to oppose secrecy in the operations of the government. It is the danger that secrecy poses for the advancement of science, and hence for the general welfare and for national security.

The policy, it seems to me, that ought to come out of these deliberations is that secrecy be held to an absolute minimum in the conduct of our government in general and in the conduct of the technological and scientific research that goes into national defense in particular. As a standard, I would suggest that the principle of absolute freedom of communication, sustained by its practical effectiveness in action, be adopted as the standard for judging the validity of security and secrecy orders.

Under our Constitution, Congress is not empowered to abridge communication; it is forbidden to abridge communication. But there is nothing in the Constitution that says Congress cannot promote communication. The McKinney commission on atomic energy has suggested the kind of thing Congress can do; that is, encourage the declassification of material now held secret in the files of the federal government.

I move to suggest, out of the experience with the Russian paper on Boolean algebra, another thing Congress can do; that is, encourage the National Science Foundation to finance

the translation of more foreign journals. Today we are translating one single Russian physics journal, because there aren't
funds enough to cover the dozen others that ought to be kept
under surveillance also. Perhaps the intelligence agencies of
the government are reading these journals. We may hope
they are. And if they are, they are undoubtedly getting important intelligence information out of these journals. But
they don't help the scientists of the country by stamping
"secret" on the things they are learning.

2

Science, Censorship, and the Public Interest

THE WORK of the Moss Committee (see "Secrets of Nature") had raised an issue for the agenda of the 1956 convention of the American Association for the Advancement of Science held in December in New York. This paper was prepared for a conference on the positive as well as the negative aspects of public information in science.

IT IS NO SECRET that scientists today are enlisting the assistance of writers in order to talk to their fellow men and to one another. There is even a special and different kind of writer for each purpose. The writer who helps to mediate communication to the public at large is, of course, a science writer. The writer whose job it is to facilitate internal communication— the writing of formal papers, reports, and manuals, addressed to other scientists, to engineers, and to technicians—is called a technical writer. Science writing and technical writing now have formal status as professions, with the organization of their respective national societies and the promulgation of their codes of ethics and standards.

The need for professional editorial skill is plain to any-one who has ever tried to write about science for the public. One would think, however, that such help would not be needed to mediate the internal communications of science. Communication between one scientist or one engineer and another would seem to present a situation with ideal match-ing of impedance between transmitter and receiver. The report, the paper, or the manual is addressed to a small audience. The members of this audience may be presumed to be knowledgeable. They have reason to be interested, and they are compelled to understand. Yet the technical writer is now accepted by the scientist and engineer in industrial, gov-ernment, and university research organizations as a full-fledged partner and collaborator in the preparation of papers and reports.

Such concern with the technique of communication in this ideal situation suggests the frailty of human communi-cation under any circumstances. It gives us also an impressive measure of the importance of communication in the process of research. It is not too much to say, in fact, that without communication there can be no research. Bishop Berkeley's dictum applies in an exact sense. Like "the tree in the quad" that does not exist if no one is there to perceive it, to borrow from Ronald Knox's restatement of the point, new research has no existence until it is communicated from the scientist to his brothers. The fact is, there is no "fact" in science that is final or significant in itself. Work has meaning only as it is connected to the general fund of knowledge and thereby established as a base for further increase of knowledge. It gets so connected and established only by communication. No discovery is ever the work of one man or group of men working in isolation from the concerns of the community of science as a whole. On the contrary, because significant questions are always of wide interest in the community, many discoveries are made simultaneously by two or more independent workers or groups of workers. Simultaneity of discovery, in fact, tends to be the rule, not the exception.

This consideration of the function of communication in research underlines the highly practical significance of freedom in the communications of science. Freedom is like the air, however, and we do not appreciate its importance until we are deprived of it. Recent developments in the information policies of our federal government, therefore, are instructive. The last two decades of war and cold war have seen a widespread expansion of secrecy in the operation of our government agencies. The censorship, for obvious reasons, has pressed most heavily upon science. Not only does it blanket large areas of applied science. The technological revolution in warfare is pushing the frontiers of knowledge; as a result, much work in basic science is classified as "top secret," "secret," and "confidential." And because people, as well as documents, are classified, censorship reaches far outside the government payroll to embroil a frightening percentage of our scientific establishment in the security system.

All of this has been said before, and it has been the subject for more eloquent protest and indignation than will be sounded here. But there had been no systematic inquiry into the spread of censorship until a year ago, when the so-called Moss Committee of the House of Representatives undertook its investigation of government information policies. This committee has given us a model demonstration of the exercise of the congressional investigative power. Its quiet and thorough work deserves much better coverage by the press, especially by scientific publications. Testimony before the committee has developed, for the first time, the magnitude of the problem of censorship.

Witnesses have agreed that censorship since the outbreak of the Second World War has locked up something like 100,000 file drawers full of classified documents in the city of Washington and at United States military and government installations throughout the world. The Army estimates that it alone has two million classified documents in its files. Such an accumulation of secret material must be deeply disturbing to anyone who prizes the institutions of our democratic society. It is a measure of the degree to which we have permitted anxiety about national security to compromise our traditions and principles.

When the legislators of the new American republic settled down to implement the broad generalities of the Constitution with statutes on specific questions, one of their first acts was to write a public information statute. It was as sweet and simple as the First Amendment; it told the executive department to keep proper records of its activities and to make them accessible to the public. Over the next one hundred and fifty years and especially in the last twenty-five years, the executive department encrusted this simple injunction with exceptions and procedures that made it more and more difficult to find out what the government was doing. In the First and Second World Wars the statute was invoked to empower the executive to do just the opposite of what the statute ordered: to make things secret. This situation was so embarrassing that Congress after the last war wrote a new statute permitting the executive to withhold information from the public in the name of the national security.

Now, of course, there is need for secrecy in the operation of government. But censorship has flourished in recent years throughout the executive department without supervision or review by the legislature or by the courts. The Moss Committee is the first agency to undertake such an investigation.

The secret documents that cram the files in Washington relate, of course, to all kinds of concerns of government—

to intelligence reports and to forgotten purchase orders as well as to current scientific research. Some of these documents can be junked without declassification; there may be good reason, in connection with delicate questions of diplomacy, for keeping some documents classified indefinitely. Some documents, however, should never have been classified, especially in realms of fundamental science, and ought to be immediately declassified. But it is clear from the testimony before the Moss Committee that most of these documents will never be declassified. The sheer magnitude of the task and the scarcity of qualified personnel, they say, will make it impossible, no matter how well intentioned we are and how determined we would like to be. The best the Army hopes to do is to declassify about 10 per cent of the documents in its custody, a maximum of about a quarter of a million. Declassification at this rate could not even keep up with the current rate of classification. All of the testimony points to the conclusion that we must seek prevention rather than cure. The most that can be hoped is that some brake on the rubber stamp will slow the accumulation of secret papers.

This is especially important for science, because research tends to stay classified once the rubber stamp has made its mark. Most strictly military censorship has its own built-in, automatic declassification. The order of battle cannot be kept secret for long, because military plans are self-disclosing as they are put in operation against the enemy. Similarly, the data surrounding the development of a new weapon are disclosed to larger and larger numbers of people as the weapon progresses from the laboratory and the factory to the field. But there is no such automatic process for research. Work in science will stay locked up unless sufficient pressure is brought to bear upon the military to declassify it.

Many fields of science, according to testimony before the Moss Committee, are now compromised by the taint of secrecy. Philip M. Morse, of the Massachusetts Institute of

Technology, told a wry story in this connection. He published what he thought was a novel and significant contribution to queueing, or waiting-line, theory. This is a branch of mathematics that has many uses in a world in which increasing numbers of people are standing in line; it can help planners to schedule the landing of airplanes at crowded airports or to decide how many cash registers to install at a supermarket. When his paper was published, Morse found himself subjected to catcalls from certain colleagues who had been associated in a secret wartime project with Bernard O. Koopman, now at Columbia University. Koopman, they said, had done the work long ago. Morse had never heard about it because he had not been involved in that particular project and Koopman's work was still classified. When Morse sought to get the work declassified, he was told that, while Koopman's paper was itself concerned with a no longer classified project, it incorporated reference to work by a man named Clark that was still classified. The reason Clark's paper must remain classified, the censors explained, is that nobody has been able to identify this man Clark or to find his paper. Under the circumstances, Morse has taken the only sensible action: he has yielded that salient in the territory of queueing theory to the censors.

Secrecy has injured science in another aspect. It has added a smell of the sinister to the climate of sensation which has surrounded the popular discovery of science as the source of new technology for war and peace. Consider the recent dictum by a federal judge holding that "many of the younger generation of pure scientists, specifically engaging in research in physics," have succumbed to the blandishments of a foreign power. The judge was careful to make it clear that he was "not saying this about applied scientists, engineers and chemists, but persons who have engaged in pure science." But we cannot blame the censor exclusively for the poisoning of the public relations of science. The sensations have been expanded and inflated by the publicists of science, even by the well-intentioned, to the point where many of our fellow citizens have science firmly identified in their minds as an accessory activity of the weaponeering, home-appliance, and pharmaceutical industries.

This brings us to our second concern, science writing, addressed to the public outside science. This function of journalism has assumed an obvious new importance in our life. The theoretically informed citizenry of our democratic society must be especially informed today about the work of science if it is to make wise judgments in public affairs. But sound public information about science is also integral to the life of science itself, for this is an era in which science must turn to the public for its support.

Science writing has shown great improvement in matter and form in this country in recent years. Most scientists will agree that it is distinguished by greater accuracy and by less flagrant affronts to good taste. As a result, they have accepted the notion of collaboration with science writers, just as they have accepted the notion of collaboration with technical writers. But we have far to go. The principal appeal in the popularization of science is still the one-note siren song of utility. Science, in the public mind, is a means to ends—to all kinds of exciting and useful ends, to be sure: to the spaceships that are being delivered this year by our automobile factories, to cancer cures, to bigger bombers and faster jets. As such, science is worthy of public support, the citizen says, provided that it comes through with more of the same. There is peril for science, however, in reliance on this distorted view. The same citizen is showing signs of ennui and anxiety at the prospect of further miracles.

There are other deficiencies. The current vintage of science writing shows a tendency to evade the difficulties of exposition; knotty topics are suspended, instead, in a solution of rich and beautiful prose. In the newer media of communications, which have more recently discovered that science is a matter of large public interest, the popularization of science is confounded by the rituals of mass entertainment. One standard routine dramatizes science through the biography of a hero scientist: at the denouement, he is discovered in a lonely laboratory crying "Eureka!" at a murky test tube held up to a bare light bulb. Another treatment invites the audience to identify itself with a hopelessly fatuous master of ceremonies who plays straight man for kindly, condescending Dr. Science.

All of this, we are told, is what the public wants. But even if it could be shown that the public had a taste for such dubious entertainment (the Hooper ratings are against it), it would still be hard to see how it promotes the popularization of science. The suspicion grows that the mass-communications image of science reflects not the public taste but merely lack of ardor on the part of these popularizers.

But publishers and producers are learning that the half life of bunkum in America is growing short. It is increasingly dangerous to underestimate the intelligence of the American public. Recently there have been notable additions to the casualty list of the American press. And stars tend to burn out faster when exposed to close inspection on the TV tube.

It is an equally good rule, however, for the science writer not to underestimate the ignorance of his public. This applies not only to the public at large; it holds equally well in addressing the otherwise educated members of our society. The scientifically ignorant include most of the spokesmen and articulators of the public consciousness—our scholars, artists, writers, lawyers, and legislators and our administrators and executives in business and government.

It is this ignorance that underlies the divergence, in the academies of America, between the scientific and the humanities faculties. This is an old story, of course, dating back to the mid-nineteenth century. It arose from the need to specialize, which has sharpened with the increasing complexity of civilization. But the gulf has widened and deepened in recent years. Ignorance of science is advertised today as the warrant of the self-styled humanist. The argument goes this way: "The aim of education is a decent, moral world made up of decent, moral people. Science must therefore be secondary, because science cannot help anyone to be a decent, moral person. Science is vacant where value is concerned. The humanities provide the value."

The humanities, by this line of argument, are staked out as the territory of the anti-rationalists. "Reason," they say, "must ever be the slave of passion." Science can show us how to achieve our ends. But for motivation and purpose we must seek guidance elsewhere, in tradition or faith, in the sensibilities, emotions, and yearnings that well up in the human spirit, beyond the understanding and control of reason.

To argue thus is to ignore how much the outlook of all men in our time is conditioned by science. In politics, the choice of the aims of national policy is profoundly conditioned by what we know, from human biology and from cultural and physical anthropology, about mankind, its history, and its place in nature. Never again can a nation assume the mantle of a "master race" or take up the "white man's burden" or proclaim a "manifest destiny." Cultural relativism has even invaded the world behind the Iron Curtain, where the nineteenth-century naïvetés of Marxism are undergoing revision. The politics of the world are modified, equally, by what we can do with what we know. The vision of the United Nations and its technical agencies is that of a world at peace because it has eliminated human destitution, misery, and disease. Contrast this vision with the old-fashioned morality that held poverty and privation to be the natural terms of existence in this life—for the poor, that is.

In personal morality, the notion of the good life and of what men live for has been deeply modified by scientific understanding of the cosmos, of the origin of life, and of the structure of the human personality. Reason is the instructor of passion in other departments of our culture. Consider, for example, the bearing of science upon aesthetics. Recent investigation of the giant molecules has shown us how nature achieves, in extraordinary perfection, the aim of art: in the molecule, function is the expression of structure; it is what it is because of the way it is made.

Such are the concerns that inspirit the scientist in his work. They are not different from those that move the painter or the composer, the historian or the poet. The motivating drive could never have been less than passions which all men share and which inspire the best achievements of men in all fields of intellectual endeavor.

This is the aspect of science most neglected by science writing. It is, I submit, the facet that is most susceptible of popular appreciation and comprehension. The preoccupation with information should give way to popularization of the objectives, the method, and the spirit of science. If the public is to support the advance of science for motives other than utility, then people must be able to share not only the useful but the illuminating and the beautiful ideas that come out of the work of science.

3

Sputniks in the Sky

UNTIL OCTOBER 4, 1957, "science" had been synonymous with "the atom." Now it means "space."

The members of the Women's City Club of New York, who ordinarily occupy themselves with more strictly civic matters, were troubled now by general questions about the context in which they carry on their constructive labors. This was an effort, in December 1957, to help them find answers to those questions.

E VER SINCE the morning of October 4, we Americans have been asking ourselves uncomfortable questions. On that morning the first man-made satellite of the earth shone in the sky. This achievement crowned the generations of discovery in science that have so profoundly altered the outlook of man and symbolized to all of the peoples of the world the awesome power of modern technology that is so rapidly changing the conditions of their existence. For us Americans, however, it seems that the most important feature of this historic event is that the satellite is called Sputnik, not Vanguard. As if to make us feel even more uncomfortable, the Soviet Union not only launched the first artificial satellite but proceeded to launch the second. Now two Sputniks are crossing and recrossing the American sky. As we look up to search for their gleam among the stars we are assailed by questions.

Let us try to face some of those questions here today.

Is this really—as Edward Teller, the "father of the H-Bomb," has said—a Pearl Harbor?

Should we drop everything and get busy making bigger bombs and bigger missiles to deliver them?

Is there something wrong with American science that the Russians have beaten us into outer space?

Is there something wrong with American education? Are the scientists it produces outclassed by the Russians?

Is our country now a second-class power?

These are the kinds of questions that people have been asking during the first weeks of what is now called the Age of Space.

But in what sense is the launching of the Sputniks really a defeat? Why should we Americans accept as a defeat this triumph of the human imagination, this compelling demonstration of man's understanding and mastery of the forces of nature? The circling of the Sputniks in the skies is as much the work of Galileo, of Kepler, and of Newton as it is the work of technicians and rocketeers of the twentieth century. We can claim that this event is an American triumph—the achievement of Robert Hutchings Goddard, our own American "father of the rocket." It is equally the work of Hermann Oberth, who is touted by the Germans as their "father of the rocket." Certainly these men contributed as much to the launching of the Sputniks as Konstantin E. Tsiolkovsky, who is credited by the Russians as their "father of the rocket."

As for the fact that the Soviet Union got a satellite into space first—that is the most trivial aspect of this historic event. The question of priority is really the reverse side of a familiar

process in the history of science—the simultaneity of discovery. The fact is that just about every significant development in science and technology throughout history has been
achieved simultaneously and independently by two or more
men, working in ignorance of each other's progress, in different laboratories and in distant parts of the world. Our
satellites might well have been up before the Sputniks, had
our space research program been given greater priority and
the use of more adequate launching vehicles already in our
possession. In any case, our satellites will be up tomorrow.

The Sputniks circling the skies have a scientific significance
that far surpasses their superficial symbolism in the momentary impasse of world politics. They are up there to give
science—and, that is to say, mankind—a window on the universe, an observatory outside the obscuring and protecting
blanket of our atmosphere. The atmosphere, by filtering out
cosmic rays from interstellar space and high-energy radiation
from our sun, makes life itself possible on earth. But this
filter also makes it difficult to answer important questions
man has learned to ask about the nature of the universe.

Most of what we know about the universe comes from
analysis of the light of the stars—from the spreading (with
a spectroscope) of the white light of the stars into the spectrum of wave lengths that make it up. The spectrum betrays
the presence of the elements that make up the substance of
a star and tells us much else about the star, its interior dynamics, its motion, and so on. Now, it happens that the wave
lengths that would tell us most are filtered out by the atmosphere and never reach our spectroscopes. There are many
fundamental questions that can be answered only from a satellite circling in space outside our atmosphere—or from an
observatory planted on the moon.

The satellites now circling the earth, even in advance of
their more elaborate successors, have already told us, by their
very circling and orbiting, a great deal about the outer atmos-

phere and about the shape of our earth. Within our lifetime we can expect to see an observatory, probably unmanned and robotized, established on the moon. Within a few generations scientific expeditions will be going off to the other planets. Beyond, in the eons to come, there open vistas of human adventure and achievement that we can just begin to imagine now.

Yet all this has been taken by some of our most influential fellow citizens as a defeat. Before the world, they have taken it on themselves to declare that our country has sustained a major disaster. They have dismayed our allies with studies, reports, speeches, and manifestoes which declare that the primary significance of the satellites is to require us to make more horrendous weapons. In a species of counterattack by press-agentry, our satellite program was speeded up a matter of eight or ten weeks and put under klieg lights. Thereupon our scientists and engineers were exposed to humiliation before the world as the first Vanguard vehicle burned up on the launching platform.

If we have suffered a defeat, then it is a defeat by proclamation—a defeat by press handout. When the history of this occasion is written, I think, it will be seen that our primary defeat occurred on Madison Avenue, not in outer space. In this public relations contest, Madison Avenue has become our sunken road at Waterloo. Fortunately, we can spare a battalion or two of press agents more easily than Napoleon his Imperial Cavalry.

But there are other questions to be asked and answered here. Whether or not we have been defeated in some manner or form, it is well for us to ask whether or not our scientific establishment, for example, is in a healthy condition. This is a question we ought to ask without the stimulus of somebody else's satellites. If we are concerned, however, primarily with whether or not we are being equipped adequately with the weapons of modern warfare, then we are concerned with engineering, not science. The design of bombs and rockets involves well-established knowledge, knowledge that is ready to be put to use by the engineer and technician, whether for weapons or for plowshares. We, the most powerful industrial nation of the world—with an administration in Washington that is run by industrialists, with a general as President—ought to be in a position to achieve whatever technological and military objectives are judged necessary to our defense. In the recent uproar one can detect more than one note of salesmanship by parties interested in government procurement orders. President Eisenhower and members of Congress have remarked on this aspect of opinion making in our country during the past few years.

But what about American science? I suggest that the question "What is wrong with American science?" ought to be reversed. Instead we should ask: "What is right with Soviet science?" It has certainly been a shock to all of us—who have lived so long with a picture of the Soviet Union as a benighted country suffocated in a fog of orthodoxy and political repression imposed by a ruthless dictatorship—that people living in such a nightmare could ever achieve anything significant in science and technology. As a first step in recovering from this shock, we ought to re-examine the folklore with which we have been reassuring ourselves throughout these forty years of the Russian Revolution. The time has come to take a more honest look at the country to get a more candid appraisal of its people, its resources, and the sources of its power.

When we take such a look at the scientific establishment of the Soviet Union, one of the things that impresses us, first of all, is that its tradition is a very old one, going back many generations and paralleling the history of science in Western Europe. It is only in recent times that Europe has been divided into an East and a West on political grounds. The common cultural heritage of Western Europe has been eagerly imbibed by the people of Russia at least since the reign of Peter the

Great, in the late seventeenth century. And the Russians have participated in the cultural life of Europe with all of the distinction that can be expected of a great people, in literature, music, the arts, and the sciences.

At least two Russian names must be counted in any list of the movers and shakers in the history of science. There is Lobashevsky, whose non-Euclidean geometry is the beginning of some of the most profound developments in modern mathematics and lays the foundations of modern physical theory. And there is Mendeleyev, the chemist, who discovered the periodicity of the elements and worked out the great table of elements, which classified all of the elements known in his time and predicted the existence of all of the naturally occurring elements that have been discovered since.

A great cultural tradition can perpetuate itself and even achieve successes as well as heroism in an autocracy. There has been autocracy in Russia beyond memory. It has held its reins tightly and harshly or slackly and benignly from period to period. But always the nation has been ruled by an autocrat, ever since it came to consciousness from the grave in which the Tatars and the Mongols and other conquerors from the East had buried it in earliest times. When we consider the wealth of the cultural heritage of Russia, we Americans, who are so used to freedom, must be reminded that freedom is not bestowed by a Bill of Rights. We are made to realize that freedom is a fundamental passion in the human system, and the tyrant and the autocrat has never been able to extinguish it. There is another lesson for us here: that the intellectual tradition of Russia is perhaps more immune to secret police and terrorism, more cunning and clever in the way it resists and eludes the inquisitor, than our own intellectual tradition may be.

Soviet science today reflects another aspect of Russian intellectual tradition. The scholar from earliest times has been accorded the same reverence that was given to the priest, for the earliest scholar was a priest and hence the vessel of the Church that gave the Russians their identity under foreign conquest and occupation. In the time of Peter the Great some of this esteem was transferred to the scientist. Ever since then, the scientist has been regarded as on an equal plane with the most highly styled of the nobility. Indeed, there is an intellectual nobility in Russia that dates from Czarist times and still perpetuates itself; Russia has the same kind of intellectual dynasties that abound in Britain. For generations the British have known the names of Huxley, Darwin, Mill, and Keynes. So, in Russia, families have produced generations of great scholars. Thanks to the accidents of history that have brought so many of Europe's best intellects to our country, we are inheritors of one of these great lines in Otto Struve. The chairman of the astronomy department at the University of California, Otto Struve, is the son of Ludwig Struve, who was director of the observatory at Kharkov; Ludwig, in turn, was the son of Otto Struve, who directed the Pulkovo Observatory; grandfather Otto Struve succeeded his father, F. W. G. Struve, who was the founder of that observatory back in the late eighteenth century. Today, in Russia, one of the leading young men in physics is named Vavilov. His grandfather was a physicist and a member of the Imperial Academy; his father is a physicist and a member of the Soviet Academy. He also had an uncle, a distinguished geneticist and academician, who was a victim of the Lysenko crisis.

What all of this suggests, of course, is that the Russians have been working at science for a long, long time. The Russian Revolution—as we learned from De Tocqueville about the French Revolution—did not proceed to destroy everything created by the old regime. On the contrary, it perpetuated much of what it found. And, again in parallel with De Tocqueville's wise insights into the French Revolution, the Russian Revolution was not so much a new start, a fresh beginning in history, but rather an acceleration of deep trends and movements already under way. For us Americans it is of the first importance to understand that the Revolution and Lenin did not invent science in Russia; the Soviet regime makes no such claim—on the contrary, it celebrates the names of Mendeleyev, Lomonosov, Lebedev, and other great figures in the history of science in Russia.

What the Russian Revolution did in science was to open up its great tradition to participation by all the youth of the country. In the process of setting up its educational system and eliminating illiteracy in the nation, the Revolution broadened the base of Russian science and brought a vigorous new infusion of talent and capacity into an already great tradition. One can no longer properly speak of "Russian" science, for many of the best men in Soviet science come from the junior republics of the Soviet Union, from Armenia, Turkestan, and so on.

But, because the Soviet Union is a poor country, just completing its transformation from an agricultural economy to a modern industrial economy, as President Eisenhower said the other day, they have had to use their resources carefully. They have had to pick and choose, and give up some things in order to accomplish others. They had to make these hard choices in science just as they had to make them in deciding between capital and consumer goods. Where they have concentrated their efforts, in one or another region of science, they have been very good. But by the same token, they have little to show in areas they have neglected.

I have a vivid picture of this in my mind brought away from a visit to the laboratory of William Fowler at the California Institute of Technology. Professor Fowler has three elegantly instrumented but relatively low-power accelerators (atom smashers), with which he is investigating the so-called thermonuclear processes that go on in the interiors of the stars. These processes generate the energy of stars, some of which we see as starlight; they also conduct the synthesis of the elements upward from the naked elementary particles of matter, building up the heavier elements from the lighter ones. This experimental astrophysics is leading to a new conception of the life history and evolution of stars and has bearing on some of the really grand questions of cosmology. Fowler told us that work of this kind is not going on in the Soviet Union; either they can't afford it or they haven't been interested.

On the other hand, Fowler and other physicists who have been to the Soviet Union tell us that the scientists there are exceptionally good in the very high energy realms, up in the billion- and ten-billion-volt range. At Dubno, near Moscow, they are putting the finishing touches on the first ten-billion-volt nuclear accelerator to be built anywhere in the world.

An important bit of background to this development is the fact that it is only within the past three or four years that Soviet physicists have got out of their Los Alamos. That is to say, they have just been released from the laboratories of applied physics, where they made their atomic weapons. They got back to basic research, to "real" science, seven or eight years later than our scientists. The lavish support the Soviet scientists are now enjoying in their venture into the ten-billion-volt energy range is, in a sense, their reward for the crash program of weaponeering—which must have been just as unpleasant for them as for our physicists.

According to Donald Hughes, of Brookhaven National Laboratories, the Soviet scientists have so far neglected the vital field of neutron spectroscopy—the technique by which American physicists have recently been exploring the interior structure of the atomic nucleus. Nor do they have any good research reactors—that is, nuclear reactors designed especially for research rather than for power or the manufacture of plutonium—at work in their program. Hughes and other physicists tell us that, as a result of the neglect of these important areas in physics, the Soviet scientists are dependent upon the work we have done in America for the education of their students and that one of the standard physics textbooks in the Soviet universities is that written by Victor Weisskopf, of M. I. T.

Out of this same spotty work in physics, however, came the first really successful hydrogen bomb. That was the bomb that employs lithium deuteride instead of liquid deuterium as the thermonuclear fuel, a stratagem since adopted, apparently, in the making of our hydrogen bombs. And out of equally spotty work in technology came the first satellite.

The same is true in other fields. In the biological sciences, for example, the modern disciplines are almost completely neglected. The reason for this is that the biological talent in Russia has been mobilized to achieve immediate objectives in agricultural research. We had our Luther Burbank, the practical, empirical manipulator of the genetic processes, a generation ago. The Russians have had their Lysenko, who was much the same kind of simple scientist. But Lysenko was a clever bureaucrat and a salesman who knew how to entrance the rather unsophisticated men who wield political power in the Soviet Union. He sold them a bill of goods, apparently promising to achieve much needed miracles in agricultural research by his simple, naturalistic, and quite unscientific methods. In his contest with real scientists for control of the country's agricultural research, he won hands down and was able to get the science of genetics labeled as anti-Marxian heresy. As a result, the Soviet Union has missed almost completely the historic advances that have been made in biochemistry and biophysics on this side of the world.

In sum, the Russians are as proficient as anyone else in the fields they go into. In the fields they don't go into, they suffer, and will continue to suffer, just as we would also suffer if we were to follow their example.

Our science, by contrast, is a well-rounded establishment. Our intellectual resources have been enriched by the presence of refugees, like Albert Einstein and Enrico Fermi, who fled here from the political turmoil of Europe. Partly as a result of this infusion of talent and leadership, American science, we can say, is now pre-eminent in every field.

What characterizes American science above all is that it is carried forward by individual initiative and enterprise. The really novel work in science is not done by a committee or a team working under some project or program on behalf of a commission or bureau, but by the individual scientist. He has his own bright idea, his own questions to ask about nature, his own particular curiosity, his own initiative and goals. The progress of science is like the creative process in any other field. It cannot be programed in advance or conducted for some predetermined goal. It comes out of the head of the gifted, trained, and dedicated individual man. Thus the flourishing state of science in our country may be taken as evidence that our Constitution is still in working order.

The free winds of liberty are vital to the life of science for another important and perhaps somewhat curious reason. The great developments in science come very often by accident. They come through the convergence of unrelated pieces of work which, when the next stone is laid, suddenly reveal themselves to be an edifice with an unforeseen structure and significance. Obviously, such developments cannot be programed. All that society can do to encourage science is encourage its scientists.

Our scientists who have visited the Soviet Union all find themselves up against an uncomfortable sensation that they are under challenge by vigorous, ambitious, and able competitors who are out to make their country's name famous. The first reaction of the American scientist is the feeling that he had better get home and get to work if he is to uphold our country's reputation. But when he gets home and thinks this over, he comes to the conclusion that he doesn't really want to "do science that way." And he is right! We don't do science in order to make our country great and strong; we support science as a supreme exercise and expression of the highest faculties of man. The drive to achievement in science arises out of a profound need in the human system. Albert Einstein called it the "passion for understanding." It is a thirst that is as elemental in human nature as thirst itself.

As the Russians have shown us, science can survive under autocracy and even flourish for a while as a means to an end. But science cannot last for very long under centralized direction without going rigid and sterile. If we and the Soviet Union don't use the power that science gives us for our mutual destruction in the next few years, then we can hope, perhaps, that the Soviet scientists will begin to do science the way we do it. They will then be even better at it than they are now.

The things that are wrong with American science are the same things that are wrong with Soviet science. There has been much too much emphasis during the last fifteen years on "applied research," which means engineering, not science. Even under the heading of "basic research," which is supposed to mean real science, there has been too much program and project work imposed upon the talents and energies of American scientists. We have come to resemble the Soviet Union in another aspect. There has been a tendency, promoted by an ignorantly conceived and stupidly managed personnel loyalty and security system, to impose intellectual conformity and political orthodoxy in our country in recent years. Scientists have been among its most prominent and numerous casualties.

The Sputniks have equally given us second thoughts about our educational system. The Health, Education, and Welfare Department report on Soviet education treated us to some really staggering surprises. Most of us learned for the first time that education in the Soviet Union is now universal, free, and compulsory through high school. There are now 1,500,-000 children graduating from the Soviet high schools each year, as compared with 1,300,000 children in America. Two million of these high school graduates are enrolled in technical schools, which are equipping them to perform functions equivalent to those performed by technicians here. They also have 1,900,000 students in their universities and colleges, as compared with 3,000,000 in our country. The Soviet Union, theoretically at least, offers the opportunity of a college education to every qualified high school graduate, and it pays the student to go. We hear talk here about how the overweening power of the Soviet state is employed to compel students to go into science and engineering. The proper word is "induce," not "compel." The student's stipend provides a means for luring talented young people into fields that the state wants to encourage and helps to ensure that the most talented go on to graduate school. Some 70 per cent of the Soviet college-grade students are enrolled in courses in the sciences.

"The Soviet Union," President Eisenhower told us, "now has in the combined category of scientists and engineers a greater number than the United States, and it is producing graduates in these fields at a much higher rate." He added: "This trend is disturbing."

It is a pity that people find such news disturbing. Of course, it is disturbing if the world is threatened with war. But it ought to be a source of great satisfaction and pride to all of us that another two hundred million people have moved into the twentieth century out of the depths of poverty, ignorance, disease, and desperation that engulf two thirds of the human race. If we can keep the peace, we may look forward to seeing these two thirds come up alongside us too.

In comparing our educational system with that of the Soviet Union, President Eisenhower urged us to "remember that when a Russian graduates from high school, he has had five years of physics, one year of chemistry, one year of astronomy, five years of a foreign language and ten years of mathematics."

To get this impressive recital into perspective we should recognize first of all that the Soviet curriculum is not another secret weapon of the Communist party. It is just old-fashioned, traditional European education. The European secondary and college education is designed for the chosen few. It is a rigorous program, meant to produce a real intellectual elite. The Soviet Union has made this program universal and compulsory for all of the children. But some of the Scandinavian countries are doing the same, and so, more recently, are the British. To make possible a high quality of training, the educational systems of all these countries separate the talented students from the untalented at an early age. The untalented get trained in a trade; the talented go on to preparatory school, to college, and ultimately to graduate school.

For us Americans, this separation of the sheep from the goats at an early age is repugnant. The egalitarian traditions of our country and, especially, of our educational system constitute a noble feature of our heritage. We admit, in all candor, that in trying to educate everybody and educate them all equally well, there has been some downgrading in the quality of American education. But our idea is to give everybody an equal break.

To catch up with the Soviet Union in science education—if that is what we are after—would be no simple matter. Before we try to do it, we should consider what we really want. We cannot produce great scientists by stuffing little heads with chemistry and physics and mathematics. Great work in science comes out of an exposure to the whole fabric of the culture. The questions scientists are concerned with are not mean little technical issues, but important questions that concern and interest every man. They get asked only by men who have the large view and generous interests that come from literature and the arts as well as science. The only way we will produce great scientists is by improving our educational system in every department and at every grade.

Just about everyone now agrees that a federal aid for education bill should get through the next Congress, and there is an increasing likelihood that it will. But that is not going to solve the problem. Education in America is uniquely a local enterprise and the principal responsibility that our political system lays upon the individual citizen. We so often conclude a discussion of politics with the plaintive statement: "We can't do anything about it, except cast our one ballot." Here, in education, there is something more that the individual citizen can do. Sputnik or no Sputnik, we ought to be doing it.

As we undertake improvements in our educational system, we must bear in mind that we cannot raise scholars and scientists as means to an end. We do not educate our children as instruments of national power. We educate them because we prize them as people. And we have, each of us, a vision of how marvelous life can be for our children if they can realize their full capacities as human beings. If we are in a race with the Soviet Union, then the way to take the lead is to refresh our understanding of our traditions and renew our conviction in the ideals by which we live.

4

Science, Disarmament, and Peace

THE TERM "arms control" was not yet in vogue when the Americans for Democratic Action assembled for their annual Roosevelt Day dinner in New York City in January 1958. The now somewhat bald word "disarmament" was therefore on the agenda. "Peace" had only recently been reinstated in the common currency of United States political discourse. So there is no doubt that "science" helped to secure for both of these words their place on the program of the evening.

It has been pointed out to me that the "shameful agreement" alluded to on page 198 has been amended, so that the security agents do not have unlimited access to the university personnel files—only to the files on such members of the faculty as the university administration itself may select as warranting investigation. This is one of those well-intended "reforms" of the personnel security and loyalty program that end in compromising the integrity of men and institutions more gravely than before. The university president is now deputized as a security officer and custodian of the privacy of the members of his faculty.

193

THERE IS a rare wisdom reflected in the joining of science, on tonight's agenda, to the issue of disarmament and the hope for peace. More often, during the past three months, we have been hearing talk about science in connection with armament and the waging of war.

A tide of anxiety cuts across all of this talk. Science has become the subject of a new and unaccustomed worry and concern. Is American science good enough? Is some other nation's science better? What the worriers are worrying about, of course, is still another question: Is American science delivering? Delivering the warheads, the rockets, and the control and detection systems equal to the ever mounting perfection of twentieth-century warfare?

Now, without doubt, this is a grave question, and one to generate anxiety. I submit, however, that the question is misdirected. When we know what it is we want to get delivered we should address the procurement order, not to science, but to technology. Science is concerned with discovery of the unknown; by definition, we cannot prescribe in advance what it is we want science to discover. The work of science is to increase our understanding of the universe around us and of the world that is within each of us. It is concerned as much with the detection of error as with the disclosure of truth. The things we can learn by scientific investigation must be regarded, therefore, not as means, but as ends in themselves. They may or they may not, in addition, prove useful for some practical purpose. As for usefulness, man invariably finds destructive as well as constructive uses for everything he takes up in his hands. But this exploitation of the already known, which we call technology, must be clearly distinguished from the discovery of the unknown, which is the work of science.

One who is anxious about the military security of our country might still be moved to ask whether American science knows as much as some other country's science. The answer to this question is one we all ought to comprehend by now: There are no secrets in science. Nature has secrets, but these are open to investigation and discovery by the scientists of all nations. Most often, in the history of science, the major discoveries have been made simultaneously by two or more scientists, working independently of one another and in ignorance of one another's work. In our obsession with secrecy during the past fifteen years we have surely disrupted the work of American scientists, but we have not prevented scientists in other countries from discovering the secrets we were trying to hide. Science is in the public domain and belongs to all of the people in the world. It is only in our troubled times that we have learned to speak of American science, or German or Russian science. Whatever these jingoistic phrases are intended to suggest, they are a contradiction in terms.

But now let us settle this anxiety about science. I venture to declare that the further advance of science can add little to mankind's already well-secured capacity to destroy itself. It is difficult to see how we can improve on the ultimate. The thermonuclear reactions are the ultimate source of energy in the cosmos. We may well be able to find improved methods for harnessing their destructive capacity. But this is technology.

Contemporary weaponeering is essentially a process of miniaturization, of packing more devastation into a smaller and more portable warhead. Of course, our military technologists have other problems to solve: how to adjust the power of the explosive to the size of the target, and how to minimize radioactivity for those occasions when one hopes to occupy the target area oneself. There are, furthermore, unimaginably complicated problems to be solved in the making of the vehicles to deliver these warheads to their destinations. This calls for the programed invention of electronic circuits of exquisite complexity yet unfailing reliability, for the development of new fuels that employ unfamiliar kinds of combustion, for the synthesis of new materials, in accord with specifications prepared in advance, to withstand stress and shock at hitherto unheard-of temperatures.

I do not demean the character of these problems and the quality of intellect that must go into solving them when I say that this is not science. It is technology of a high order, and it is exploiting whole regions of knowledge only recently won from the unknown. On some salients along the front, the ambitions of this fantastic technology are raising questions for true scientific investigation. But the fact remains that the immense research and development activity sponsored by the Pentagon will contribute practically nothing to human understanding and can yield little else but an increase in the efficiency, flexibility, and enormity of our destructive power.

In sum, if anyone is anxious that our progress might be lagging in military technology, then the authorities to consult are not scientists but the technologists. I myself am puzzled that there should be so much anxiety on this heading. Technology is what we are supposed to be good at. After all, our country is the most powerful industrial nation in the world.

I must now confess to you, however, that when I contemplate our achievements in military technology I am filled with anxiety of another kind. During the past ten years, we have permitted our military power to become an overriding, all-enveloping absolute. To meet its demands, apparently, we must compromise the soundness of our currency and bankrupt what remains of our free-enterprise economy, we must set aside essential outlays for health, education, and welfare, and we must suspend our Bill of Rights. There must be some alternative to this squandering of our intellectual and human resources on weapons that are too frightful ever to be used. I find no comfort in the thought that homicide today is suicide or in the assurance that sanity is now compulsory in the affairs of state. Suppose we do manage to keep this time-bomb peace?

Science, Disarmament, and Peace

What kind of a country, what kind of world, will we live in then?

Now, it happens that scientists can tell us more about what that world will be like than any other group of citizens. They have been living inside the near edge of that world for most of the past fifteen years.

Their experience makes it clear, in the first place, that it will be a world without much science. In the weird distortion of values that has encouraged us to lay out unstinted billions for arms while we starve our educational system, we have placed our younger generation of scientists, the postwar crop, under cruel economic pressure. As a result, a dangerously large percentage of them have been abandoning the universities and their careers in science for higher-paid jobs in technology and industry. The ever mounting torrent of money for research and development has flooded over into the universities themselves and there conscripted the time and talent of our senior scientists. Science in our universities depends upon the federal government for more than half of its current support, and more than half of this support comes from the Department of Defense. All of this money is project money; that is, it is paid for services rendered. To some degree these payments are a camouflage for grants-in-aid, laid out to support the scientist's own work. But, by and large, most of it represents work on someone else's idea of what is necessary and worthwhile, and little of it can be credited to the advance of science. You don't get science when you give a professor a contract to do research, let us say, on solid fuels for rockets—even if you tell him: "Make that research *basic!*"

As for the next generation of American scientists—our high school science teachers have been giving up the teaching profession in favor of employment as engineers and technicians in industry. Who can blame them, on their old-fashioned, pre-inflation teaching salaries, for yielding to the temptation of a living wage?

197

There is another aspect of the experience of our scientists in this period that has implications for us all. More than any other element in our society, they have suffered abridgment of their civil liberties and invasion of their domestic privacy as the result of our national loyalty neurosis. The retirement of the congressional committees from this field has left a deafening and quite deceptive quiet. Our university faculties remain in the toils of the federal personnel security system. The universities that are party to classified federal research contracts —and that means practically all of them—are also party to a shameful agreement that opens their files on all of their faculty members—not simply those cleared for classified work, but all of them—to investigation by federal security agents. No matter what niceties of administration are invented, what imitations of due process are preferred, the fact remains that the protections hedging the sovereignty of the American citizen have been breached and nowhere more ominously than in the very citadels of our liberty, the universities.

How can this downgrading of the individual be reversed in a world that lives in the shadow of the ninety-minute war? Who can talk of human dignity among a people that is being taught to scramble at the siren's wail and tomorrow will learn to cower in underground shelters? What place is there for liberty in the garrison state that brands dissent as treason? How can scientific talent be spared for investigation of fundamental questions when the question of the hour is the design of an electronic brain to decide when the moment has come to push the push button?

If we want to talk about science, plainly we must assume the world will keep the peace. But that is not enough. If we want to believe that science has a future, as well as a fruitful past, then we must assume disarmament.

There is a deep connection between science and the social order of self-governing democracy. Scientific investigation is uniquely an individual process. A scientist has no system of absolutes to tell him whether he is right or wrong, no court or consistory to which he can repair for confirmation and approbation of his work. He can trust no authority but his own judgment. It should be no surprise, therefore, to discover that scientists tend to be highly individualistic, independent men. Men of this stamp may, of course, turn up in autocratic societies. They may die at the stake, as did Giordano Bruno, or they may succeed in outwitting tyranny, as did Galileo. But, naturally enough, they will flourish more readily in social orders that cherish the individual and respect his rights. As Albert Einstein observed: "It is quite possible to assert that intellectual individualism and the thirst for scientific knowledge emerged simultaneously in history and have remained inseparable ever since."

We can see why it is, therefore, that science and self-government have advanced together over the past five hundred years. It is not only that technology, enriched by science, has eliminated famine and pestilence as necessary conditions of human existence and made possible, at long last, the abolition of slavery as the underpinning of high civilization. The advance of science during this period has brought an equally revolutionary change in man's outlook upon the world.

All of us today are Newtonians, at least, in physics; we think of the universe as a great mechanical system open to our understanding to the furthest depths accessible to our instruments and our imagination. Our children, of course, are a good deal more sophisticated; they are making themselves at home in the new cosmos of interchangeable matter and energy, elastic time, and curved space. In biology, all of us are Darwinians; we perceive the unity of our species with all other living things and find a new reverence for life in the realization that we are the terminal point of its evolution on our planet. Inescapably, too, we are Freudians in psychology; the subconscious, we now realize, is natural to our make-up, not the enemy of reason but the generator of its passion.

All of us, in brief, are scientists. With the overthrow of received authority and the banishing of superstition, we are comprehending that it is man's destiny to make himself.

The brief history of intellectual individualism has now brought humanity to the threshold of its destiny. The choice for the future is our own to make. If we choose peace and life in preference to war and death, we can envision a swift acceleration in the evolution of our species. In the universal understanding that no man is a natural slave, that all men are brothers, we would not long delay the organization of a world order appropriate to this understanding. A world in which the individual man is sovereign would soon eliminate the international anarchy of sovereign states.

The thirst for scientific knowledge has supplied the means as well as the motives for the choice of world peace. It is now technologically possible to eliminate, before the end of this century, hunger and disease from the lives of the two thirds of the world population whose misery and destitution submerge their existence at a subhuman level.

In the light of what we know and what we can do, we can now cease to regard peace as an interval between wars. The making of peace becomes an objective that can fulfill the genius and passion of man so long as the evolution of the cosmos permits his existence.

Here, then, is the alternative to our present commitment of our liberty and safety to the protection of ever more terrifying armaments. The flowering of science and democracy in our nation is the example that set off the revolution of the destitute that now shakes the world. The material deficit that blights their existence can be balanced by our enormous agricultural and industrial surplus—now going to waste and destruction. Surely the self-governing citizens of our country can find here new ways to exert our power and influence in international affairs and show the world the promise of peace.

5

The Revolution in
Man's Labor

St. John's, at Annapolis, Maryland, is the college of the Great Books. The convocation in April 1959, to which I contributed this essay, was called to bring the besetting questions of our times into the light that is shed by readers of those books.

In the darkest hours of human despair life could never have seemed so transient as it appears to the present generation. Man has survived the cruel trials of natural selection only to face at last the direst of all threats to his existence: himself.

In an arms race that consumes the treasure and genius of civilization, one side—the one we tremble to call our own— has accumulated sufficient destructive capacity to annihilate the other twenty-five times over. And that other side, by this time, has equipped itself with ten times the power to destroy us. Between us we are in a position to exterminate the entire species three times over. Neurosis, senility, stupidity, accident —any of these at any moment may push the button on Apocalypse.

While time permits, we may stand in wonder at what man has wrought. He has taken in his mortal hands the source of energy that lights the universe through all eternity—or at least for 10 billion years past and 50 billion years to come, in the finite terms in which we measure infinity today. He can ignite stars on earth hotter than any that shine in the firmament. In the dread rehearsal of our last hour more than 300 such stars have already winked their blinding light under the roof of our increasingly polluted atmosphere.

We may marvel at the depth of understanding of nature and nature's laws that makes such deeds possible. Here, on the scale of destructive might, is a measure of the power of the rational method. In the chancelleries of the world the importance of natural philosophy is at last comprehended. The decisions of statesmen in every land are now heavily conditioned by regard for the destructive power of science.

It is ironic, though it is inevitable, that the threat now laid to human existence should be leveled by those same nations in which human life has for the first time experienced abundance. In North America and Europe west of the Urals, entire nations have enjoyed a well-being that has been reserved in the past to the fortunate elite. These nations are the first to have discovered, in the words of Bertrand Russell, "how to prevent abject poverty, how to prevent the pain and sorrow and waste of useless births condemned to premature death, and how to substitute intelligence and care for the blind ruthlessness of nature."

Why is it that the most fortunate people on earth should be on the verge of treason to the entire human race? To say that violence is natural to human nature is to fall into tautology. If this statement means anything at all, it ignores the great plasticity of the human personality. It may be that the original sin was the enslavement of one man by another in the organization of the first high civilizations. In the behavior of the modern national state, the resort to force and violence is sanctioned by all but one or two churches and by the most eminent moral philosophers. How else could states, living together in anarchy, decide which is to have enough when there is not enough to go around?

But in the very age in which we live there has come an essential change in the condition of human existence. The terrifying destructiveness of modern technology bespeaks a corresponding capacity for constructive solution of the ills of mankind. The revolution in man's labor that has come with the present amplification of our capacity for mass murder makes it possible for all men at last to enter into the human estate. The way of life that we are privileged to enjoy is now possible for all mankind. That is the essence of the change in the condition of man. If the nature of this change were more widely comprehended by citizens and statesmen, I have faith that an equal change could be worked in man's relationship to man.

But this declaration does not come escorted by a thunderclap. Its truth is not widely credited. The possibilities of human fulfillment to which it points are not generally comprehended even by those citizens and statesmen whose own style of existence furnishes the most compelling evidence in its support. The revolutionists try to forget the revolution. We embrace the good fortune that is ours and claim it as our birthright. In fear, we suppress the memory of the recent past and, in a world of increasing impermanence, persuade ourselves that our estate is perpetual.

To such a state of mind it may be salutary to recall that the entire biography of man is but a recent event in the history of the earth. We surmise that our genus originated in a recognizable approximation of its modern form not more than one million years ago. In the five billion years that the earth has revolved around the sun, those million years are the last fifteen seconds of a day.

The first evidence of our species is dated on the order of 100,000 years ago, within the last two seconds of the earth's first day. In the flaked stone and sharpened bone we see that evolution has already assumed a new dimension. Man appears unique among the animals: he can transmit acquired characteristics to his offspring. Human infancy, then as now, was prolonged, and the primitive society of the family and tribe was already engaged in education. In the long, slow accretion of skills recorded in the exquisitely worked tools and weapons buried in the cave floors, we can see how successive generations selected and rejected and improved upon their heritage.

At some turning point, man mastered fire. The blackened bones and earth in the cave middens are not the only testimony. The vegetation over large parts of the Northern Hemisphere shows that Stone Age men used fire to open up grazing lands for the wild game on which they preyed. With this new mastery of nature, the human species, perhaps 40,000 years ago, radiated over the entire earth, crossing for the first time into the Western Hemisphere. Before the history of civilization began, men had occupied the margins of the Arctic ice, the desert, the prairies, the mountain forests, and lonely islands in the distant ocean. These were the cultures of day-to-day survival—of hunters, fishermen, food gatherers, inured to menace, formidable antagonists in the struggle for life.

The history of civilization, of the settled urban community, goes back no more than 10,000 years, less than two tenths of a second ago. By that time the food gatherers had brought all of the food crops and all of the domestic animals we know today under cultivation and husbandry. They had learned also another use for fire. By confining it in a furnace they could raise the temperature from the 400 or 500 degrees of the open campfire to 1,000 degrees. Such temperature drives out the water of crystallization in pottery and bricks and made it possible to store the harvests and build cities.

Now, at last, want and the daily struggle for enough food to survive were lifted for a few members of the species. The new technology of agriculture required the labor of only four families on the soil to produce enough food to support themselves and one more family. The allocation of this surplus was secured by a social invention, the institution of slavery. In the ruins of the earliest cities we see the image of the societies that built them: at first temples, later palaces, surrounded by fortifications and the hovels of the slaves.

Since it was now possible for the labor of four families to support a fifth in occupations other than agriculture, the range of technology broadened. The furnaces became hot enough to smelt copper and iron. The wheel and the sail appeared. The pulley and the lever, the pump and the bellows, and other mechanical contrivances came into use. With the technological base thus broadened, the way was opened to high civilization and the beginning of recorded history.

In the record we discover three major centers—the Mediterranean, India, and China. Later, in apparent independence of these, came the high civilizations of the Western Hemisphere. But in all of these centers, history and civilization were an experience of the few. The life of the rest of mankind, from Rome to Cathay to the central plateau of Mexico, was wretchedly the same. Everywhere within the marches of civilization the ratio of four families out of five enslaved to the soil prevailed. And the first urban masses freed for other crafts and functions were enslaved in other ways.

Civilization, however, was a success. The human population expanded. Where it had taken ten square miles of wilderness to support a single human being in the primitive economy of food gathering, now a few acres of agricultural land sufficed to sustain each human life. But the population of the agrarian civilizations pressed everywhere, at all times, on the margin of subsistence. As the land under cultivation expanded, so did the population; when harvests failed—or when the land failed under unwise exploitation—the population shrank. The fortunes of the most famous ancient states waxed and waned with the harvests and with outbreaks of epidemic disease. From the outside they were threatened by those they called barbarians, peoples still in transition from the Stone Age to neolithic culture. But as the slow trial-and-error advance of technology furnished weapons and more secure means of communication and the rulers learned to manage ever larger social organizations, states blossomed into empires, and history moved into the modern era.

In one form or another the institution of slavery persisted in almost every center of civilization on into the history of our own republic. Thomas Jefferson himself, whose eighteenth-century enlightenment is evoked by the pleasant architecture of this college, once recorded his opinion that "some numbers of men are natural slaves."

If we wonder what life was like for ordinary people in those high and far-off times, we need not dig into archaeology or scratch for illumination in the history books that have so largely ignored them. We can see their technological contemporaries struggling for the same sort of life in the world today. They constitute, in fact, nearly two thirds of the human race. Principally in the Southern Hemisphere, they are the peoples of what we have come to call the underdeveloped regions of the world. There, four out of five families are still bound to scratching their subsistence from the earth. Their life expectancy, until very recently, was between thirty and forty years. This means that most of them die in infancy, at birth, or in childbed. Their nutrition ranges from 1,300 to 2,000 calories per day, at least 500 calories below the minimum required to sustain the vigor of life. As late as the beginning of this century, famine and pestilence kept their increasing numbers in Malthusian equilibrium with the yield of the soil. The primary source of energy for their day's labor, as for neolithic man 10,000 years ago, is the metabolism of their own bodies. Literacy is the skill of a few in the village; ignorance and superstition are the shelter and solace of life.

Here and there we can find some tens of millions of men in a still lower estate. They are men of the Stone Age and in the first transition from food gathering to the cultivation of jungle gardens. But they are quickly disappearing, some dying with their gods, others engulfed without trace in acculturation to the twentieth century.

Contrast their condition with that of the inhabitants of Western civilization. In our own country, the labor of one family in eight on the farm yields a harvest equivalent to an average of more than 10,000 calories per capita per day for the entire population. From this cornucopia we consume an average of a little more than 3,000 calories each, feeding the surplus to domestic animals in order to upgrade the protein content of those 3,000 calories to a hitherto unheard-of 30 per cent. Life expectancy is moving from sixty to seventy years. Famine and pestilence are echoes of Sunday-school Bible lessons. The primary source of energy is the combustion of fuel. Our per capita income, a term of pure mystery to most of our fellow men, exceeds $1,800 a year and equips us to hanker for wants that are unknown even as luxuries elsewhere in the world. Almost all of our children are graduating from high school, and nearly 30 per cent of them are going on to college. The largest and the fastest-growing segment of our labor force is no longer in manufacturing, which long ago succeeded agriculture, but in distribution, the service industries, and the trained professions.

So far as our citizens are concerned and for the overwhelming proportion of Europeans west of the Urals, material want has been effectively abolished. The improvement in their well-being above that of the general level of mankind was reflected two centuries ago in the steep increase of the population of

Europe, the New World, and the other frontiers occupied by Europeans. The expansion begins with the invention of the steam engine and accelerates to the highest rate of growth ever experienced by a major population at mid-nineteenth century, when mechanically generated energy for the first time displaced the energy of human muscles. From 150 million in 1770, the white population has increased sixfold to nearly 900 million. In the same period the colored people of the world have only doubled their numbers, the largest increase coming in the last fifty years. The ultimate arrival of the white people in the condition of freedom from want is now testified by the leveling off of their population growth. With the increase in their production outrunning even their spectacular increase in numbers, they have found it possible and desirable to limit the size of their families and so to conserve and amplify the improvement in their well-being.

How did it happen that more than one third of the human race arrived in a condition of such material advantage over the rest? To answer the question we must go back 400 years in the history of Europe, well back into the last tenth of a millionth of the last second of the world's day. At that time, in the European civilization that was rising from the ashes of the Classical Age, a new movement of discovery was under way. We may evoke the spirit of this epoch in the person of one man, who personifies it in all its boldness and diversity; this was Leonardo. In the models of his inventions—displayed here at the college—we behold a Promethean vision of what was to come. The least successful of his inventions declare his reckless aim: to comprehend the forces of nature and subdue them to his purpose. But it is in his paintings that we see his most profound contribution to the emerging inquiry of science. "He is a painter," says the British mathematician J. Bronowski, "to whom the detail of nature speaks aloud; for him nature expresses herself in the detail . . . [He] gave science what it most needed, the artist's sense that the detail of nature is significant. Until science had this sense, no one could care—or could think that it mattered—how fast two unequal masses fell or whether the orbits of planets are accurately circles or ellipses."

It was the commitment to the inductive method—which begins with the detail of nature—that was to change the condition of man. This was the way to take the faculty of reason out of the cul-de-sac of mere logical tautology and on to the discovery of unity in nature. The first scientists were deeply imbued with the Classical conviction of order in nature, but the inductive method alerted them to discern the never ending variety in which nature's unity finds expression. In a brief few years the scientific movement swept from Tycho and the perfection of his observations, to Copernicus and his boldness in choosing the sun-centered alternative, to Kepler and his ellipses, to Galileo, who perceived the analogy between the motions of planets and the fall of unequal masses on earth, and on to Newton, who encompassed all motion in a single great world system. The triumph of the new method of natural philosophy was complete by the end of the seventeenth century.

Beginning in the eighteenth century, science gained its ascendance as a major enterprise of our civilization. Newton's physics was extended to every branch of inquiry into nature and everywhere extirpated the fallacies, myths, and nonsense that had been cherished from earlier years. The universe ceased to be a realm permeated with vitalistic, purposive, and capricious forces and opened up its most distant reaches to exploration by the human mind.

During the past century, the movement has gathered constantly increasing acceleration. It was a century and a half, for example, from the discovery of the force of gravity to the discovery of electromagnetic forces; less than a century thereafter to the discovery of the force that binds the atomic nucleus; and now less than a generation to the measurement of the weak forces that attend the mysterious decay of the ultimate particles of matter. Newton's grand generalizations are today encompassed in still more comprehensive statements of nature's underlying theory. Most recently the search for unity in nature, its perception sharpened by the inductive method, has uncovered the subterranean, looking-glass world of anti-matter. Nature apparently guarantees that there shall be no end to our inquiry. Each successful generalization uncovers new gaps in our experience and asks new questions.

Since ours is a civilization of action, there has been a parallel acceleration in the application of new knowledge. The nature of combustion—which had vitrified neolithic pottery and smelted the ores of the Bronze and Iron ages—was not comprehended until the end of the eighteenth century. The discovery of oxygen began the science of chemistry. Where once men could purify a mere half dozen metals, there is now not a single metal in the table of elements that is not finding its way into use in modern technology. The fixation of nitrogen from the limitless ocean of the air a scant two generations ago removed the threat laid by nitrogen exhaustion to the world's food supply. From the study of the giant molecules of life has come the organic chemical industry, which imitates life in the synthesis of new reagents, dyes, drugs, and materials. Mathematics itself, the once inviolable muse of speculative thought, has given birth to mechanical computers able to conduct centuries of calculation in a few hours, and to robot control systems that manage most of the major operations of our technology. Even astronomy has joined the applied sciences; it is from astrophysics that we are learning to subdue the inferno of the thermonuclear reactions, the last step that remains before man achieves access to the ultimate and, for all practical purposes, infinite source of energy on earth.

Until the scientific enterprise began 400 years ago the rate of invention hugged the time base line. The stock of technique increased by arithmetic progression, as often as not by accident and without real understanding of the principles involved. For the past three centuries, however, the progression has been geometric, climbing steeply toward parallel with the vertical co-ordinate. Now invention has entered a new phase. It exploits understanding already established; it responds not merely to necessity but to opportunity presented by new knowledge. So long as the enterprise of science is nurtured by society, technology will move forward with it.

Thus, as man's understanding deepens, his environment grows ever more responsive to his wants; the world's resources become as rich as his imagination. Does our appetite for metals at last exhaust the abundant ore beds of the world? According to Harrison Brown and his associates at the California Institute of Technology, we may turn to the granite of the continental masses and extract not only the full spectrum of mineral wealth but the fissionable elements that will provide the energy to power this "age of granite." Or we may turn to the oceans, with their limitless supply of hydrogen for energy, plus all of the minerals leached out of the continental rock by the rains and rivers. Do we require food? According to studies by the Food and Agriculture Organization, we can, with sufficient investment, expand the world's arable land seven times. The output of the land may meanwhile be multiplied past any prediction by the manipulation of life processes in plants and animals. Beyond the land lie the seas, in which the major portion of the earth's organic matter is turned over in the great interlocking cycles of life.

The outcome of the revolution in man's labor thus brings the elimination of want within the reach not only of the living generation of men but of all the generations we can foresee. Those latter-day Malthusians who panic at the world's immediate prospective population growth may leave it to later generations to decide how numerous they want to be. Want is no longer a challenge to technology, but to economics and politics. It is a social problem.

Not the least of the social problems posed by technology is the question: How can human dignity and freedom be maintained in a world organized to sustain the logistics of abundance? The management of the high technology of the future might find it in its power and convenience to tamper with the genetic constitution of the species or with the psychological processes of individual human minds.

But such questions beset us already in a society that is willing to contemplate suicide and listens every noontime to the wail of sirens. Is this the only face that we can turn to the world's dispossessed, to the 1,500 million beyond the pale of Western civilization?

They have heard the news of the revolution in man's labor. They are impressed by the example of our own nation more than that of any other. Thanks principally to death control, they are living longer and feeling well enough to do something about their plight. The political turmoil of the no longer colonial peoples provides the principal dynamics of this era of international political conflict. It is the power vacuum created by the breakdown of the old order in those regions that sucks the two great power systems to the edge of catastrophe.

In an acutely tender way, the wishes of these aroused people should be on our conscience. They are still extracting the irreplaceable resources of their lands to feed our voracious appetite for raw materials. Presently, in fact, we import from overseas sources iron ore, bauxite, oil, and a host of precious commodities in a greater volume than ever before. In some sectors our technology is perilously dependent upon the riches they supply so cheaply. The good will and compliance of the natives have immediate relevance to our price structure.

We cannot stop at the churlish counsel that the colonials should reduce their numbers. Their population is rising because the modicum of sanitation introduced to protect the white colonials in their midst has reduced their rate of mortality as well. Their numbers are increasing, according to

United Nations studies, at a rate that exceeds 1 per cent per year. Since the end of the Second World War their material condition has been in corresponding decline; their calorie intake has actually fallen.

To offset the claim of population growth and reverse the decline in their condition, they must increase their production at a rate greater than their population growth. The larger the differential, the faster will their lot improve. Such an objective is not only technologically but politically and economically feasible. Our own industrial growth has averaged 2.5 per cent over long periods; it has even reached 5 per cent under intense pressure. The growth of our agricultural output has correspondingly proceeded at the rate of 2 per cent in normal times. In response to the economic cycle and to administrated prices and other regulatory devices, it fluctuates over an even wider range. Under forced draft attained by political pressures obnoxious to our citizenry, the U.S.S.R., the first under-developed country to come up to twentieth-century standards, has been achieving gains in industrial output at the rate of 8 per cent. The goals of their present agricultural programs are correspondingly high. Reports from China suggest that the government of that country has set no less ambitious objectives.

The success of both kinds of political and social management is proving increasingly attractive to the emergent economies of India, Southeast Asia, Indonesia, South America, and Africa. In their eyes, it is the results that count. As Prime Minister Nehru recently observed in the hearing of the American television public, hungry people are not ready to learn what we mean by freedom.

The task of industrialization involves some simple equations from classical economics. It is well known that the creation of capital requires savings. As Adam Smith long ago explained, saving means that the satisfaction of current want must be set aside to provide for future satisfactions. But when there is not enough to meet current want to begin with—which is the case in a Malthusian economic system—someone must starve to provide capital. Compulsion is usually necessary to persuade people to starve. In the present mood of the colonial peoples, however, they are ready to starve if it will do any good. And there are plenty of indigenous leaders ready to furnish the compulsion. This is what Prime Minister Nehru had in mind when he spoke of the secondary priority accorded to freedom in his electorate.

Now there is another alternative. The colonials do not have to go it alone. If we had conviction in our political and economic institutions and traditions—and a better understanding of their place in history—we would not willingly see these peoples submit themselves to compulsion. Out of the surplus capacity that troubles our market place we could meet a substantial portion of their need for capital equipment. Thanks to the labors of the international civil service of the United Nations and its accessory technical organizations, we have a pretty good idea of what it would cost.

Something on the order of $500 billion over the next fifty years would secure an average per annum gain of 2 per cent in industrial production and a corresponding increase in agricultural output in the areas concerned. This global figure comes out of reasonably detailed local studies; many of the projects are ready for preliminary cost accounting. Not all of the $500 billion would have to be supplied from outside. At about the halfway point, the new industrial centers would begin to generate some additional capacity of their own.

The bedrock investments, however, are not particularly attractive to the world's capital market. These involve such elementary public utilities as communication systems, including highways as well as railroads, and dams for flood control and irrigation. Investment in such projects would call for the kind of funds we now write off on armaments. On the whole, we would have to take a long-range view in looking for return on our investment. It would come eventually, however, as these economies cross the first hump toward the solution of their food problem.

Our technology is especially qualified to contribute to the soaring demand for electrical energy which will attend these industrialization programs. In a mature industrial system, fuels are, by overwhelming tonnages, the biggest commodities in circulation. The mines and oil fields, the railroads, pipelines, docks, and huge materials-handling depots that deliver coal and oil to our central power stations constitute one of the major activities of our economy. If the underdeveloped countries had to lay such foundations to achieve their electrification, they would have to wait for years. Here is a splendid market for our surplus of atomic bombs. A bomb is merely a high-speed reactor. Re-engineered and hooked up to a turbogenerator it becomes a power reactor. These high-density packages of energy, so well adapted for delivery by airplane and rocket, make it possible to electrify the frontier from scratch, with no preliminary investment in heavy engineering and construction. Hopefully, these man-made stellar engines will light the sky with the light that comes from windows.

But the demand for huge volumes of energy, heavy equipment, and big investment would not come at the outset. First there comes lead time for planning and then engineering. Many of the early gains in these areas would be achieved, anyway, with very little expenditure on capital goods. The first requirement is for brains and knowledge.

An example of what can be accomplished in this phase of the undertaking is furnished by Mexico. For the past twenty years the Rockefeller Foundation has been working with the Ministry of Agriculture and Animal Husbandry of that country. At a cost of something less than $2 million per year, American agronomists have been supplied to Mexico, and young Mexicans have been trained in the agricultural sciences. In this period, the food production of the country has mounted 80 per cent. The gains have been achieved by improved yields of Mexico's own staple crops, the development of new varieties of wheat and potatoes, and the establishment of something like our own county-agent system for farmer education. Not a single tractor or fertilizer plant is in the expense account; the money has been spent for the intangibles of information, education, and expert consultation. The 4 per cent per annum gain safely exceeds the increase in population and has brought an improvement in the people's diet that is already showing up in the vital statistics.

Somewhere in our material and intellectual resources we can certainly find the capacity to expand on this precedent. If we could make a beginning we would soon have additional wealth and brains available for the task as a result of the attenuation of the arms race on which our prosperity now rests so heavily and insecurely. Whether our present distribution of values permits us to think we can afford action on these lines or not, political and economic necessity will soon supply crude compulsion.

As the principal revolutionists in the revolution in man's labor, our people more than any other have created the conditions that now confront mankind with the choice between extinction and the achievement of its yearning to fulfill its humanity. Surely it will not exceed our capacity for social invention to assume the role that ought to be ours in the making of that choice.

In Defense of Education

HIGH SCHOOL TEACHERS all over the country have been going back to college. They are learning the "subjects" that were neglected in the course of their teachers-college training in "techniques." The National Science Foundation provided the first financing for the movement; the National Defense Education Act greatly amplified the funds available. Washington University, in St. Louis, Missouri, where I spoke in October 1959 to a group of high school teachers enrolled for the study of physics, has been one of the most successful centers for this leavening of method with matter.

W E ARE GATHERED HERE, at the expense of the United States federal government, to talk about education. This is as it should be. Public education was one of the generous promises of the American Revolution to the children of our country. America was, in fact, one of the first modern nations to achieve universal free public education.

But we should also remember that public education has been carried on in our country all of these years without the intervention of the federal government. Federal aid for education is a new bit of jargon in our political life, and it has been in controversy for most of the time that it has been in circulation. Now, suddenly and bountifully, federal funds have been made available for the encouragement of public education in America. A quite unprecedented act of Congress has appropriated $300 million to this end.

Significantly, the title of the act is the National Defense Education Act. Robert Hutchins has observed that there is a theme for a depressing spell of introspection in the fact that federal aid to education has become available for the first time under the heading of "defense."

Hutchins also points out that the United States, alone among the major nations of the world, leaves the function of education to local governments, the weakest and smallest units in the political system. Now, this arrangement may try one's patience, but it comes straight out of the Constitution. That document reserved not only education but the police power to those local units of government which come under the closest surveillance of the citizenry. The writers of the Constitution were good readers of history. The police power and education have figured again and again in authoritarian societies as primary instruments of tyranny—police power for the short run and education for the long run.

How then explain the sudden reversal in tradition and staunchly defended fiscal policy that has brought federal aid to education? The crucial date is October 4, 1957. On that day, the first man-made satellite began orbiting our planet, and it turned out not to speak English very well.

In the first rebound from the shock and chagrin of seeing someone else get there first, the President hastened before Congress with a special message. The secret of the Soviet triumph, he revealed, was Soviet education. The President's own astonishment was shared by everyone as he reeled off the figures. It was as if an American satellite had gone around to the other side of the moon and discovered there an entirely new and unknown civilization.

Of course, the Soviet Union is right here on this planet, and its territory is, in fact, as large as the face of the moon. That its educational system could have been concealed from the American people suggests that our press may be doing as poor a job of informing the American people about the Soviet Union as it claims the Soviet press has been doing in handling the traffic in the other direction.

The President of the United States had to break the news that, as early as 1950, 75 per cent of the children growing up in the Soviet Union were going through ten years of education. Moreover, the Soviet Government had declared its intention to extend the same opportunity to 100 per cent of the children by 1960. In the Soviet Union, the President revealed, the school year runs a full ten months, six days a week. During the last six years, 40 per cent of the time of all the children is given over to science and mathematics. They get six years of algebra, geometry, and trigonometry, five years of physics, four years of chemistry and biology, and a year each of astronomy and psychology.

For a few days following these revelations, the children of America could be seen skulking furtively between home and school, not advertising their existence by the usual skylarking. Their educators rushed to their defense, explaining that in those five years the Soviet child gets no more than small daily doses of physics and in the aggregate no more than an American child soaks up in his one-year course—if his school teaches the subject. But our political leaders accepted no such reassurance; they placed the education lag second only to the missile gap.

There was no time for consideration of constitutional questions; the hour called for action. Congress overturned a century and a half of tradition and appropriated the handsome figure of $300 million for the aid of American education.

The National Defense Education Act betrays the improvisation that is said to be characteristic of democracy when it is stirred to sudden strenuous efforts. It is perhaps more significant of the spirit that moved and carried the act that it was most warmly supported in Congress by those elements that had been most vocally opposed to federal education in the past.

The emphasis which the act places on the teaching of science is a plain indication of the kind of imbalance that might be imposed upon our educational system under centralized federal control. There is no suggestion that our educational system may be equally deficient in the teaching of other subjects—foreign languages, for example, or the reading and writing of English. Nor is there a hint that the deficiencies in the teaching of science, whatever they are, may be symptoms of deeper ills in our educational system, calling for other remedies.

Educators know these well and have been talking about them with eloquence for years. It is to the credit of American educators, moreover, that they have put the National Defense Education Act funds to many good uses, not all of them contemplated by the authors of the act.

The global statistics of our educational system are enough to suggest the kind of problems that confront the administrators and teachers. Since 1929, our country has been spending a steady 3 per cent of its gross national product on elementary and secondary education. This means that the expenditure has increased, all told, from $3 billion to $15 billion a year. The expenditure per student has multiplied, on a dollar basis, four times. Allowing for inflation in the interim, it appears that expenditure per student has doubled. This is not a bad performance at all for the weakest and smallest units in our political system. It compares favorably with the administration of higher education—a far smaller enterprise and so presumably more flexible, especially since much of it is in private hands—where expenditure per student is down one third.

But if we look at this doubling of the expenditure per student in the lower grades a little more closely, we find that it must be considerably discounted. An important element in the increase is the heavy expenditure on real estate, bricks and mortar, and capital equipment. The biggest investment has been in high schools, which have multiplied three times in number across the country in this thirty-year period. The over-all increase also reflects the suburbanization of the country, which has required the building of new schools in the new communities surrounding our metropolitan areas. From the global statistics it is difficult to tell how much of the increase is going to support the process of education that is supposed to animate the bricks and mortar. One discouraging indication is that our teachers are teaching just as many children per teacher as they did thirty years ago—and that means too many.

The condition of science education in our country demonstrates the fallacy of the misplaced concreteness that builds beautiful new schools and fails to hire enough teachers. The U.S. Office of Education shows, for example, that in the good old days, at the turn of the century, some 56 per cent of the high school children were studying algebra, whereas in 1953 only 25 per cent were exposed to the subject. The corresponding figures for geometry were 27 and 10 per cent. Around 1900, 19 per cent of the high school students were learning physics in a given school year; that figure was down to 4 per cent in 1953. Some 25 per cent of our high schools have no science teachers at all, and 25 per cent are no longer teaching geometry.

Of course, the high school enrollment has vastly increased in this period, and it may be argued that those who can absorb the hard subjects are being taught them in as large numbers as ever. But a survey of the "intellectual resources" of the United States recently conducted by the National Academy of Sciences shows that more than one third of the students graduating from high school with I.Q.'s of 145 or above—that is, the I.Q. of a reasonably well-qualified physicist—are not going to college. For this deplorable waste of capacity, the study found economics to be responsible only in part. Sheer lack of incentive was the major factor.

Let me give you some suggestion of the kind of thing that saps the incentive of some of our children. In 1957 we graduated 31,211 engineers in this country; of the total, 81 were women. Out of 596 engineering Ph.D.'s granted in that year, one was received by a woman. Among 2,104 advanced degrees in biology, there were 500 granted to women; out of 4,400 advanced degrees in physics, women received 300. That's about half the population deprived of incentive.

To this half of the population you may add the male offspring of such substantial minorities as the Negroes and the Latin Americans. You may also add a factor for the finding, made by George D. Stoddard and his colleagues at the Iowa University Child Study Center some years ago, that the I.Q. itself is a variable that responds to the environment and increases in direct ratio with incentive and the availability of good schooling.

So, if our country actually needs more scientists and more engineers, more than it needs more string musicians, lawyers, historians, and poets, it is clear that reforms of a more thoroughgoing and more constructive kind must be instituted, reforms that will take a longer view of the condition of American education than is expressed in the National Defense Education Act, which, on the face of it, is limited to the duration of the cold war.

But $300 million, to be spent over a five-year period, can do a lot of good if it is well administered. And it does seem that these first federal funds to flow into public education have been put to imaginative use. The numerous conferences and seminars, the summer fellowships for teachers, and the stipends that have brought you here to Washington University will surely upgrade the quality of the teaching of science in our schools. Hopefully, such activities may actually increase the output of scientists and engineers. But, what is more important, I think, the effort is going to improve the quality of science education for all students, whether they go on in the sciences or not.

While we count our blessings, however, we must not forget the terms on which these funds were pressed upon the educational system. This is important, because those terms contravene the very spirit of education as it has been conducted in our society. Not so long ago, it was universally agreed that the aim of education is the perfection of the individual, the evocation and realization of his humanity. Under the terms of the act, education—and the individual as well—becomes a means to an end, subordinated to the demands of national defense. The essence of what the defense measures are supposed to defend has been forgotten. The object is no longer the perfection of the individual; the individual is to be perfected as a kind of weapon in the sciences that give the modern state its military power. Presumably, if the same overriding absolute of "defense" required it, the process of education might also be suspended for the duration.

The confusion of ends and means that is embodied in the terms of the present federal financing of public education is not exclusively a product of demagogy and panic in Congress. It bespeaks a confusion in public opinion about ends and means, with respect to education, with respect to science, and with respect to the place of the individual in our society.

Consider the profound misunderstanding of the educational process, in the first place, that is represented by the idea of education for defense, or for any other end but its own. In effect, it is demanded that children be educated now so that at some later date they can put their knowledge to the service of the state or to some even more profitable use. As Norbert Wiener has said: "The goose that lays the golden egg has become a Strasbourg goose with his feet nailed securely to the floor of his coop, to be crammed with information, not cracked corn, to the end that from the degeneration of his brain, not his liver, a profitable commodity may ultimately be drawn."

Along with this utilitarian view of the process of education has come the crackdown. Away with the frills! The time has come to stop teaching students and start teaching subjects!

Now, there is no doubt that it is quite feasible to teach subjects to students. It has been done throughout most of the history of education, and done with some success. And it is an easier thing to do, both for the teacher and the school principal: with a little discipline, to reduce the student to the proper state of passivity and pump information into his head.

But every conscientious teacher must reject this approach to teaching along with the premises that it holds about the human mind. Alfred North Whitehead has put it this way: "The mind is never passive; it is a perpetual activity, delicate, receptive, responsive to stimulants. You cannot postpone its life until you have sharpened it. Whatever interest attaches to your subject matter must be evoked here and now; whatever powers you are strengthening in the pupil must be exercised here and now; whatever possibilities of mental life your teaching should impart, must be exhibited here and now. That is the golden rule of education and a very difficult rule to follow."

The rule is, of course, especially difficult for teachers who have come through that other kind of education, the kind that reduces learning to courses, and courses to credits toward a certificate. But teachers were children once. And the curiosity, the capacity to wonder, that motivates the child at the beginning of his education at least, is a universal heritage of all children. It survives in all too few graduates of our educational system.

The subversion of values becomes apparent again when we consider the prevailing misapprehension of the place of science and mathematics in human experience. These are not bodies of received knowledge packaged in mean little books out of which everything useful can be taught and learned. These are ongoing human activities that should challenge and enlist the young—all of the young who are ever exposed to the experience of learning about them.

It is a bleak and narrow view of geometry, for example, that puts it on the curriculum as a subject to be taught in the event the student should go into engineering or science. Of course geometry is useful. But it is a great deal more than that. For Euclid it was not a "tool subject." To almost every student, on his first exposure to Euclid, there comes one of the really great moments in education, a moment of giddy insight into the capacity of his own mind.

John Aubrey, the Restoration diarist, tells how one student, Thomas Hobbes, back in 1631 made his acquaintance with geometry:

"He was 40 yeares old before he looked on geometry; which happened accidentally. Being in a gentleman's library, Euclid's Elements lay open, and 'twas the 47 El. libr I. He read the proposition. 'By G—,' sayd he. (He would now and then sweare, by way of emphasis.) 'By G—,' sayd he, 'this is impossible.' So he reads the demonstration of it, which referred him back to such a proposition; which proposition he read. That referred him back to another, which he also read. *Et sic deinceps*, that at last he was demonstrably convinced of that trueth. This made him in love with geometry."

There ought to be, and there probably is, an equally effective way to teach algebra backward. The fact is that people who have been teaching youngsters arithmetic under proper experimental conditions have been finding that the children learn it much faster by the axiomatic (that is, a sort of Euclidean) method than they do by having it beaten into their heads to the cadence of a yardstick. The same kind of respect for the natural mathematical capacities of children comes out of the work by Jean Piaget, the Swiss psychologist, who has developed convincing evidence that children learn topology, a relatively highbrow branch of mathematics, long before they ever become arithmeticians.

It is an equally spiritless and dehumanized view of physics that holds it to be a tool subject, necessary for such later grand undertakings as the designing of a reactor for the generation of electrical power or the fabricating of a weapon of mass destruction. Physics has direct relevance to the life of the student. It offers him an immediately rewarding experience, because it holds answers to his questions about the world.

Consider the experience of one lively child, named Albert Einstein. When he sat down, at the age of sixty-seven, to write what he called his own obituary, he told this story:

"That sense of wonder seems to occur when an experience comes into conflict with the world of ideas that are already sufficiently fixed in us. Whenever such a conflict is experienced hard and intensely, it reacts back upon our thought in a decisive way. I experienced a wonder of this kind as a child of 4 or 5 years, when my father showed me a [magnetic] compass. That this needle behaved in such a determined way did not at all fit into the nature of events, and could find no place in my unconscious world of concepts, in which, I suppose, effects were associated with direct touch. I can still remember—or at least I believe that I can—that this experience made a deep and lasting impression upon me. Something deeply hidden lay behind such things! The development of the thought-world must be a continuous flight from such experiences of wonder."

The flight from wonder that Einstein speaks of began in

an organized way only about 400 years ago. As a result, our perception has been extended far beyond the world of "direct touch." The progress of science has broken into vast new realms of wonder. It has stretched the range of perception from the recognition of atomic events that take place in 10^{-18} second (a billion billionth of a second) to the detection of galaxies that signify their existence by light waves that started toward our earth 10^{10} years (ten billion years) ago. What is more important, it is an open universe, in which the reason and the imagination will continue to enlarge the horizon of human experience.

The emphasis is always placed on physics in the talk of the deplorable state of science education in America. The achievements of physics have indeed given us much to contemplate in the way of splendor and terror during the first half of this century. But I venture to say that biology has equal surprises in store for us in the second half of the twentieth century. Infants may lose their sense of wonder soon enough about the physical world, but it is a long time before a person stops being concerned about the life processes going on inside his own body. The wonders of the living world are usually the first to excite the curiosity of the child.

V. B. Wigglesworth, of the University of Cambridge, tells this story of how his career in physiology and biochemistry began:

"I was five years of age when I made the most important discovery of my life. A caterpillar I had imprisoned in a jam jar wrapped itself in silk, and then some days afterward emerged under my close and astonished observation, a butterfly. Later on, I learned that others, including Aristotle, had anticipated me in the discovery of insect metamorphosis."

Wigglesworth improved upon his discovery of insect metamorphosis by isolating the remarkable "juvenile" hormone that controls the process, a discovery that has implications far beyond the field of insect physiology.

In arguing for an approach to science education that has respect for the child's integrity as a person, I have distinguished between science as understanding, on the one hand, and science as a tool for use in the solution of practical problems, on the other. In making this distinction, I do not mean to elevate one aspect of science above the other. Science has this complementarity embedded in its nature. It is at once understanding and, as J. Bronowski has said, "command over the hidden potential of nature." Possessed of understanding, men will always also exercise the control it gives them, whether for good or for evil purposes. But they cannot command nature wisely without deeper understanding, and the object of that understanding is ultimately man himself.

For the student, an education in science is essential to his self-recognition and to his orientation in time and space. Without a grounding in science, he is cheated of full participation in the life of his century. Our children ought to have a better education in science because they are entitled to it, not because there is some utilitarian end to which knowledge now crammed into their heads may someday be put. An understanding of science is as much needed by students who are not going to realize the objectives of the National Defense Education Act as it is necessary to those who will go on to be scientists and engineers. It is needed profoundly by those who are going on into public affairs, into business, or into other positions of responsibility in the management of our society. Ignorance of science on the part of our public administrators and our industrial leadership underlies much of the sterility in the making of national policy that has characterized our country's role in history during the last fifteen years.

Finally, of course, a sound education in science is needed by students who are going on to be scientists and engineers. Their work is a calling, not a craft or a trade. Their gifts and training are not passive instruments to be put to use by others more skilled in the management and manipulation of our social institutions. They are not to regard themselves as armorers or weaponeers, nor yet as Strasbourg geese, at the command of either governmental or industrial power. They have an inescapable and direct moral responsibility for the practical uses to which their work will be put. To fulfill that responsibility they must have an understanding of the relationship of their special field of science to the whole enterprise of science. In high school they have almost their last chance to get that broad view before specialization confines their intelligence and energy to some narrower field.

7

The Economics of
Disarmament

WHEN I UNDERTOOK this study of the economic consequences of disarmament, there was only one other such effort in print, that issued by the Friends' Service Committee in Philadelphia. Other organizations have since addressed themselves to the question, notably the National Planning Association, the Committee for Economic Development, and the Bureau of the Budget. There seems to be no dissent from my major conclusion, to the effect that a substantial portion of any reduction in the military budget will have to be offset by increases in public spending in other areas.

The study by the Bureau of the Budget, one of the last undertakings of the Eisenhower administration, submitted to the President two days before he left office, is especially instructive. Projecting a cutback of $23 billion in national security expenditures, the report sees three quarters of the total, or $17 billion, absorbed in other federal activities, especially public works. Another $2.3 billion would go to assist the capital development programs of the underdeveloped nations—a figure that comes satisfactorily close to my own estimate of $2.5 billion as our proper share in that effort (see Chapter 8, "The Economics of Underdevelopment").

With the inevitable so calmly accepted in such authoritative quarters, I would be inclined to moderate the note of pessimism on which my study closed. Hindsight also calls for a correction of a key figure involved in my estimating. I placed the "multiplier" (see page 242) at 2.5. It appears that the multiplier stands closer to 2.0 these days. Retention of corporate earnings and the tying up of funds in equities that are inflated out of all proportion to earnings appear to account for the difference. As a result, a military budget of $40 billion stirs up something like $80 billion, rather than $100 billion, of total economic activity. By the same token, it will take higher rates of federal expenditure in non-defense activities to achieve equivalent stimulation of the economy as a whole.

The paper was presented in the Graduate Lecture Program at Case Institute of Technology, Cleveland, Ohio, in November 1959.

W E ARE LIVING in a period of prolonged prosperity, which we owe in a significant degree to nuclear physics. It is the nuclear warhead that makes the intercontinental ballistic missile a tactically decisive weapon. Under the threat of push-button war, the national defense has become primarily a technological effort. We find it convenient to carry on this effort, without apparent sacrifice, alongside a booming peacetime economy. For that portion of the labor force involved in national defense, the production of large standing rockets surely provides more interesting employment than service in a large standing army. Such employment is more gainful as well, and the purchasing power of the six million or so who are engaged in the defense effort goes to swell the unprecedented demand for consumer goods and services. Providing we avoid the unthinkable, no one seems disposed to ask why this arrangement of our economic life should not work indefinitely.

In recognition of what science has thus contributed to the well-being as well as to the security of one nation, science too has had its share of prosperity. This year the total national expenditure for research and development exceeds $5 billion. Most of the outlay, of course, goes to the development of new weapons and substantially all of it to the exploitation rather than the increase of knowledge. Nonetheless, it has financed such technically sweet accomplishments as the engineering of the thermonuclear reactions and has made large incidental funds available to more or less basic research. Something on the order of $1 billion has been earmarked for investigation of outer space, $600 million for oceanography, $100 million to build a linear accelerator two miles long, and $75 million for a steerable radio telescope as big as Yankee Stadium. The possibility that some other nation might do it first has even enlisted federal support for digging a hole in the ground—the romantic Mohole project, which seeks to run a drill through the earth's crust down to the mantle. As the new entrepreneurs of science have learned, the national pride as well as the national defense is at stake. Have our biologists secured less than their proportionate share of the freely flowing funds? They have failed to point out that some other nation's biologists may yet beat us to the synthesis of life.

But not all of our scientists have found the same satisfactions in this era of prosperity. Many are perturbed by the identification of science with military technology. They find in bigness no guarantee of excellence and place the trained imagination above the giant instrument. They see the true mission of science compromised by public support that is promoted and rendered on the wrong premises. They are troubled by their own preoccupation with the tasks of weaponeering. But most scientists, like most other men, feel a duty to country that comes ahead of the sense of membership in the general community of mankind. In the present period the scientist may console himself that he is designing weapons not for use in a hot war but for prolongation of the technological stalemate that is the cold war. He may go even further and take pride in his achievement as a practical pacifist. His science has made war technologically obsolete: thermonuclear war is not an extension of diplomacy. Even the morally blind exponents of political power seem to understand that mass murder is mass suicide.

The arms race may thus be economically advantageous, and the stalemate in the arms race may furnish a permanent deep freeze for irresolvable conflicts in the anarchy of nations. But there is nonetheless a world-wide yearning for disarmament. Who can tolerate the prospect of the Third World War? Who would not rather see the genius and treasure of civilization expended on the urgent tasks of peace? Even in one-party and one-press nations, where it is difficult to hear the voice of the people, disarmament has emerged as a popular cause capable of exerting effective pressure on unresponsive governments. Of all the open questions in international politics this is the single one that has now come under negotiation. For the moment—and for another few months at least—the first de facto agreement on disarmament is already in force. Nuclear weapons tests have been suspended, and they may stay suspended even without formal agreement.

So some degree of disarmament now appears to be in prospect. All at once we face an entirely new set of problems. The serious mention of disarmament sets off a tremor in the United States economy. We are compelled to face a question we have been avoiding for a decade: Can the United States peacetime economy maintain its high prosperity without heavy government spending in the arms economy?

It is hard to remember that the question was once put another way. At the outbreak of the Second World War there were fears that our economy could not afford the enormous task of armament. But it was the war effort that started the boom in which we are still living. The war that brought privation and destitution to other nations launched the United States economy to new heights of productivity and prosperity. After twenty years the war economy has become an integral feature of our normal economic life. And normalcy today has come to mean an unprecedentedly high rate of economic activity. The gross national product this year moved on to the unheard-of figure of $450 billion, and is on its way to $500 billion in 1962. The median family income of the American people now exceeds $5,000. For the most compelling evidence of the well-being of our fellow citizens we need only to look at the transformed face of the country. America has rehoused itself in the suburbs.

But the enjoyment of prosperity has been disturbed by circumstances that somehow do not fit the traditional picture of a sound economy. The federal budget has never diminished in this period without once more resuming its apparently limitless growth. At $70 billion per year, federal spending represents 15 per cent of the total economic activity of our nation. Despite high personal and corporation taxes, the government has shown a deficit in four years out of five. The national debt now crowds the $300 billion line, and the fixed charges on it run to twice the federal budget in prewar years. Recently the treasury encountered difficulty finding takers for its short-term notes and now must seek a statutory increase in the long-term interest rate in order to avoid a printing-press inflation.

The citizens most disturbed by this state of affairs are those who ought to know most about it, the businessmen. One may suppose they would like to encourage disarmament. Surely, they abhor war as deeply as any other members of the community, and they long for the return of a solvent federal government, cut down to natural size. After twenty years of experience with a war economy in our midst, the businessman would be happy to take the old-fashioned business cycle, with its booms and busts, in exchange for the new kind of business cycle, in which the ups and downs in the economy are a function of what the federal government spends on arms. The most recent recession, the downturn of 1957, from which the present represents the upturn, was set off by nothing more than a momentary reduction in the current rate of arms expenditure. The Administration was forced to this painful action because the statutory debt ceiling hovered too close and Congress was not on hand to lift it, as has been the routine custom at almost each session of Congress for a generation.

Such sentiments are felt with special poignancy in those corporations whose single customer is the federal government. Since the government spends some 80 per cent of its arms-procurement outlays on the products of these corporations, the nation may be said, for the first time, to have a true armament industry. It is somewhat larger, measured by sales, than that bellwether of the economy the auto industry, and it is developing a bellwether record of its own. During the 1957–8 recession the geographic center of the industry was plain to see; the national recession was a depression in California. Nonetheless, the armament industry dreams of getting out of the arms business. Each of the enterprises engaged in it has a line of peacetime products under development in a back laboratory. It is sometimes difficult, however, to figure out what washing machine or what industrial process will ever need a feedback control system with a frequency response on the order of a microsecond.

Presumably our business leadership has given a great deal of thought to the question of how disarmament may affect the economy and what activities might take the place of armament in our economic life. They have not, however, shared their thoughts with the public at large. In fact, the only projections of our economic future to issue from authoritative business and academic sources, even in recent months, have envisioned an armament industry burgeoning with the economy as a whole, in some cases growing relatively bigger, on into the indefinite future to dates as far off and remote as 1975.

Failing advice and counsel from these quarters, I should like to urge the economics of armament and disarmament as a proper subject for the concern of physical and natural scientists. These citizens need feel no timidity about the discipline of economics itself. It owns no concepts that offer any inherent difficulty to minds that are trained to cope with the multiple variables of nature. The data are all familiar and are only too numerous and incomplete.

The members of the scientific community have a personal stake in the prospect of disarmament. At least half of our engineers, outside of civil engineering, are engaged in the design and development of weapons. For them the cycle of armament expenditure means a cruel new economic experience —high-income disemployment, as they are laid off 2,000 to 6,000 at a time upon completion or termination of a contract. Research scientists are even more deeply involved in the arms program. Fully half of them are directly engaged in military projects; the remainder are dependent upon research grants from defense funds for half of their support. Certain of our universities are jostled and dwarfed by the huge research enterprises they conduct for the government, sometimes under the aegis of an associated research institute but often right on the campus. Beyond these straightforward ties, an unreckoned percentage of appropriations to science by way of other agencies of the government reflects Congress's enthusiasm for science as a somehow necessary, although quite mysterious, antecedent to the technology of armament.

Upon looking into the economics of disarmament one soon makes a decisive discovery. It appears that economic compulsions play as significant a role in establishing the size of the national arms budget as any consideration of the military necessity.

To understand the nature of these compulsions we must make a brief excursion into recent economic history, back to the years when our economy was a normal, though no longer quite classical, industrial economy. This means going back thirty years to 1929, the peak year of the last free oscillation in the untrammeled business cycle. In those days economics was ruled by laws that were widely regarded to be as natural and immutable as those of physics. We shall try to see the workings of the economy through those laws.

Going back then to 1929, we behold our immense country shrunk down to a small fraction of its present size. Our population shrinks to 120 million; our gross national product shrinks further, down to less than half its present size (to less than one quarter its present size in current dollars). A relatively modest element in the picture is the federal government; its budget represents but 3 per cent of the gross national product.

The median family income falls even more steeply—down to $1,750. To help us appreciate this figure we have a six-inch shelf of volumes that were issued by the Brookings Institution in the 1930's under a title that reflected the contemporary preoccupation of the economists—*The Distribution of Wealth and Income in Relation to Economic Progress*. From careful investigation of the way families allocated their income—giving up nutrition, say, in favor of other necessities, such as rent—it had been determined that an income of $2,000 per year would just maintain an adequate nutrition. The Domesday Book of the Brookings Institution shows that two thirds of the families of the United States lived on that income or less. In sum, two thirds of the families of this country lived at—or below—the level of bare subsistence. They included the families of the unemployed; in those days of normal oscillation in the business cycle unemployment averaged about

15 per cent of the labor force. They included also most of the families who lived on the farms, and in those years one out of five families was engaged in farming. Thus, something like half of the American families had breadwinners who were underemployed or unemployed. Recently, we have become aware of the fact that the same waste of irreplaceable human lifetime underlies the destitution of much larger populations in the underdeveloped regions of the world.

Altogether these subsistence-income families lived on less than one quarter of the total national income. The top third got the other three quarters. In its best years, therefore, the pre-war United States industrial economy conducted its significant transactions with only one third of the population. The other two thirds of the nation lived outside. They had real enough needs, especially since they lived within hailing distance of the one third who were inside the economy. But they could not come into the market with what economists call "effective demand."

The Brookings Institution showed that if their annual income could have been brought up to something on the order of $2,500—giving them enough to finance an adequate diet plus a modicum of effective demand for the hard goods of the industrial system—the economy would have had to expand its output by 20 to 30 per cent. A parallel study by the Brookings Institution found that the then installed capacity of industry was inadequate to meet any such increase in demand.

So there was want, but not exactly in the midst of plenty. The United States industrial economy was already the world's largest and most impressive. But it functioned as a kind of accessory appendage attached to a poor nation made up preponderantly of people who, by and large, did not participate in the benefits of industrial civilization.

Within this accessory industrial economy the business cycle prevailed. Classical economics regarded this situation as quite normal. The classical economist can take this detached view because he does not look at the economy as a whole; he looks at the workings of the system from the inside, from the point of view of the individual businessman. When the economy is on the upgrade, according to classical theory, the businessman goes into the market for materials, equipment, and labor, hoping to buy at a lower price and sell at a higher. He tends, however, to overproduce—that is, to exceed effective demand —as the system approaches full employment. Goods then are plenty, prices falter, the pace of business slackens, and the downturn starts. Now the businessman reduces his output, curtails his purchases, and cuts his payroll. With unemployment rising, the downturn accelerates toward the bottom of the cycle. At last, with stocks depleted, prices rising, and wages at minimum, the entrepreneur finds the right conditions and the courage to initiate another round.

Of course, there is a great deal more to the classical description of the business cycle than this simplified account suggests. But it serves to illustrate the point that classical economics envisioned the behavior of the economic system as the simple sum of the actions of its entrepreneurs, as if it were a Maxwellian gas composed of identical atoms. To the cause and cure of the troubles of the system as a whole, it brought the same sound homilies that it prescribed for the conduct of the individual businessman.

It was thus the simple mechanism of prices—established by the immutable law of supply and demand—that kept the system from running down or running over. Through prices the total output of the system was registered and reported back through innumerable feedback loops to the individual entrepreneur. Control engineers are not surprised to observe that this self-regulating system has an inherent tendency to oscillate, for such behavior is natural to all self-regulating feedback systems. But, since the oscillations of the economic system involve the well-being and security of people, economists were expected to do something about it.

In 1929 the economy reached a more than classical peak. It was not only that investors speculating on margins were dangerously exposed in an overinflated stock market. The American family, buying hard goods on the newly discovered installment plan, was equally exposed to the hazard of over-extended credit. Seeking to expand its markets, the industrial economy had been reaching out beyond the one third of the people who were its regular customers and had encouraged a tremendous inflation of consumer credit. This time, when unemployment approached its maximum, the banking system was to find that it had placed its own credit in jeopardy.

The economic slide continued into the early 1930's. Unemployment exceeded 25 per cent of the labor force; the gross national product contracted to $56 billion, half of the 1929 peak and smaller than the 1959 federal budget. The median income of American families fell to $1,100 per year, and three quarters of them were submerged below the $2,000 subsistence level.

In the Great Depression the classical correctives somehow failed. Prices, for one thing, did not fall nearly as far as wages. So the unemployed—and those who managed to remain employed under "share the work and reduce the wage" programs—could not enter the market for anything but the barest necessities of existence. There was no prospect that recovery would come spontaneously; classical economics had no prescription to offer for the national illness.

At this point there began to be talk outside academic circles about a new approach to economic questions, the work of a school of University of Cambridge economists identified with the name of John Maynard Keynes. Classical economists regarded them as heretics. For their anti-classical heresies, however, the Keynesians derived a kind of legitimacy from the princely traditions of seventeenth-century mercantilism. Like the mercantilists, they looked at the economy from the outside, regarding it as an organic system made up of differentiated component parts, of which the entrepreneur was one. The classical economists, as spokesmen for the rising bourgeoisie, had rejected this patrician viewpoint and had redrawn the economic picture in the perspective of the individual entrepreneur. By standing outside the economy and studying it as a whole, however, the Keynesian school was able to present a new description of the business cycle and prescribe methods for controlling it.

Their analysis begins with a truism which says that the rate of production depends upon the rate of consumption. This observation gains significance in the next step of the analysis, where it is observed that the wages earned in current production are not all spent on the purchase of the goods produced. Given the inequality in the distribution of income as between corporations and the upper-income groups on the one hand and the lower-income groups on the other, some considerable portion of the current income from production is saved and not spent on current consumption.

Now, of course, if this process were to go on, all of the money would ultimately go into savings and the system would grind to a stop. But Keynes now observes that some of the savings are invested. These investment funds generate the production of capital goods. Such goods do not go into current consumption; they go to expand the productive capacity of the system. Some portion of the income earned by the producers of the capital goods does, however, enter the market for consumer goods. Depending upon what proportion of that income is saved and what is spent for current consumption, this additonal purchasing power amplifies the total demand for consumer goods by the so-called multiplier effect. In an economy with a low rate of saving, the multiple transactions set in motion by this injection of money into the system may add up to a purchasing power worth 50 times as much as the original expenditure on capital goods. In a mature economy like that of the United States on the other hand, the multiplier has a value of about 2.5; that is, $1,000 expended on the investment side of the ledger will generate a total of $2,500 in gross national product.

Servomechanism engineers, whose profession is the design of self-regulating machines, recognize this interaction between the investment and consumption sectors of the economy. The two sectors may be likened to a pair of coupled feedback circuits. A small input to the lesser circuit, representing investment activity, excites a large amplitude of output in the larger, or consumption, circuit, and hence a higher rate of activity in the system as a whole.

From this analysis Keynes and his colleagues went on to the question of control of the business cycle. Their model of the economy opened up a strategic point for action—at the coupling of the investment and consumption circuits. They pointed out that public works provide an activity equivalent to investment in capital goods. Public works themselves obviously do not enter the consumption circuit, but expenditure on public works generates income that is expended on consumer goods. With the multiplier at work, government expenditure on public works would thus produce an amplification in the activity of the system as a whole. Guided by this understanding, government expenditure could damp the oscillations in the business cycle and even permit the economy to aim at full employment.

These ideas were tested out on a grand scale in the United States in the later 1930's. It is, of course, practically certain that the officials responsible were not all Keynesian economists; nor did they frame their policies with the idea of testing a new body of economic theory. They simply had to do something about the plight of the unemployed. The political climate in the United States rejected the notion of a dole, the bleak solution that had been adopted in England. So the imaginative spenders of the Roosevelt administration produced a vast and varied program of public works, from the

Grand Coulee Dam to murals in the local post office. By 1936 the federal budget had climbed to the unheard-of figure of $9 billion, or nearly 15 per cent of the gross national product.

These expenditures had the predicted multiplier effect: from the low point of $56 billion the gross national product ascended to something on the order of $70 billion. The gain was equal to approximately 2.5 times the $4 billion expended on public works. Thus, in the late 1930's, the economy was restored to something like normal activity, although not to the 1929 peak.

But the United States industrial system was still inadequate to the true material needs of the nation's population. It could count no more than one third of the nation in the constituency equipped with purchasing power to exert effective demand on its output. Two thirds of the nation remained outside the system on subsistence incomes or less. The story is that Franklin D. Roosevelt, confronted with the picture presented by the Brookings Institution studies, was urged to incorporate the findings in his campaign speeches. He responded: "I can't go to the people and say that two thirds of the nation is ill housed, ill fed, and ill clad. It would be too discouraging!" So he made it one third!

The establishment of the war economy in 1941 accomplished almost overnight the most hopeful economic objectives advanced by the New Deal, objectives that for two terms had eluded the Administration's boldest budgets. Now the federal budget climbed from $9 billion to $32 billion, to $76 billion, and ultimately to $98 billion. Full employment was attained late in 1942. The nation's most bitterly destitute citizens, the Okies and Arkies, against whom nature as well as economics had conspired, were summoned from shanty towns and relocation centers in California, Oregon, and Washington to build ships and aircraft. Full employment of the nation's industrial plant was simultaneously achieved and then followed by an immense program of capital expansion that added

20 million tons to steel capacity and made aluminum a heavy metal. In four years the gross national product mounted from less than $100 billion to more than $200 billion. With the material wants of the lowest-income groups implemented by purchasing power, the economy bulged dangerously with effective demand. Want in the midst of plenty gave way to satisfaction in the midst of scarcity. Despite shortages in all lines, the consumer economy expanded to unprecedented size. The multiplier effect of huge government expenditures outside the consumer economy would have expanded it to even greater size had the goods been in supply. Rationing and price controls locked up the excess purchasing power in savings and staved off the worst of the inflation until the end of the war.

It was this excess purchasing power that confounded the gloomy predictions of economists during the first few postwar years. Against a precipitous decline in federal spending and a heavy discount by inflation, consumer liquidity carried the consumer economy to fulfillment of the boom that had been pent up by wartime controls. As early as 1948, however, the gross national product leveled off at $250 billion and the boom slackened. Where this turn of affairs might have taken us we cannot tell. The country was still a long way from prewar normalcy, with the federal budget at $33 billion and with corporate liquidity maintaining a high rate of investment. Then, all at once, uncertainty was banished. With the onset of the cold war and the outbreak of war in Korea, the war economy resumed its place in the American landscape. The federal budget climbed again to more than $60 billion and the gross national product rose with it, past $300 billion and on to $400 billion.

Today, even after the inflation discount and after allowance for the increase of our population, our industrial economy is more than twice its prewar size. It now counts within its primary market not one third but two thirds of all the nation's families. Fully two thirds of our families in 1959 enjoy incomes above the subsistence level, even though the cost of subsistence has inflated from $2,000 to $4,000. And only one third can now be reckoned as ill housed, ill fed, and ill clad. This popularization of well-being challenges the aspiration of mankind. It is the substance of the "American Celebration" that has engaged the talents of our publicists over the last half decade.

The celebration is qualified somewhat, in the privacy of our national conscience, by the realization that it must depend in part upon the war economy. Out of the $70 billion expended by the federal government, $60 billion is expended upon war, including interest and pension obligations incurred in past wars. Of the $60 billion, about $40 billion represents direct spending on the military establishment and on the development and procurement of arms. This $40 billion employs directly some 3 million federal employees plus some 3 million workers in the war industries, or approximately 10 per cent of the labor force. But it is clear that the injection of this $40 to $60 billion into the economy has a very much larger effect on the total activity of the system. Armaments, the product of the war economy, do not enter the markets of the consumer economy; the income generated in their production does. The war economy thus meets the specifications of the investment circuit and serves the same function in setting and maintaining the scale of total activity. On a reasonable estimate for the present value of the investment multiplier, the $40 to $60 billion war economy accounts for $100 to $150 billion worth of business—that is, 25 to 33⅓ per cent of the economic activity of the nation as a whole.

We must therefore credit to the war economy a very substantial portion of our progress since 1939. It is perhaps no exaggeration to say that it has brought that second third of our families above the subsistence-income level and into the primary markets of the consumer economy. The maintenance of the military establishment and the procurement of arms thus play a role in the economic life of the nation quite independent of their function in the national defense and surely no less significant.

So long as armament is not used, it serves its economic purpose in an ideal way. The income created in the development and production of arms represents a clear net gain to the total purchasing power available to sustain the consumer economy. The armament itself does not enter the market to compete with other goods for the consumer or investment dollar. Thanks to the rapid advance of science and technology, the rate of obsolescence in armament is high; so the task of armament can never be completed. If we can be sure that our terrifying armament will never be used, we need not think of stopping.

But no one can live with the assurance that the arms race can go on indefinitely. Weapons of mass destruction are coming into the armament of another and yet another nation. Decision concerning their use is being delegated to lower and lower levels of command.

But if we want to think seriously about disarmament, we must consider also the economics of disarmament. The war economy is not likely to be totally or suddenly dismantled. But if it is to be curtailed in the performance of its vital economic function, then some other activity must take its place. Tax cuts paralleling reduction in military expenditures would stir some action. But since these funds would be released primarily to corporations and individuals in the higher-income brackets, they would be sterilized to a substantial degree in savings and so would not exert the multiplier effect. In the long run the federal government must find appropriate ways to generate activity in the investment circuit of the economy.

No stretching of the terms of this elementary discourse is needed to show that public works and public services provide the economic equivalent of armament. Plainly, the products of these undertakings do not enter the consumption circuit, whereas the income they generate does. It would be an easy and inviting task at this juncture in our history to write a program for public works. The prosperity of the American household has been accompanied by a profound depression in the public domain.

Some 10 million children are going to school in overcrowded classrooms in buildings long since on the condemnation list. With fifty and sixty students in a class, teachers are reduced to serving as underpaid auxiliaries of the police force. Our universities have been swamped by a 100 per cent increase in enrollment, and expenditure on higher education per student has fallen by one third. Happily, public works expenditures need not stop at bricks and mortar. Investment in the educational process itself can also serve our ulterior economic motive. In fact, expenditures for teachers' salaries would secure an even larger multiplier effect: they have substantial needs in current consumption not implemented by their present purchasing power. The same economic logic favors generous public works expenditures on the arts. If the idea of publicly supported repertory theaters, opera companies, and symphony orchestras still seems chimerical in the cultural climate of the United States, there is at last a growing disposition to do something about the "ballet gap."

The voluntary hospitals in every community in the country are bankrupt; with their non-professional staffs getting less than the $1.00 per hour statutory minimum wage, their housekeeping is in such decline that hospital infections have returned to the list of public health hazards. More than half of their interns and a high percentage of their residents are recruited from overseas, doctors whose training could never qualify them for practice in the United States and who come here hoping that the sweatshop experience in our hospitals will advance their careers when they return home.

Our central cities, deserted by the newly well-off families, have been abandoned to the lowest-income groups and racial minorities, setting up an ugly new pattern of metropolitan segregation. Slum clearance, without adequate funds or planning, has failed to overtake the spread of blight. The collapse of public transportation and strangulation by motor traffic threaten soon to make our cities not only uninhabitable but inaccessible. In New York City the engineering drawings for the Second Avenue subway have been gathering dust for twenty years. As the costs of construction mount each year—now to something like $250 million per mile—it is argued that building the subway can no longer be financed. (Looked at in the proper perspective, of course, the expenditure of $250 million per mile could be the best reason for building a subway!)

In the decade before the war we made but a beginning on the work of conserving and restoring our wasting national resources. The task of the Reclamation Bureau on the High Plains is only half completed; the Soil Conservation Service brought no more than 30 per cent of the land under sound practice. Solvent and thriving after a generation and backed solidly by every chamber of commerce in its territory, T.V.A. reminds us that similar plans for the Columbia and the Missouri river basins are lying on the shelf.

On all of these headings the government has been underspending since 1939. The present $10 billion non-military budget, discounted by inflation, barely exceeds the last budget of the Hoover administration. There is reproach to every citizen in a mere listing of the areas of neglect: education, hospitals and health services, housing, urban renewal, public transportation, soil conservation, reclamation, afforestation, air and water pollution, navigation and flood control. Practically the only public works to receive substantial financing in this period are airports and highways; we doubtless owe the promotion of these undertakings to the several industries that have major stakes in them. The neglect is not, of course, chargeable solely to the federal government. In the framing of programs to fill the void of a shrinking war economy, municipal and state governments as well as the federal government must take the initiative and put their share of the investment on their budgets.

When it comes to that twentieth-century region of the public domain, the endless frontier of science and technology, we find ourselves on the defensive. The task here is to maintain big budgets already established but compromised by their identification with the arms race. In the future we may expect the industrialization of the underdeveloped regions of the world to supply a moral equivalent for arms in the encouragement of research. A long lead time devoted to research and engineering must intervene before massive capital development can begin in these regions. It is here that large numbers of research scientists and engineers disemployed by disarmament may find challenging tasks—perhaps not so exciting as the design of missile control systems but sure to leave more enduring monuments.

The Friends' Service Committee, in Philadelphia, has made the modest estimate that we could spend something on the order of $20 billion a year for the next ten years on programs such as those sketched here. That is not quite enough, obviously, to replace the arms budget. But this estimate comes from relative amateurs. When business executives, the leaders of the major political parties, and labor leadership bring their experience and understanding to the task, we shall surely hear some challenging proposals.

We may wonder why we have not already heard from these quarters. On this question John Kenneth Galbraith, of the Harvard economics faculty, supplies some enlightenment: "Every corner of the public psyche is canvassed by some of the nation's most talented citizens to see if the desire for some merchantable product can be cultivated. No similar process operates on behalf of the non-merchantable services of the state. Indeed while we take the cultivation of new private wants for granted, we would be measurably shocked to see it applied to public services. The scientist or engineer or advertising man who devotes himself to developing a new carburetor, a new cleanser or depilatory, for which the public recognizes no need and will feel none until an advertising campaign arouses it, is one of the valiant members of our society. A politician or public servant who dreams up new public services is a wastrel. Few public offenses are more reprehensible."

It may be, after all, that our problem is psychological, not economic. We see the nation enriched in consequence of utterly wasteful public expenditure upon armament that is destined for the scrap heap. But we cannot be persuaded that we may enrich ourselves twice over by public expenditure upon public works. The mental block, the King Charles's head, that explains this breakdown in public reasoning is to be found in the classical propensity to look at the welfare of the nation from the point of view of the individual businessman. That point of view regards the government as an unbusinesslike business enterprise subsidized by hard-earned taxes. Public expenditure, accordingly, is rated as profitless expense to be incurred only under compelling obligation. Of all public obligations, the national security alone elicits willing support for really large-scale expenditure.

The long-term yield of public works as contrasted with the absolute wastefulness of armament shakes this preference not at all—the long-term yield so often collides with private interest. This aspect of public psychology suggests that perhaps some activity as purely wasteful as armament might prove more acceptable than public works.

John Maynard Keynes had such an impasse in mind when he made this suggestion: "If the treasury were to fill old bottles with bank notes and bury them at suitable depths in disused coal mines, which are then filled to the surface with town rubbish, and leave it to private enterprise with well tried principles of *laisser faire* to dig the notes up again, the right to do so being obtained of course by tendering for leases on the note bearing territory, there need be no more unemployment, and with the help of the repercussion [the multiplier] the real income of the community and its capital wealth also would become a great deal greater than it actually is. It would indeed be more sensible to build houses and the like, but if there are political and practical difficulties in the way of this —the above would be better than nothing."

Much as he aroused classical economists by his advocacy of public spending, Keynes would have been scandalized had he lived to see the essential economic sense of this suggestion demonstrated in the management of the United States economy today. A prudent investor and conservator of capital for his college at Cambridge, he never dreamed of a national budget set permanently at 15 per cent of the nation's gross national product, the bulk of it going into the irrecoverable sink of armament. His idea was that the government might smooth out the hills and valleys of the business cycle by judicious spending on fruitful and otherwise neglected undertakings. By well-timed deficit financing we could borrow from the boom to maintain full employment through the bust. The expansion of the economy would thereby be sustained on an upward curve to that ultimate epoch when not only full employment but full investment would be at last attained and the benefits of an industrial civilization extended to all of its inhabitants.

Thanks to nuclear physics and the drive for permanent preparedness against push-button warfare, the advance toward full investment in the United States economy has been accelerated beyond all expectation. It took the Industrial Revolution three generations to bring the first third of the nation into full participation in the economy of abundance. In little more than a decade the second third of the nation has joined the celebration.

Now we have come to the crisis in this reckless exploitation of the power for achievement and destruction that science has placed at the will or whim of mankind. It is a crisis which today's man of science as a member of society is well prepared to understand. Society requires expert counsel in the choice that it must make of the ends for which it will use the means at its command. The old viewpoint that looks at the life of the economy from within cannot see the future beyond the next turn in the business cycle—or the nuclear catastrophe that may bring it to a stop. The perspective that sees the economy from the outside can plan for the day when three thirds of the population will share the material benefits of industrial civilization.

8

The Economics
of Underdevelopment

MORE THAN ONCE in the pages of this book I have argued the feasibleness of a capital development program that would eliminate want from human life before the end of this century. Though the century now has less than forty years to run, I still believe the aim is feasible. In December 1960, in the old Friends' Meeting House that is the center of the Swarthmore College campus, I was emboldened to consider why the prospect must seem so remote.

IN SAN FRANCISCO, fifteen years ago, fifty-two nations wrote the charter of the United Nations. In 1960, the membership of the United Nations has risen to ninety-nine. The late-comers are the new nations of the world. They are also the nations of the world's poor, and their poverty mocks the legal and diplomatic fictions that rank them on a par with the nations that preceded them into the twentieth century. Yet these new nations, just now translated from colonial status, found themselves at home in the UN; for poor nations were already in the majority in the Assembly (but not, of course, in the Security Council). Now the poor nations are in the overwhelming majority, as poor people have always been, the world over.

But the poor people of the world have set upon the course of self-government with determination and hope. At Rehovoth, in Israel, last summer, the delegates of forty nations gathered to consider the role of science in the advancement of the new states. Abba Eban, formerly his country's ambassador to the United Nations, expressed their mood: "There is no law of nature confining scientific and technological progress to the developed nations of the West. New nations do not have to tread long and tormented paths. They can skip the turbulent phases through which the Western industrial revolutions had to pass. Nor is there any need to pay the price in human suffering which Western man had to undergo in his odyssey across the centuries. For we live in a world of sharpened social consciousness. New states are more fortunate than were the older industrial countries, in that they have at their disposal both the promise of twentieth-century science—and the conscience of twentieth-century society."

What are the chances that the poor of the world may at last escape the subjection to material want that cheats them of their claim to the human estate? What are the chances that they may do so and not have to pay the historically established price of subjection to the debasement and cruelty of power? One measure is the gulf that lies between them and the realization of their hopes.

The poor of the world, identified by the average personal income of national communities, constitute two thirds of the human species. About one third of the two thirds are Chinese not now represented in the UN and for this reason, as well as for reasons that will be apparent, will not be reckoned in our consideration of the questions before us here. With this exception, most of the poor live in the Southern Hemisphere. The bottom half of the world reaches northward well past the Equator, roughly to the 45th parallel in the Old World and to the 30th parallel in the New World. Here personal income— a common denominator that scarcely represents in fact what it is supposed to suggest—averages less than $100 per year. A more significant measure of their situation is average nutrition, estimated at about 2,000 calories per day—compared with the United States minimum public health standard of 2,500 calories. The same figure will serve as an index of clothing and shelter. Life expectancy, in consequence, ranges between twenty-nine and thirty-nine years; the upper figure—a consequence of the introduction of elementary public hygiene—is a new factor in the projection of world population trends.

These bare statistics define the condition of poverty which is now known to the world as underdevelopment. This is not a new condition of human life. Not more than two centuries ago all of the nations of the world were underdeveloped. Development is relative, and by such a standard some of the now poor nations of the world were once better off than the presently rich. The historical novelty is the rich nation. From the beginning of history, there have been rich and poor people. It is only in the last century that such a distinction could be drawn between nations. Only in our lifetime have we come to know rich nations in the sense that entire populations are well-to-do by comparison with the citizenry of poor nations. Until almost the present day, participation in the life of civilization has been the privilege of class, bounded by the unequal distribution of less than enough to go around. Now it is a right asserted by the entire citizenry of nations.

The poverty that blights the lives of the 1.2 billion people who concern us here has been the common experience of almost all of the 25 billion people who have lived and died in the 10,000 years since the agricultural revolution. It is an aspect, universal in time and place, of civilization based upon agriculture. In the agricultural civilizations of the Tigris and Euphrates valley and in the agricultural nations of the world today, the land engrosses the primary energy of the people. The underdeveloped nation is formally defined as one in which 75 per cent or more of the citizenry subsist on the land. In the underdeveloped nations, as in the agricultural civilizations of the past, biological processes in the tissues of men and beasts supply most of the energy. It is typical of agricultural civilization, moreover, that its technology remains fixed or evolves only slowly; over long periods of time the culture affords the same ratio of tools and resources to the labor of people. Production, therefore, increases only as population increases. Bringing more land under exploitation by the same technique does not increase individual nutrition; it only feeds more people the same or a smaller ration, depending upon the rate of population growth. Since demand always rises to equal supply—to put the Malthusian law in Parkinsonian terms—agricultural civilization affords most of the people, from generation to generation, an unchanging subsistence at the edge of insufficiency.

Whatever land and labor yield by way of surplus above necessity has always been appropriated, through such institutions as rent and taxes, to support the small group of people at the top of the political and social order who carry on the life of civilization, its government, its commerce, and its ostentation. The agricultural, pre-industrial technology supported great cities and made possible enduring expressions of human aspiration and imagination. But, however splendid and powerful the city or the empire, the life of the people was always constrained by the Malthusian equation which says that bare necessity multiplied by increasing numbers will always overtake supply. Over long periods of time, in some regions of the world, well-being did increase. But wherever man has occupied the land long enough, increase in demand has always ultimately encountered decline in resources. This is the plight of the poor nations of the world today, from the Mediterranean basin, where man has exploited the land longest, to Latin America, where the land is not yet fully occupied.

Over the past 200 years, some twenty nations with populations totaling 600 to 800 million have evolved an entirely different way of life. In industrial civilization, the great innovation of Western culture, it is industry, not the land, that engrosses the primary energy of the people. Only one United States citizen in twenty-six is today employed in agriculture. Industrial civilization supplies its always rising demand for energy from chemical and physical sources. In the United States, central power stations furnish each citizen the year round with electrical energy equal to the output of eighty-five human beings, and internal combustion engines put the capacity of as many more on call. It is typical of industrial civilization, moreover, that its technology grows constantly in diversity and complexity; even in the short run it affords a rising ratio of tools, resources, and energy to the labor of the people. Once it attains a critical state of internal complexity, the industrial system generates its own continued expansion, each innovation in technique exciting further innovation by reverberation through the system as a whole. The laws of its growth, arising from the internal interdependence of its parts, are not solely economic but technological as well. Production increases, therefore, without any fixed reference to population growth and may be set at any desired multiple of population growth.

As a result, for most of the people and from year to year, industrial civilization affords a subsistence that rises constantly above the long since surpassed level of necessity. Beyond the capacity of the population to consume what it produces, given existing inequalities in the distribution of purchasing power, the system produces enormous surpluses. They are sufficient, in the first place, to maintain the continued expansion of the system's productive capacity at no perceptible cost to current consumption. Beyond this classical capital requirement, surpluses supply the livelihood of the increasing percentage of the population that is engaged in what, by traditional standards, are essentially non-productive functions—certainly not "work" as it is known to the poor of the world. There is the further surplus of unused capacity, surely a cruel waste in a world afflicted by want. And there are yet more surpluses to be squandered on the waste and folly of gigantic armaments that can serve only to bring industrial civilization to a catastrophic finish.

It is plain that the rich nations of industrial civilization have found the way out of the Malthusian cul-de-sac. They have exchanged the equilibrium of insufficiency for a constantly rising and expanding abundance of material goods. The ultimate capacity of their industrial machine does not appear to be limited even by resources, for the stock of resources comprehended by technology constantly expands.

The disparity between the rich and the poor nations of the world has begun to trouble statesmen as well as moralists. The disparity has sharpened in the fifteen years that have brought the rich and poor together in the council chambers of the UN. The rich have grown richer, while such increase in production as the poor nations have managed barely maintains the steady state of destitution. Greece, Kashmir, Korea, Indochina, Cuba, the Congo, Algeria, and Lebanon—the international crises of this period testify that the peace cannot be kept secure in a world of rich and poor. The hope and determination of the poor nations is now answered by increasingly genuine concern among our political leaders.

How does a nation make the transition from agricultural to industrial civilization? Since the end of the Second World War the question of development has had the central place in Western economics that was occupied by the business cycle in the prewar era of boom and bust. It must be admitted that these studies do not flow from preoccupation with underdevelopment alone. During this same period the free-enterprise system has had to yield its claim to be the sole vessel of technological and economic progress. The centrally planned and directed industrial system of the Soviet Union has been expanding at an astonishing pace, growing in capacity from year to year at rates two and more times greater than the highest rate of growth ever achieved in the development of industry under capitalism. There is persuasive evidence, moreover, that the industrial revolution in China has been launched at a still higher tempo. Economists have, accordingly, been reexamining the classical theory of development and have been looking beyond theory into history.

The classical theory, with its roots in the ethos of Protestantism, held that expansion arises from saving. The entrepreneur abstains from the enjoyment of current consumption and saves his current income for investment in the prospect of a future increase in income. The interest rate is the monetary expression of his option as between the marginal utility of an increase in his current consumption and the marginal productivity of capital. Saving was thus the function of the capitalist and thrift was his distinguishing virtue, setting him apart from the aristocrat whose ostentation adorned the summit of agricultural civilization.

B. S. Keirstead, of the University of Toronto, is one of the economists who has consulted the early history of capitalist development. He states his conclusion in blunt language: ". . . if interest is the reward for abstinence, it [has been] paid to the wrong people."

"When society taken as a whole abstains," Keirstead explains, "the *per caput* consumption of its members is less . . . than it would have been if the new net saving had not taken place. . . . The individual members who abstain, however, may be divided into those who do so voluntarily and those who do so involuntarily . . . Historically most social abstinence has been imposed and enforced. It is not possible to get people on the margin of subsistence to abstain voluntarily."

Great Britain, before its industrial revolution, had an agricultural civilization. The largest number of its people accordingly were living on the margin of subsistence. Abstinence, Keirstead finds, had to be imposed and enforced on a large scale.

"The industrial revolution in Great Britain," he says, "began with an accumulation of commercial capital [voluntary] and a transformation of the conventional forms of agriculture [involuntary]. . . . The Enclosure Act, passed by a Parliament of merchants and landowners, forced severe abstinence upon the displaced farm workers and small proprietors . . . During the crucial initial stages of the industrial revolution, England was governed with great severity by the representatives of three small groups: the squirearchy, that is the lesser landholders who depended on rents from village land; the landed aristocracy who had largely allied themselves with manufacture and trade by reason of the enclosure of tillage land for sheep grazing—thus rendering their rents and profits dependent on the price of woolen yarns and cloth—and the new merchants and manufacturers who found wealth in the woolen trade. The acts of enclosure, the harsh laws penalizing offenses against property, the mercantile system, indeed the whole framework of 18th century law was designed to encourage woolen export, the development of related export trades and the formation of capital . . . [all at the expense of] the harshness and severity of the lot of the unemployed poor, the displaced agricultural worker, not yet employed in the new industries, who bore in the interim a disproportionate share of the enforced abstinence."

For those who abstained involuntarily, the task of accumulating the capital for the British industrial revolution was prolonged over a century and a half. We have the contemporary journalism of Charles Dickens to tell us explicitly about the situation of the nation's poor at mid-nineteenth century. The

Romantic movement, with William Blake as its most passionate moral spokesman—"And was Jerusalem builded here Among these dark Satanic mills?"—marked the end of eighteenth-century Enlightenment. It was in this period, as Francis D. Klingender has observed in *Art and the Industrial Revolution*, that science lost its enchantment for the artist. He quotes the romantic painter B. R. Haydon complaining that he was "not happy in Manchester. The association of these hideous mill prisons for children destroy my enjoyment in society. The people [in society] are quite insensitive to it." It may be said that the classical apologists of the British industrial revolution, long after the fact, remain insensitive to its human costs.

The same may be said of the prevailing mythology of our own industrial revolution. There is little sense of history in our economic literature, and what little history there was is now being rewritten. The Populist movement, the Wobblies, the violence at the Homestead Works, the Chinese coolies buried under the ties of the western railroads, and the squalid history of the slums in our eastern cities, occupied by successive waves of scorned minorities and now being bulldozed out of sight—all remain in memory to show that the enormous wealth of a virgin continent did not obviate the need for abstinence in the accumulation of capital. Compared with the archetype of the British industrial revolution, however, our revolution was of shorter duration, and it carried further as well as faster.

The record of the briefer and more recent industrial revolutions of Germany and Japan is the same. Industrialization in these two nations was promoted by the authority of the state, which imposed on their severely disciplined populations the abstinence necessary to ensure the supply of capital.

With each industrial revolution the path grows shorter. The nation next in line is able to draw upon an already existing and expanding stock of technology. Discovery and invention accumulated over a long period of time before they culminated in the modern industrial system. But now that the fully articulated and self-fructifying system is in being, the task of industrialization is reduced to rote replication. So the path is shorter. But those who travel it suffer no less torment. In its forty years, the Soviet industrial revolution compressed a century or two of abstinence on the time scale of classical economics and found the methods of coercion necessary to the task. The Soviet records appear to be exceeded in all respects by the Chinese.

With the Southern Hemisphere on the eve of its industrial revolution, the conscience of twentieth-century society must be wracked by the prospect that yet another 1.2 billion people must be so pitilessly used. Against the appalling precedents of history one maintains the hope, if not the confidence, that the transition from agricultural to industrial civilization does not require the immolation of the living generations.

There are grounds for hope, I believe, in the understanding that economic laws, no matter how they themselves defy our understanding, are man-made. As such, they are subject to amendment by reasoned action. What is more important, they are subject to changes arising out of the nature of the industrial system they are supposed to order.

Consider the nature of capital formation as it goes on in the mature industrial economy of the United States. It comes out of the true surplus of the system's gigantic productivity. This is a very different kind of surplus from that which is extracted by coerced abstinence. There has never been such a resource available to the will and need of man throughout his entire history. The implication is as enthralling as it is obvious: It is now possible to generate capital by technological rather than economic processes. Our surpluses should relieve the poor of the need to submit to enforced abstinence.

If it be argued that we have here confused the two senses of the term "surplus"—the economic and the technological—the answer is to be found in the peculiar effects that our productive surplus has already exerted upon the workings of our economy. The percentage of the gross national product that turns over in the (strictly speaking) non-productive sectors of our economy—in sales and distribution costs, in flamboyant styling and lavish packaging, in an ever expanding public sector, in the burgeoning professions, and so on—has been growing every year; the percentage is now on the order of 60! The most powerful factor working against disarmament is the fact that arms procurement represents fully 25 per cent of the output of our durable-goods manufacturing industries.

Through such surplus modes of consuming our surplus, our economy has learned to maintain its prosperity and continued growth. Waste has become a built-in compulsion of the system, and the percentage of waste ascends with each advance in technology. With unemployment and technological disemployment now exceeding five million, we are going to see further innovation in wasteful expenditure: the digging of underground shelters is due to commence under powerful economic compulsion, though the activity will not promote either the safety or the sanity of our society.

The logic of this discourse is not mine. It is the inverted logic of pre-industrial, scarcity economics attempting to cope with the distribution of abundance. There are, of course, more logical and less wasteful ways to utilize the surplus. Under the headings of education, medical services, city planning, and public transportation one can run up a substantial budget of pressing domestic wants. But we are concerned here with want overseas.

The fact is that the present rate of investment maintained by the underdeveloped nations of the world—something on the order of $10 or $15 billion per year—comes to a fraction of our arms budget. It would seem that our surplus capacity could absorb the entire requirement plus enough more to spare them the entire burden of abstinence and get their industrial revolutions moving forward.

Unfortunately, such a miracle remains technologically unfeasible. The first step on the path to industrialization for the poor nations is to raise the output of their land and at the same time move their underemployed rural populations off the land. Almost everywhere this requires enormous enterprises toward the restoration of depleted soils and the rationalization of water resources. Simultaneously they must put enormous investment into what economists call "social-overhead capital" —that is, the generation and distribution of power, the construction of country roads, national highways, and railroads, and the building of the villages, towns, and cities of their new civilization. Up to this point the principal investment is labor, and the principal source of capital for these heroic undertakings will be the underemployed people themselves. Finally, but still concurrently, there comes the task of industrialization in the narrower sense of building the mines, mills, and factories. Here, of course, the relevance of our surplus capacity is direct.

At the outset, however, the principal and most universal need in the underdeveloped regions is for technical assistance —that is, for consultation, education, and training, especially in the agricultural technologies. Here the experience and techniques of other poor nations may be more helpful than ours. Presently the most fruitful effort in development is being conducted precisely along these lines by the technical agencies of the UN and, so far as the United States is concerned, by our universities and certain private foundations. Such activity does not consume much of our surplus, but some few United States citizens have found rewarding careers in the work.

The next most urgent category of external assistance comes under the heading of expendable supplies and equipment. Food is one item of interim necessity, and Public Law 480 has made it possible for the United States to chip away a little at the gigantic surpluses heaved up by the scientific revolution now under way in our agriculture. Fertilizers, farm equipment, trucks and autos, food processing and preservation machinery, steel for construction uses, textiles, and the like also come under this heading. Each poor nation, early in the process of industrialization, will seek to reduce its dependence upon imports for these commodities. In the interim, however, they represent a substantial part of the assistance needed. Happily, the inventory of need corresponds well with the inventory of our surpluses, starting with an automotive industry operating at 60 per cent of its capacity.

The items of more permanent capital equipment—rolling mills, machine tools, dynamos, and the like—are those that give our folk economists the severest turn! Why should we build up our competitors?

The answer, of course, is that American business makes most of its overseas sales to its "competitors" and sells little to the poor nations. Outnumbering the rich as they do, the poor constitute a very much larger potential market. In our capital-equipment industries, year after year, we have the largest unused capacity—to meet boom years they must be heavily overequipped. The requirements of the Southern Hemisphere industrial revolution could level out their "chickens today and feathers tomorrow" cycle for years to come.

This recital would seem to lay a foundation for an overseas capital investment program of really staggering dimensions. From available studies, however, it seems that the needs of the underdeveloped countries are not likely to solve the problem of disposing of our surplus. The most thoroughly worked out plan is the Mediterranean Project of the Food and Agriculture Organization of the UN. It is designed to double the per capita income of that underdeveloped region by 1980. Out of the total annual increase in investment of $12 billion necessary to achieve this goal, FAO calls for $1.5 billion from outside the region. Similarly, India, in its third five-year plan, sets up an investment goal of $5 billion per year, of which $1 billion is to come from outside. Projecting and averaging such figures for the entire Southern Hemisphere, one comes up with a total annual investment of about $50 billion, with $7.5 needed from the Northern Hemisphere. On the precedent of the American share of UN budgets, this sets a figure of $2.5 billion for our capital assistance program. This calculation agrees roughly with the projections made fifteen years ago in the paper implementation of Point Four, and it is in line with the analysis made in the summer of 1960 for the Senate Committee on Foreign Relations by the Center for International Studies at M.I.T.

The figure of $2.5 billion is a small one. It scarcely approaches the scale of profligacy on which we have come to manage our economy. It is a W.P.A., or early New Deal-sized, figure compared with the D.O.D. cold-war figures we live with now. But we did not make this calculation to solve our domestic economic problem; the object was to estimate the need of the poor nations.

For them this small figure is vital. The principal investment they will make in their future, especially at the outset, is labor. The $7.5 billion of external assistance supplies a major portion of all their needs beyond. These are the items of equipment and supplies that would otherwise call for cruel abstinence, that would slow down and prolong the task of construction if they are not available when and as needed. Such collaboration by the rich nations will not reduce the labor, but it will remove a major portion of the agony from the task.

The United States share of the projection turns out to be in scale with the present "foreign aid" program of the country. Little of the present expenditure is available, however, for useful investment; the bulk of it is in support of military programs. The projected United States investment of $2.5 billion per year is also smaller than the current rate of United

States private investment abroad. But, again, little of these funds are going to the poor nations, and the portion that is, as we shall see, contributes disproportionately less to their economic growth.

The $2.5 billion figure thus represents a true net addition to the present rate of United States investment and expenditure overseas. Even though the figure is a small one, it is difficult in fact to see where it is going to come from. Plainly, little of this financing can be attractive to private enterprise. Especially at the beginning, the heaviest investment will be in the low-yield agricultural and social-overhead undertakings, the kind of investment that, even in our country, is normally conducted by the government. Turning to our federal government, it can be shown that the export of goods—of the expendable supplies and equipment so much needed by the poor nations in the early phase of their development—makes more sense than the export of gold which now troubles our fiscal managers. It can also be shown that the purchase of such goods from industry for shipment overseas is, insofar as its domestic economic effect is concerned, precisely equivalent to expenditures for arms.

The economic assistance program as sketched here is not unprecedented; it is modest and it commends itself to our humanity. Why, then, is it so unlikely to come to pass? The question brings us to the economics of underdevelopment, about which nothing has thus far been said.

This is a branch of economics which involves the rich as well as the poor nations and our own as much as any other. Remote and truly underdeveloped as Mauritania, Sumatra, and even Guatemala may seem to us, we are well known to the natives of these places. We are well known at least to those members of the community who have had the good fortune to escape the land. For the only way to make a living in the poor nations outside of subsistence agriculture is in conducting—or becoming otherwise involved in—economic relations with the rich country that happens to have the biggest stake in the poor country's resources.

The most prosperous members of the community will be, of course, the large landholders, ranging upward to the Shah himself, with whom the officials or entrepreneurs from the rich country are able to write a properly legitimate contract permitting them to extract and cart away the country's resources. There are also the merchants who make a living from the peripheral trade that develops around the pivotal resource-extraction industry. With the beginnings of urban life, native people will also find their way into other crafts and professions, and a few happy places have developed tourism. There are, finally, the straw bosses and workers in the mines and on the plantations, who constitute the largest group in contact with the outside world, but still a small percentage of the population. The poor nations, of course, have had different histories and present an immense variety of situations, from the outright colonial dependency, such as the Congo, whose native culture is that of the Stone Age, to India, which had a high civilization before the history of modern Europe began. It is characteristic of all of them, however, that their economic life outside of subsistence agriculture is dependent upon the poor nation's economic arrangements with the rich.

Our own country, as much as any of the classical colonial powers, is profoundly involved in such arrangements. Our domestic economy depends upon them to provide a host of vital raw materials, both agricultural and mineral, which we otherwise could not secure or could produce only at very much higher cost. As the statements of the corporations engaged in this business show year after year, the arrangements are lucrative. In the poor countries that yield agricultural commodities, the arrangements typically encourage one-crop plantation agriculture—sugar, tobacco, coffee, and so on—which ties up large portions of the best land and employs a small percentage of the native population. In these agricultural lands, relations with the rich nation will so little disturb the extra-economic, non-monetary subsistence agricultural system that the poor nation typically becomes an importer of food to supply its emerging urban population.

If the commodity is a mineral, the rich nation will typically haul away the ore in the raw and never in more than a semi-processed condition. Thus, bauxite will be loaded onto ore boats at a dockside cost of $4.00 per ton, ultimately to acquire a value of $450 per ton when it is rolled into aluminum sheets. Although most oil is still hauled away in the same raw condition, some of the Middle Eastern princes have learned of the value added by manufacture, and refineries have been built at the fields.

Thus, apart from the rents and royalties paid to whatever native recipient is validated to accept them, the extraction of raw materials yields little to the poor nation's economy. To Venezuela, for example, oil represents 90 per cent of its exports. The expenditures by the oil companies in the Venezuelan economy, apart from royalties paid to the government, represent no more than 20 per cent of the value of the export and employ no more than 2 per cent of the country's labor force. To the countries of the Middle East, oil represents a corresponding percentage of their total exports; some 5 per cent of the value of the commodity at dockside goes to wages and employs less than 1 per cent of the people. And once these irreplaceable resources have left the native port they have ceased to yield value to the poor nation's economy.

Since the yield on investment from the extractive industries runs upward from 20 per cent, it is difficult to tempt capital from the rich nations into making necessarily lower-yield investments in the development of more integrated economies in the poor countries. Nor does one find much disposition on the part of the native mercantile people to tie up their fluid capital in fixed industrial investment. As for the collectors of the royalties and rents, they are to be found, in appropriate seasons, in the capitals of Europe, in New York and Beverly Hills, on the beaches of Florida, and afloat on the blue Mediterranean. The return of the native economy is in *haute couture*, Cadillacs, and air conditioners, not capital equipment. The sum of these arrangements, then, is stagnation.

It is plain that economic development cannot get under way in the poor nations until these arrangements are fundamentally changed. Economists who face the facts come almost invariably to the conclusion that the necessary changes can be accomplished only by social revolution. That is the conclusion at which Paul A. Baran, at Stanford University, Martin Bronfenbrenner, at the University of Wisconsin, and Edward S. Mason, at Harvard University, have severally converged from their diverse starting points in economic philosophy.

Revolution, unhappily, profoundly complicates the prospect of substantial United States participation in overseas capital development programs. So far we have been unable to come to really comfortable terms with the merely political revolutionists who have come to power in the Middle East and in the Far East. The Cuban crisis is especially discouraging because it shows what can happen when United States economic interests become directly embroiled in a social revolution.

The makers of United States foreign economic policy— meaning citizens as well as statesmen—must reconcile themselves to certain features that are sure to characterize the impending industrial revolution in the Southern Hemisphere. First, with or without social revolution, industrial development in these regions will require radical revision of their present economic arrangements with us, yielding to them a higher return from their labor and resources and permitting them to build diversified and integrated economies around their key resources. Second, the economic development of these regions is going to involve central planning and management by the state. The market economies of the poor nations could not begin to generate the capital and enterprise required. Because the efficient units of heavy industry are "lumpy," the task of industrialization must proceed by five-year plans and great leaps forward.

In other words, the economic development of the poor nations is going to collide directly with tangible United States economic interests all around the world. These are, to be sure, the interests of private industrial concerns, not of our nation as a whole. But our economy as a whole has been the beneficiary, as will be demonstrated when the price of sugar, aluminum, and oil begins to reflect returns paid to the country of origin.

Perhaps even more important than the economic repercussions is the prospective affront to the official United States ideology as propounded from Washington and by orators at industrial conventions. The leaders of the poor nations talk all kinds of economic heresy and have no compunctions about undertaking enterprises in fields that are classically reserved to private enterprise. It may also be observed, however, that it will be a long time before their governments begin to play as large a role in the economic life of their nations as our government has come to play in ours.

In other words, if the United States is to play its part in easing the poor nations' path to self-sustained economic growth, it must be prepared to do so at some cost to United States interests, real and imaginary. There are others ready to assist them if we do not; Western Europe and the United States no longer hold an exclusive franchise on the Southern Hemisphere. What is needed is a larger conception of our national interest, one that is larger than the commercial and industrial interests that happen to be embroiled in the turmoil of change at any given moment and one that comprehends our inescapable involvement in the common destiny of our species.

9

The Economics
of Abundance

THE RURAL AGRARIAN REPUBLIC of the United States has evolved into an urban industrial democracy. The Center for the Study of Democratic Institutions, at Santa Barbara, California, which is now the main activity of The Fund for the Republic, is dedicated to "clarifying basic questions of freedom and justice raised by the emergence of twentieth-century institutions."

This paper was presented for discussion at the Center in April 1961 and published by the Center in its series of "occasional papers." In abridged form, it has appeared also in *The Nation*.

I had a curious experience with the material developed here. Presented in a lecture to undergraduates at Newark College, a new campus of Rutgers University in New Jersey, the facts and figures engendered gloom and depression on all sides. On the other side of the continent, in a lecture to undergraduates at the equally new Santa Barbara campus of the University of California, the same story was received with buoyance and hope. Perhaps it was the difference in climate between our east and west coasts, never more in contrast than at the end of winter. Perhaps we must look to the burgeoning new communities of the West for the social resilience and political inventiveness needed to accommodate our material abundance.

THE ADVANCE OF SCIENCE has for many years been undermining the two pillars of our economy—property and work. Each at length has fallen from its place. Property is no longer the primary source of economic power, and ownership no longer establishes the significant, functioning connection between people and the things they consume. Work occupies fewer hours and years in the lives of everyone; what work there is grows less like work every year, and the less the people work, the more their product grows. In the place of work and property, illusions and old habits and compulsions now support the social edifice. Public understanding must eventually overtake this transformation in the relationship of modern man to his physical environment. Fundamental changes in the social order—in man's relationship to man—are therefore in prospect and are already in process.

It is difficult and perhaps dangerous to forecast where these changes may lead. Full employment, for example, now seems to be not only an unattainable but an outmoded objective of economic policy. What takes the place of wages in a workless society? If such a question must be asked, then others follow. Does profit remain a useful standard of accounting in a propertyless society? But these questions are not only too big; they are premature. Before they can even be asked, the scientific revolution that occasions them must be more closely examined.

As the withering of these institutions from the life of society suggests, property and work are artifacts of civilization. In the kinship economies of pre-agricultural societies they

have no place whatever or appear only in the faintest ana-
logues. The wampum hoard that confers prestige in one culture becomes the potlatch of another. Hunting and food
gathering are not work, but adventure, assertion of manhood,
magic and craft.

Property and work make their appearance with the agricultural revolution. They are devices for gathering and impound-
ing the surplus that four families at work upon the land can
now produce to support a fifth family off the land. Property
is the institution by which the church, the state, and their
individual agents assert their control over the land as one of
the two primary factors of production. Work is the institution
by which they assert their control over the other primary
factor of production—the energy of human muscle. The word
"work" signifies toil and at the same time the product of toil;
it is the measure ("according to his works") of the portion of
the product that may be allocated to the unpropertied worker.
The two institutions together furnished the rationale for the
compulsions necessary to assure the removal of the surplus
from the land. Thanks to these arrangements, even fairly
primitive agricultural technologies were capable of supporting
substantial urban civilizations, as in Mexico.

In the feudal societies identified with agricultural technology, land was the only economically significant property.
It was typically inalienable, except by order of the suzerain; it
was cherished and maintained from generation to generation,
physically occupied by its possessors, who enjoyed all the
rights of usufruct as well as the power to exploit. In medieval
Europe the land so completely dominated economic life that
the taking of interest was synonymous with usury, a crime as
well as a sin. It took a religious revolution to establish the
practice of selling things for more than they cost and to secure
propriety for profit in the worldly virtue of thrift.

Profit, thrift, and the accumulation of capital brought an
entirely new kind of property into ascendance in economic

affairs. This was the machine. At first the machine had the
same immemorial look of permanence as the land. It embodied
a high ratio of brute material to design and was built for depreciation over at least one generation of ownership. Through
such time periods, ownership of the machine carried the same
stability of power and place as ownership of the mine or
plantation.

It was not long, however, before the ratio of design to material in the machine began to rise and then reverse. As the
machine became ever less substantial, its lifetime grew shorter.
Today the economically significant industrial property is not
the machine, but the design, and not so much the design as the
capacity to innovate design in process and product. This is
scarcely property at all, but is rather a capacity inhering in an
organization. To have that capacity encumbered by gigantic
plant can be hazardous. This is what the steel industry has
found in the present technological free-for-all that has brought
steel into competition with materials—glass, ceramics, recon-
structed wood, plastics, and exotic new metals—no self-re-
specting steelmaker ever heard of fifteen years ago. The most
profitable manufacturing enterprises are those that show a
shrinking ratio of plant to output and a rising ratio of instrumentation to plant. Not only the plant but the product and
the very industry in which the company is engaged may be
subject to obsolescence. The decisive factor of production is
research and development.

As the nature of property, in the sense of the thing that is
owned, has changed, so has the nature of the social institution
of property. Property was subverted by another social institution, the corporation. With ownership represented by stock
certificates, the proprietor ceased to occupy the premises. The
right of property vested in the stockholder, as Adolph A. Berle
and Gardiner C. Means made clear long ago, was reduced
to the right to vote for the directors of the corporation
(if the stockholder bothers to return the proxy statement)

and to a claim on earnings (if the directors declare them out in dividends on his class of stock). Even these vestiges of power are delegated today to a third party for the increasing percentage of the voting equities in American industrial enterprise which is held by insurance companies, pension funds, and mutual investment companies.

The vitality in research and development that determines the fortunes of a corporate enterprise is commonly valued at one dollar on the balance sheet. This accounting fiction hypothecates the talents of the men who make up the organization, and the common stock certificate is a thrice-removed share in that hypothecation. Under the circumstances, it is hard to see how the stockholder could be vested with a larger claim. The instrumentalities of ownership have become as insubstantial as the decisive factor of production itself.

Against this statement of the terms on which the present owners of the American industrial system hold their property, it may be argued that the really giant new fortunes are being made in the old-fashioned kind of property; that is, land and the mineral riches underneath it. But even the discovery of mineral resources has moved into the realm of invention. It is par excellence a yield on instrumentation, implemented by an equally intangible talent for politics. As a result, most of the prospecting is carried on by large corporations, and ownership stands at the same remove as in other activities of the industrial system.

With the emergence of two to five corporations in control of assets and sales in all but a few realms of industrial activity, economic power has become highly concentrated in our society. But it is no longer attached to property. The power is vested in self-perpetuating managements. How they derive their legitimacy is a question that troubles a great many people, including those who exercise the power as well as their critics.

Edward S. Mason, of the Harvard economics faculty, has

astutely asked what difference, if any, this transfer of power has made. It is true that the profit margin—the yield to ownership—remains the ruling discipline of corporate management. And it is also true that operation under this discipline chronically fails to realize the full potential of industrial technology. That failure is the measure of the present business recession: with the gross national product holding steady at an all-time high, fully one third of the steel plant and comparable percentages of capacity in other industries lie idle. As the self-appointed management contemplates the troubling question of the legitimacy of its power, it must also face increasingly insistent questions about its stewardship of power.

The same transformation of the nature of property is to be seen again in the relationship of the owner to property as usufruct. There are more homeowners today in the United States than ever before in this century, more than 60 per cent of the occupiers of dwelling places compared with less than 50 per cent in 1900. But whereas 30 per cent of the homes were mortgaged to 40 per cent of their aggregate value in 1900, more than 60 per cent are mortgaged to more than half their aggregate value today. The builders and bankers of the new suburbs will tell you that the ownership of one out of six homes there turns over every year. Plainly, the so-called homeowner is buying not a home but a housing service, much as he buys transportation, not a car, from the auto industry. Rarely has he paid more than half the purchase price before he turns in the old house or car for the new model. By the same token, the total installment debt represents, from one year to the next, by far the major property interest in all of the other consumer durable goods in use in the country. The householder is correct in regarding these transactions as the purchase of a service rather than property. For the objects themselves are self-consuming, being designed for depreciation to desuetude in a thousand hours of service.

In sum, the typical American consumer owns no property

in the classical meaning of the term. Out of current income he pays for services currently rendered. Through income set aside in social security taxes and in pension and insurance funds, he reserves a claim on services to be rendered in the future.

Mention of the social security now provided for the overwhelming number of United States citizens brings this discussion to the topic of work. Social security is one of the devices evolved in the recent history of our industrial economy to help solve the problem of "distribution." This, as is well known, is the last frontier of economics. Viewed from the vantage of the economy as a whole, it is the problem of finding people qualified to consume the increasing abundance of goods produced by a declining number of workers. From the point of view of the individual citizen, it is the problem of finding work in a shrinking labor market in order to qualify as a consumer of that abundance. Thus, as we shall see, the primary function of work in our economy today is to secure not the production but the distribution of goods. This is clearly a different situation from that which prevailed in the valleys of the Tigris and Euphrates 7,000 years ago, when surplus had to be extracted from scarcity by coercion.

Modern industrial technology produces a vast material surplus of goods, many times greater than the needs of the workers engaged in producing it. That surplus goes begging for consumers because technology has subverted the social institution of work. The subversion of work began, of course, with the displacement of the biologically generated energy of human muscle by the mechanically generated energy of steam engines. The reciprocal steam engine gave way after little more than half a century to the steam turbine, the generator of electrical energy in the huge quantities that are measured in kilowatts. Studies conducted many years ago, when muscles were yielding the day's work to steam, showed that one man can put out about 48 kilowatt-hours in useful work in a year. On that basis, the 750 billion kilowatt-hours of electricity generated in the United States puts the equivalent of eighty-five slaves at the disposal of each man, woman, and child in the population.

But this is an old story. The new story is the disemployment of the human nervous system. In industrial production the function of the human worker has been to set the tool, start up the machine, supervise its performance, correct its error, and keep its parts in working order. The machine has been doing all the work, including work that exceeds human physical capacity. But, for lack of a nervous system, it has had to depend upon human beings to regulate its operations.

The robot, or artificial nervous system, is the steam engine of the present phase of the Industrial Revolution. Unlike the steam engine, it does not announce its presence by huffing and puffing and it has no easily recognized anatomical structure. But it does have a single underlying principle, which is as clear-cut and universal as the idea of converting heat into mechanical energy. This essential idea is known to engineers as feedback.

Feedback is the principle that underlies all self-regulating systems, including living organisms. The nearest and simplest example of feedback in action is the household thermostat: A mechanical sense organ absorbs a little of the heat generated by the household heating plant and thereby makes a measurement of its output. This small fraction of the output is fed back in the form of a signal to correct the input of fuel to the heating unit. By this feeding back of output to input, the household heating plant is made to regulate itself.

Now, the principle of converting heat to mechanical energy is embodied in about half a dozen economically important heat engines—including the steam turbine, the internal combustion engine, the gas turbine, and the rocket engine. The feedback control systems in our economy, on the other hand, appear in a host of species and varieties—electrical, electronic, pneumatic, hydraulic, mechanical—and in such diversity of design and appearance that they have only the essential feedback principle in common.

An accurate census of these robots has not been made. But the evidence is strong that they now outnumber the human workers employed in industry. Our entire energy economy —from the steam plant out across the high-tension lines to the rotating machinery of industry—is now subject to automatic control. The new technology of atomic energy is critically dependent upon automatic control; dozens of feedback circuits in the depths of a nuclear reactor control the dreadful flux of atomic particles in which no living things could survive. Our petroleum refineries and almost all of our chemical process plants are today so highly robotized that their entire operations are controlled by one or two human operators stationed at the central push-button control panel.

It is only a few steps from here to the fully automatic factory. In the petroleum industry, such a factory would make use of an instrument—such as the nuclear resonance spectrometer, which has only recently graduated from the laboratory—to analyze the output stream of a refinery. The spectrometer would feed back its reading to a mechanical computer, one of the "giant brain" variety. These machines are already equal to doing the work of the human operator at the control panel; they need merely to be equipped with instructions covering all possible contingencies in the operation of the plant. Comparing the spectrometer report on the output of the refinery with the instructions stored in its memory, the computer would check and correct the performance of the robot valves at all points on the process stream. In fact, the first full-scale refineries incorporating the principal elements of the self-regulating robot factory are now "on stream."

Obviously, the purpose in designing the automatic petro-

leum refinery is not to replace the one or two human operators who still remain on the payroll. This was the naïve idea
of a Middle Eastern petroleum prince for whom an American oil company was building a refinery not long ago. Out
of consideration for the underemployed fellaheen who were
to squat in the sand outside the refinery fence, he asked
whether jobs might not be created by disengaging the robots
from the valves. The engineers took him seriously enough to
re-examine the entire control system. They had to conclude
that no team of human beings could be trained and co-ordinated to do its work.

So, also, the dial telephone, with the ramifications of direct
long-distance and direct inward dialing, is designed not to
save the wages of human female telephone operators, but to
make the operation of the modern telephone system possible.
The heart of that system is not the dial on the telephone but
a computer in the central station known in the telephone
company as the "line marker." Its self-regulating internal
circuitry is so complex that its designers cannot tell at any
given moment just which elements in it are performing the
work at hand. The American Telephone and Telegraph Company estimates that, at the present rate of traffic, it would
have to employ all of the women in the labor force, plus
20 per cent more, to do the work of its line markers. The
task of co-ordinating the output of that many human nervous
systems in a single telephone system is quite impracticable.

To engage the robot in functions of this kind takes some
doing. The control system must be furnished with receptor
organs, like the spectrometer or the dial on the telephone, to
supply it with inputs from the world outside. And it must
be linked with the world on its output side by means of ef-
fector organs, the hands that carry out its instructions. These
may take the form of the electrical and pneumatic motors
that drive the valves on a refinery or the relays that close
connections in the telephone system.

Since the computer's function is to handle information, the easiest way to hook it up to the world outside it is by typewriter. Equipped with typewriters, it becomes a white-collar worker.

Thus far the impact of the automatic control revolution upon the industrial payroll has been felt most acutely by the production worker. Until about twenty-five years ago, the ranks of skilled and semi-skilled factory hands were the growing element in the labor force, absorbing the inward migration from farm to city. In the last ten years, however, as the index of manufacturing output has climbed from 75 to 110, the number of production workers has hovered around 12 million. It is evident that the number is now due to decline. In the electrical industry, for example, production employment shrank by 10 per cent in the six-year period from 1953 to 1959; during that same period production in this industry increased by 20 per cent. Even more striking records have been made by the larger units of the industry. In three years, from 1956 to 1959, the General Electric Company increased its output by 8 per cent and at the same time reduced its production payroll by 25 per cent. That company's non-production workers now outnumber those on the factory payroll proper. Corresponding trends are to be observed in other industries. After the last retooling, the auto industry produced more units than ever before, and yet the auto cities of Michigan were rated as distress unemployment areas throughout the year of peak production. Projection of these trends into the future shows factory workers becoming as scarce as farmers toward the end of the century.

Vocal union organizations imbued with the Luddite spirit have made the public uncomfortably aware of these developments in recent years. Less is heard of what must be the already considerable impact of the white-collar computer. This movement has only just begun. Since typewriters furnish all the necessary linkage, it is clear that the liberation of white-collar workers from their routine tasks is due to proceed at a much faster rate. Again it should be emphasized that the object is not laborsaving alone. With a computer to do the job, all the many records kept by a corporation become a deck of punched cards or a length of magnetic tape that serves as the single record for every function from inventory control to the computing of a salesman's bonus. Herbert A. Simon, of the Carnegie Institute of Technology, has pointed out that the computer so programed is not merely a clerk but stands ready to assume a large portion of the functions of middle and top management. As a decision maker, the computer can subject much larger masses of data to more sophisticated analysis in much shorter periods of time. Not only does it know the theory of linear programing better than most of our highest-paid executives; it can also learn from experience to improve its performance in the managerial function.

From decade to decade, the American economy has adjusted to the subversion of the social institution of work with flexibility and something of the same inventiveness with which it has absorbed the consequences of the subversion of property. One man-hour of work today produces what it took three man-hours to produce sixty years ago. This means that we could be producing the same national product as in 1900 with one third of the 1900 labor force. That would leave 58 million members of the present labor force unemployed. But, of course, the American people have elected to apply their rising productivity to the production of a much larger volume of goods, about six times as much as in 1900. A major part of this vast increase in output is represented by products not dreamed of in 1900. In other words, the workers disemployed by rising productivity in the old industries have been absorbed in new ones to produce an expanding variety of goods or in entirely new functions created by the flow of abundance.

They could be producing goods in even greater volume if

not variety today, but they have chosen to take a substantial portion of the gain in leisure. With the work week shortened from around sixty hours to forty hours, the much larger 1960 labor force is putting in a total number of man-hours that is only 40 per cent larger than that worked by the 1900 labor force. If the sixty-hour work week still prevailed, only 40 million workers would be needed to produce the 1961 national product and some 27 million workers would be unemployed.

This invention—the spreading of the same amount of work over the larger labor force by giving everyone less work to do—constitutes only one of the measures so far evolved to handle the problem of distribution. Moreover, it should be distinguished from the desperate share-the-work measures taken in the Great Depression, because it does not involve sharing the wage.

On the contrary, the portion of the national income going to the labor factor—that is, compensation of employees as against profit, interest, rent, and so on—has risen slowly from 53 to 73 per cent since 1900. Some substantial portion of this shift must be attributed to the decline in the number of proprietors, large and small, especially in agriculture. That the shift also reflects a gain on the problem of distribution becomes clear, however, when it is considered in connection with the way the total income is shared among the income groups. Since 1929 the share of the national income going to the most fortunate fifth of the nation's families has shrunk from 55 to 45 per cent. Almost the entire 10 per cent subtracted from the income of the top fifth has gone to the three middle fifths, improving their relative position by about 25 per cent.

This redistribution of purchasing power is another important factor in reducing the amount of work people do in the course of their lives. It makes it possible for young people to postpone their entrance into the labor market through high school and even college age, and it takes workers out of the labor market by voluntary retirement at the other end of their careers.

But the shortening of the work week and the working life still leaves untold the real story of how work has been spread in order to secure the spread of purchasing power. If work is defined with any sort of strictness to mean productive work —that is, the extraction of raw materials and the making of consumable goods from them (farming, mining, manufacturing, building, and transportation)—then less than half of the labor force, only 25 million people, are really at work.

The distribution of the abundance they produce is secured in large part by employing people in the task of distribution. This is not to say that the distributors do not serve a valid economic function. But selling and distribution costs commonly mark up the manufacturing cost of durable goods by 250 per cent. The major portion of the profit on the sales price therefore comes from the distribution process. Since gimmickry is thus made to grow by what it feeds upon, the distribution system pays a premium on waste. Its principal economic justification is that it does provide "work" and so increases the number of consumers.

To the 12 million employed in distribution should be added another 12 million, who qualify as consumers by virtue of their employment in financial, clerical, and service functions— necessary, but again not productive work even as it is formally defined in our national bookkeeping. Another large group of consumers are qualified by their enrollment on government payrolls. Certain members of the community will stoutly deny that these people ever do a day's work. Not counting the armed forces, their number now exceeds 5.5 million. If the figure looks too big, it is because we usually forget local and state governments in these calculations. The figure comes back into scale when we recognize that $132 billion, nearly 30 per cent of the gross national product, turned over in government budgets in 1959. Those expenditures not only set up 5.5 million consumers for the goods made by those more productively employed; the money also made possible substantial direct purchases of goods and so generated millions of the jobs in the production sector.

Our roll call ends with the approximately 2 million household employees and the 2 million or more who either are employed in teaching or self-employed in the professions. Those whom we have here classified as non-productive workers constituted only 30 per cent of the labor force of 1900; they make up 60 per cent of it today. Compared with the day's work that confronts most of mankind every morning, most United States citizens are not engaged in work at all.

Thus, up to the present, the American society has managed to handle the subversion of the institution of work without undue stress upon the system of distribution that has carried over from the days of scarcity. Work, the illusion of work, and pleasant substitutes for work furnish an expanding population with the purchasing power to consume an even more rapidly expanding volume of production. For most of the past twenty years employment has been "full."

It now appears, however, that the advance of technology has begun to outstrip our capacity for social invention. Before the Second World War, in the flux of technological change and the oscillations of the business cycle, the system chronically fell 5 or 10 per cent below full employment and fell as far as 25 per cent below in 1933. It is instructive to compare this experience with the present. During the past several years, despite a steady rise in gross national product, unemployment has been rising. Each wavelet in the now well-damped business cycle has left a larger number of workers high and dry on the beach. Unemployment now approaches 6 million, or nearly 10 per cent of the labor force. But this figure seriously understates the gap between the jobs available in the production and distribution of goods in the economy

and the number of people who need employment in order
to be able to purchase their share of those goods.

That gap has been filled for the past fifteen years by the
war economy that has grown up alongside the consumer
economy in our country. The rolls of the employed include
today the 2.5 million in the armed forces; they are certainly
not employed in the production and distribution of goods.
To their numbers should be added the 1 million civilian employees of the Department of Defense, whose principal employment is that of housekeeping and procurement for those
in uniform. Finally, we must add the 2.5 million workers in
industry engaged in filling the procurement orders of the
military. The total of those unemployed or employed outside
the civilian economy thus comes to 12 million, close to 20
per cent of the labor force, only 5 per cent below the unemployment peak of 1933—and this at a time when the gross
national product has reached an all-time high.

Wassily Leontief, of Harvard University, has recently
adapted his "input-output" technique to permit detailed analysis of the prospective economic consequences of disarmament.
Study of his tables indicates that even if the gross national
product is maintained at peak levels through the transition
period following an agreement to disarm, the civilian economy would very likely fall short of re-employing all of those
who would be disemployed by the cut in military expenditure. The same study indicates that by 1965 technological
disemployment will, in any case, eliminate about one fifth of
the jobs in industry now generated by the procurement of
arms (unless progress in the technology of armament continues to generate new starts on new weapons systems). In
other industries, in the same period, technological progress
promises to reduce employment by an average of close to
10 per cent.

The evidence that full employment is no longer an attain-
able objective seems to be growing. Of course, the arms

budget can be arbitrarily increased, and the size of the armed forces along with it, to offset technological disemployment in the armament industries. But no one really wants to contemplate an indefinite continuation of the arms race. Alternatively, or concurrently, some of the slack can be taken up by a thirty-hour work week, a measure advocated by both presidential candidates as long ago as 1956. After that, the work week could be reduced to twenty-five, then twenty hours. At that point the nation will have come really close to being a workless society.

No reasonably predictable rate of growth in the productive sectors of the economy seems equal to overtaking the current rate of technological disemployment. Every step of progress in automatic control reduces the capital investment as well as the employment per unit of output. As the cost of investment goes down the rate of technological progress must increase and with it disemployment. Even an expanding economy must employ progressively fewer workers in its productive sectors. At some point the terminus of full investment will be reached; even at the present level of opulence, the consumer economy shows signs of surfeit. There is, of course, a vast untapped market in the income groups at the bottom third of the economic pyramid. But how are their wants to be implemented with purchasing power when that bottom third already counts the disemployed among its members?

In the long run, larger questions must be asked and answered. If a fraction of the labor force is capable of supplying an abundance of everything the population needs and wants, then why should the rest of the population have to work for a living? Preposterous alternatives come forward: giveaway programs on television suggest that television might be employed to give the abundance away instead of trying to sell it. If production cannot be maintained at a profit under such circumstances, then why should a profit be made?

Some other standard of accounting might serve even better to reduce waste and inefficiency.

These questions are put in a deliberately extreme form. They suggest the kind of overturn in the values of our society which is already shaking the ground beneath our feet. The virtues of hard work and profit are rooted in scarcity. They have no relevance to the economics or the sociology of abundance.

Any hard work that a machine can do is better done by a machine; "hard" these days means mostly boring and repetitive, whether in the factory or office. But the instinct for workmanship, the need to feel needed, the will to achieve, are deeply felt in every human heart. They are not universally fulfilled by the kind of employment most people find. Full employment in the kind of employment that is commonly available, whether blue-collar or white-collar, has been plainly outmoded by technology. The liberation of people from tasks unworthy of human capacity should free that capacity for a host of activities now neglected in our civilization: teaching and learning, fundamental scientific investigation, the performing arts and the graphic arts, letters, the crafts, politics, and social service. Characteristically these activities involve the interaction of people with people rather than with things. They are admittedly not productive activities; nor are they profitable in the strict sense. But they are highly rewarding to the individuals involved and add greatly to the wealth of the nation. There is no question that our population numbers increasing millions of people qualified for such functions; our institutions of higher learning will have an enrollment of 6 million before the decade is out. The nation's principal economic problem has become that of certifying its citizens as consumers of the abundance available to sustain them in tasks worthy of their time.

What disturbs the scarcity economist, of course, is that such certification is likely to be provided by the public payroll.

It must be recognized, however, that these activities—along with urban rapid transit, the enhancement and conservation of natural resources, public works, the best kind of medicine, the operation of museums, and so on—have never been or can no longer be conducted at a profit. Most of these activities and institutions are now short-changed. With abundance to support the expanding portion of the population engaged in them, we may anticipate that they will assume a higher priority in our civilization.

In any event, so long as the institutions of work and property preside over our economic activities, it is clear that the distribution of material goods will be achieved as it has been in the past, by expansion of the "non-productive" payroll in both the public and the private sectors of the economy. The "peace corps" and the revival of the conservation corps proposed by the Kennedy administration are the latest steps in this direction. There is plenty of need, if not demand, for labor of this kind. A really adequate program of assistance to the underdeveloped countries might engage large numbers of disemployed factory workers in teaching their skills to people now entering on their industrial revolution. For some time to come, we can be sure, the world's work will stave off the specter of universal leisure.

As for profit, considerations other than profit are already being pressed upon the great corporations by society through government regulatory agencies. The self-perpetuating management is understandably wary of such invasion of its prerogatives. In the present ascendance of its reputation, however, it should be more concerned about its performance than its prerogatives. What is most to be asked of the corporate enterprise system is the vigorous promotion of technological progress. This, in fact, is the primary purpose served by profit in the industrial system today; as a kind of involuntary savings, extracted beforehand from the thriftless consumer, retained corporate earnings have furnished the principal capital for industrial expansion throughout the past fifty years. In the future, the "economic republic" of A. A. Berle envisions the insistent intrusion of the public interest in the councils of the private governments that operate our economy, especially when it comes to the deployment of investment funds.

Our society is probably closer to being propertyless than workless today. But the rate of technological progress is speeding up. It appears now to be moving faster than even the responsive and resilient American social order can evolve. Some of the changes may have to come in quantum jumps. For these we need economic and political leadership whose perception and judgment are not compromised by commitments to the past.

10

The Wilderness and the American Dream

THE YEAR 1892 may be taken as the date that marks the full occupation of the continental domain of the United States. In California that year the naturalist John Muir founded the Sierra Club. The frontier was now behind us; the American wilderness was no longer a realm to be conquered but a wasting asset to be conserved.

With a large and responsive constituency and an intelligent and aggressive leadership, the Sierra Club exerts an influence in conservation affairs far beyond the boundaries of its region. This is fortunate, because that region embraces most of what is left of our wilderness. The Biennial Conference of the Sierra Club is now a national forum for threshing out constructive policies in the field of conservation and mobilizing public opinion in their support.

Sometimes, as is well known, exclusive preoccupation with a cause can become preclusive. Addressing the Seventh Biennial Conference of this league of the convinced, at San Francisco in April 1961, I sought to place the cause of conservation in a larger context.

IN THE COUNTRY I come from one must know where to look to find the wilderness. It is the little wilderness at a turn in a meandering pasture stream. The stream slides in silence and so still that only the little spinning whirlpools dimpling the glassy surface at the boundary of the eddy betray the movement of the water. The overhanging branches of the alders defend the solitude of this secret corner of the world. But a cast to the open water upstream will bring the fly, floating high and dry, under the alders and down across the window of the lurking trout. The salmon long ago ceased to run in Salmon Kill, an upper tributary of the Housatonic in the Berkshires of Connecticut. Yet the trout that rises with such stealth to suck the fly will prove to be a dappled square-tail, touched with the colors of the sky and of roses, one of the natives that settled here when the glacier retreated and still hold their own in competition with the brown trout from the hatcheries.

At the foot of the flat, meadowed valley of Salmon Kill is another wilderness. Here the stream plunges into a granite gorge, tumbling in cascades of white water, filling the woods with sound, and, for a brief stretch in its passage, evoking the wild glory of your Sierras. But the great scoured rocks on which it breaks are the ruins of a dam. And on the west wall of the little canyon there rises the lichen-covered masonry of the flume that once carried the head of water down to work the great leathern bellows of the forge at the foot of the canyon. It is the mournful wilderness of one of those Piranesi engravings of the ruins of ancient Rome. These Connecticut ruins are monuments of America's first industrial frontier, the Salisbury iron district that cast the shot of the American Revolution.

From such images of the wilderness that I know, I can still construct some picture of the true wildlands of the West that your embattled organization so unselfishly defends. You have been defending them for me as for all other citizens of our country.

I have some idea of what you mean by the sense of release that you find in the high country. Somehow, the western wilderness is identified in my subconscious with our Bill of Rights. Those Gothic mountains are the keep of our liberty. There the dissenter may find refuge and the freedom at least to think his own thoughts.

Though I have never shared the actual experience—I have not penetrated the Sierras beyond the beer-can zone—I have an inkling of the precious solitude that is conferred by the mountains, "where you can be serene, that will let you contemplate and connect two consecutive thoughts, or that if need be can stir you up as you were meant to be stirred up, until you blend with the wind and water and earth you almost forgot you came from."

I understand that some portion of the wilderness that remains must be set aside not only from exploitation by technology but from the innocent uses of recreation. We need whole landscapes untouched by man so that civilization may have bench marks by which to measure its depredation of the planet. We must keep at least a few communities of nature natural, so that we may learn more fully, by scientific study, the lesson of the interdependence of life and find our place more humbly in the biosphere before we break irreparably the chain of life upon which our own existence hangs.

Through all such talk of the wilderness, however, it must be confessed, there runs a strain of misanthropy. More than once in the minutes of the Sierra Club one finds the dour shade of Thomas Malthus presiding in the chair. Misanthropy on those occasions becomes explicit. We hear the good old days recalled, when "viruses, bacteria and starvation [curbed] the growth of population." In an expressively mixed metaphor, the "flash-flood of humanity" is likened to a cancer, the cells of which "have become relatively free from the balancing forces of death and at an accelerating rate have increasingly multiplied and invaded hitherto uninvolved tissues (that is, areas of the world), especially those remaining healthy (such as wilderness areas)." In less poetic language, it is said that the remaining wildland must be closed to the multitude that might invade it in search of solitude; for the multitude, by definition, can find no solitude and the wildland would cease to be wild.

The "No Trespassing" sign at the edge of the last frontier surely marks a strange terminus to the history of our country. The men and women who dreamed the American dream not quite two centuries ago had a different vision. Thomas Jefferson was one of the first to behold the vast continent peopled from the "original nest" on the Atlantic shore, the settlers moving on from those centers where "the inhabitants become uneasy, as too much compressed, and go in great numbers to search for vacant country."

His fellow countryman Crèvecoeur could respond to the rhetorical question "What is an American?" with the proud declaration: "Here there are no aristocratical families, no courts, no kings, no bishops, no ecclesiastical dominion . . . no great manufacturers employing thousands, no great refinements of luxury. The rich and the poor are not so far removed from each other as they are in Europe. . . . We are a people of cultivators, scattered over an immense territory . . . united by the silken bands of mild government, all respecting the laws, without dreading their power, because they are equitable. We are all animated with the spirit of an industry which is unfettered and unrestrained, because each works for himself . . . A pleasing uniformity of decent competence appears throughout our habitations. Lawyer or merchant are the fairest titles our towns afford; that of a farmer is the only appellation of the rural inhabitants of our country . . .

We are the most perfect society now existing in the world."

In the 1840's, William Gilpin, prophet of the western movement, proclaimed the "untransacted destiny" of the American people: ". . . to subdue the continent—to rush over the vast field to the Pacific Ocean—to animate the many hundred millions of its people and to cheer them upward . . . to establish a new order in human affairs . . . to carry the career of mankind to its culminating point . . . to perfect science— to emblazon history with the conquest of peace . . . to unite the world in one social family—to dissolve the spell of tyranny and exalt charity—to absolve the curse that weighs down humanity, and to shed blessings round the world!"

Looking back upon the conquest of the continent in 1893, Frederick Jackson Turner was able to declare: "The existence of an area of free land, its continuous recession, and the advance of the American settlement westward explain American development."

But on this finite earth the frontier could not recede forever. In our day, we have come to an impasse—that dead end marked by the "No Trespassing" sign at the boundary of the last few thousand acres of the American wilderness. The serene splendor we behold in the mountain fastness beyond fills us with dismay when we look back upon the land we have occupied and despoiled. The wilderness holds a new meaning for our generation. It is there to accuse us: we have yet to transact the destiny of America.

History tells us that the continent yielded up its riches readily enough. Before 1840, the Salisbury iron district gave way to Pittsburgh. By 1890, the United States was the foremost industrial nation of the world. The prairies of the Midwest were the breadbasket of Europe, and the first dust storms had driven the wheat farmer back behind the 100th meridian. Pennsylvania oil was lighting the lamps of China; the great man-made crater at Bingham was already visible from the surface of the moon.

But it was not the plow of the homesteader that broke the Pleistocene cover of the prairies. Henry Nash Smith tells us that titles to less than 400,000 quarter sections were perfected under the Homestead Act; not more than 2 million of the 10 million Americans who settled in the West before 1890 came into their birthright from the public domain. Before the turn of the century, steam-driven combines brought the factory to the field and 35 per cent of the American farmers had become tenants.

In 1865, the population of the country numbered 35 million, including the 2 million newly translated from the status of slave to that of citizen. Within seventy years, the accorded span of human life, some 35 million immigrants were to be added to their numbers. We forget that millions of these immigrants were imported by wholesalers of human labor and spent their first years here in indentured servitude. Few of them, except those contracted to build the railroads and settled under mortgage to the railroads on the prairie, ever saw the open sky. The evidence of the urban squalor that each successive wave of despised minorities inherited from the last is only now being bulldozed out of sight. The memory of industrial violence at Pittsburgh, the Haymarket, Homestead, Leadville, and Coeur d'Alene testifies that our unbounded resources, there for the taking, did not displace coercion from its ruthless economic function.

Even now, sixty years after the full occupation of the continent, the vital statistics of our country show that one third of the nation remains "ill fed, ill housed, and ill clad." The unprecedented well-being of the rest of us depends to a frightening degree upon preparation for the unimaginable catastrophe of the Third World War.

We are waking now from the American dream to realize that it was a dream few Americans lived in their waking hours. The history of the New World has turned out to be not so different from that of the Old. The peril that threatens the last of the American wilderness arises, not from the reckless dream, but from the same historic forces of rapacity and cruelty that laid waste the land in the Mediterranean basin, Arabia, India, and the treeless uplands of China.

The wilderness is there, however, to recall the dream. And lately we have won a reprieve through the advance of scientific understanding. As the voracious appetite of industrial civilization consumes the last of the fossil fuels, physics is opening the way to the energy transformations that light the stars. From the life sciences we are learning to preserve and restore the land and to secure increased yield from the life processes of plants and animals. The frontier of understanding has no limits, and the curse of want and poverty may yet be lifted from the life of our species. That frontier cannot be exploited on the same selfish terms as the frontier that lies behind.

Here in America the vision of the just society has had its clearest revelation in the mind of man. When our imagination —or our conscience—falters, the insistent vision remains here in the land itself. As Archibald MacLeish has perceived:

> She's a tough land under the corn, mister:
> She has changed the bone in the cheeks of many races:
> She has winced the eyes of the soft Slavs with her
> sun on them:
> She has tried the fat from the round rumps of Italians:
> Even the voice of the English has gone dry
> And hard on the tongue and alive in the throat speaking.
>
> She's a tough land under the oak trees, mister:
> It may be she can change the word in the book
> As she changes the bone of a man's head in his
> children.
> It may be that the earth and the men remain . . .

Surely, men must save the wildland until they have come to terms with one another. Then, in its pristine beauty, the wilderness may become the heritage of all.

PART IV

Civil Defense

Civil Defense

C IVIL DEFENSE" IS A BIG LIE. The civil order is defenseless in a nuclear war. This conclusion follows from the technical considerations developed in the first of the following two essays, which was presented at Town Hall in Los Angeles during the week in which the country's most distinguished advocate of fallout shelters saw his own back-yard fallout shelter collapse in a brush fire that ravaged some of the choicer residential canyons in Los Angeles. This essay has already been published in the *New Statesman* and *The Bulletin of the Atomic Scientists* and has been widely reprinted in the daily press.

On the near side of the nuclear holocaust the civil order faces even more plainly predictable destruction. This is the other half of the contradiction-in-terms that underlies the falsehood of "civil defense." The civil order as we know it and as we would hold it worth defending must be abrogated by the measures proposed and even now being taken in its defense. This conclusion follows from the technical considerations developed in the second essay, presented as the Robert Kennedy Duncan Memorial Lecture at the Mellon Institute in Pittsburgh and published in *Science*. That history can be turned upon another course I have urged elsewhere in this book. I am so bold as to advance this possibility once more at the end of this essay on the feasibility of peace.

The Illusion
of Civil Defense

Two ominous events—the testing of giant weapons in the Soviet Union and the sponsorship of fallout shelters by our own federal government—compel each one of us to contemplate thermonuclear war at close range. We have lived with the possibility of this calamity for more than a decade. We must now reckon with its probability.

No one in this audience, I suppose, will question my declaration that the Soviet Union, by resuming the testing of nuclear weapons, has increased the danger of war. I suspect, however, that I must document my charge that shelter building in the United States also brings the Third World War closer. You should know at the outset that the documentation will bring us here and now to that close-range contemplation of thermonuclear war. When you have apprehended the nature of the war, I believe you will join me in the conclusion that civil defense is an illusion—an illusion that places our institutions and our lives in jeopardy.

The citizen who sets out to study thermonuclear war will

find himself richly supplied with literature by his government. I have reviewed this material, and I must tell you that I find it to be incomplete and uneven in quality and reliability.

The hard facts on which this material is based are the results of the weapons tests conducted by our Government over the past sixteen years—some 160 shots totaling about 120 megatons of explosive energy. In spite of the magnitude of the effort, these experiments do not answer all our questions. For one thing, the results are not available to the citizen in their entirety. In the second place, these tests have been conducted in the wilderness of Nevada and on barren coral atolls in the South Pacific. They do not, therefore, tell us what a thermonuclear explosion would actually do to a crowded city at home —or to our forests and crop lands. For direct demonstration of what might happen here we have only the experience with the nominal atomic bomb at Hiroshima and Nagasaki. But one quickly learns that experience with kiloton weapons has no direct application to the potential effects of weapons in the megaton range.

On this limited, incomplete, and uncertain data there has grown a vast secondary literature. Here one finds the fruit of speculative investigations conducted by civil defense agencies, by the Atomic Energy Commission and the armed services, by certain academic institutions and individuals, and by such quasi-independent organizations as the RAND Corporation working under contract for the armed services and other governmental agencies. Much of the material is conveniently packaged for reference in the proceedings of the several congressional hearings on the biological and environmental effects of nuclear war, and civil defense against those effects, that have made newspaper headlines during the past ten years.

Careful and critical reading of the secondary literature shows that the secondary investigations it reports are no less speculative for the fact that they have been conducted under the rubric of "operations research" and facilitated by the employ-

ment of large computers. It is evident that the assumptions fed
into the computers heavily condition the results.

The work reported in this literature is threaded with two
major strands of bias. One strong bias originates from the
desire to envision and secure an effective civil defense. As one
witness put it in the record of a congressional hearing: ". . . we
should always emphasize the survivors rather than the casualties . . . 'it is not what you have lost that is most important,
but what you have left.' " This human tendency is entirely
understandable in relation to the grave concerns of civil defense. Equally understandable is the pressure of bias that flows
from the military contribution to the literature. One would
expect military men to argue the validity of military solutions
to political problems. It is perhaps less understandable—and
surely less creditable—that their quasi-independent consultants
should tell them what they want to hear. But you should not
be surprised to learn of the conclusion to which pressure from
this quarter leads—that thermonuclear war is not only possible
and probable but also feasible.

Now those who advance the feasibility of thermonuclear
war do not claim that it is desirable. After living with the subject for more than a decade, however, these authors have
learned not to shrink from horror. They face facts from which
others recoil and distinguish between a "hopeless situation"
and a "grim one," between a situation that "could be very
serious" and one "not catastrophic," between an "unprecedented catastrophe" and an "unlimited one." From close study
of these distinctions they conclude that it is possible "to prevail
in some meaningful sense of the term" if not "win."

In the calculus of feasibility, you must realize, civil defense
plays a decisive role. Simple arithmetic shows it is the number
of survivors that makes the difference between an unprecedented and an unlimited catastrophe. Here the objective of
civil defense poses a delicate paradox. In all humanity, we must
encourage measures that can save the lives of individuals. In

the national interest, one must seek to minimize the number of casualties. But if such measures enhance the feasibility of thermonuclear war, then they may also raise the probability of war. At best, they increase the likelihood of unprecedented catastrophe. At worst, if the assumptions on which the civil defense measures are predicated prove to be wrong, they expose the nation and its people to unlimited catastrophe.

The basic doctrine of our national civil defense policy is a spartan one. By now it is familiar to most of us that "in an atomic war, blast, heat and initial radiation could kill millions close to ground zero of nuclear bursts. Many more millions—everybody else—could be threatened by radioactive fallout but most of these could be saved." No responsible official or consultant suggests that anyone can be protected against what are called the "prompt" effects of nuclear weapons: the initial radiation, heat, and blast. But people can be sheltered against fallout. It is against fallout, therefore, that the civil defense program is directed.

Even at this early stage of public indoctrination in civil defense, most people have learned to distinguish two kinds of fallout. There is, on the one hand, the fallout that has excited such concern during the recent series of Soviet tests and earlier during the last series of tests conducted by the United States. This is the world-wide fallout that follows a test explosion in the atmosphere; the radioactive fission products are transported aloft by the fireball to be dissipated in the stratosphere and to return to earth later highly diluted and after a loss of much of their lethal energy.

There is, on the other hand, the local fallout, which is of concern to civil defense. This fallout results when a nuclear weapon is burst on the ground. A major portion of the heat and blast energy is then transferred to the ground itself. The explosion scoops out a crater, and the fireball carries tons of vaporized and melted material from the ground upward in the air. The fission products are now trapped in particles of grit and dust as the material in the fireball cools and condenses. Secondarily, some of the material scooped from the crater is irradiated to add to the poisonous mass of the cloud. Only the finest particles carried upward in the fireball enter world-wide fallout. Some 80 per cent of the fission products fall out locally, the heaviest particles settling in a circle around the crater, the remainder riding on the wind to fall in high concentration on the ground downwind from ground zero.

This is the picture already engraved in the public imagination. There is a catastrophe at the target, as at Hiroshima and Nagasaki, from which few escape. And there is local fallout, from which those who are sheltered may escape.

With this picture in mind, most people are surprised to be reminded that there were no casualties from local fallout at Hiroshima or Nagasaki. The reason is that there was no local fallout in either of these catastrophes. As the President explained at the time, the two bombs were detonated at a height calculated to minimize the generation of local fallout. The President did not go on to explain that they were detonated at a height calculated to maximize the prompt effects of initial radiation, heat, and blast. These effects are suppressed by as much as 40 per cent in a ground burst in exchange for the radiological effects of local fallout or for the delivery of maximum ground shock to a hardened military target. Thus, as the saying goes in the vulgar lexicon of nuclear warfare: "You can't have everything, even when you've got an absolute weapon."

As fallout is the only effect that civil defense can cope with, you find the subject of fallout emphasized in civil defense. As one witness testified in June 1959 before the Joint Committee on Atomic Energy: "Fallout and its potentially lethal areas are important, but so are the areas of the other effects; the pendulum of interest has swung to fallout and there is some tendency to overlook the very important other effects."

It stands to reason that, if a maximum number of people are

307

to be protected against fallout, then a maximum number of people must be exposed to fallout in a given nuclear attack. Students of civil defense have given a great deal of time to the detailed investigations of hypothetical fallout attacks. In the June 1959 hearings, for example, experts from several agencies presented their findings on a hypothetical attack with a weight of about 1,500 megatons directed against military and civilian targets in the continental United States. All the 263 weapons employed in this attack on 224 targets were ground-burst. The computers, applying the ratios experienced at Hiroshima and Nagasaki, showed 30 million fatal casualties, plus 10 million surviving casualties, caused by the prompt effects of these weapons. But they showed 10 million more killed and 10 million surviving injured as the result of exposure, without protection, to the effects of local fallout. The lesson of this study was that fallout shelters might have reduced fatal casualties by 25 per cent and the number of injured by half.

Even more dramatic results were reported at the hearings held in August 1961 by a subcommittee of the House Committee on Government Operations, under the chairmanship of Representative Chet Holifield. The investigation covered a wide range of attacks, from 3,000 to 10,000 and on up to 30,000 megatons in total weight, directed primarily at military targets and employing air bursts instead of ground bursts only when the "softness" of the target permitted. The charts showed that, in the absence of civil defense precautions, total deaths might range from more than 10 per cent to substantially 100 per cent of the population, with casualties at the maximum when the entire weight of the attack was committed to ground bursts. With fallout shelters affording somewhat less protection than those envisioned in the present civil defense program, these figures were shown to be reduced by as much as 40 per cent. The study showed that with more substantial fallout shelters that would also afford "nominal protection against blast," more than 90 per cent of the population would survive the 3,000-megaton attack and as much as 60 per cent would survive the 30,000-megaton attack.

Such figures certainly favor the preparation of substantial fallout shelters. But the witness who reported on these figures was careful to moderate their impact. He pointed out that "the outcomes of future attacks are anything but precisely predictable. Fallout could create overwhelming disaster, but it might not." And he added: ". . . it depends most importantly on the kind of war the combatants may be prepared to fight."

We shall return in a moment to this question of the kinds of war the combatants may fight. The feasibility of thermonuclear war involves another big question, which I would like to take up now.

If fallout shelters can secure a substantial number of survivals, what kind of world will they "survive into"? As Governor Rockefeller's Committee on Fallout Protection defines the problem: "There are many unsettled questions as to what people should do, where they should go, to whom they should look when it is safe to leave shelters."

The answers to these questions are somewhat less precisely predictable than the casualty rate. But they have been subjected to study, and the recuperation of the nation from at least one of the possible wars has been projected in a preliminary way.

Ignoring the question of whether the weight of the attack was applied to military or civilian targets and whether casualties were caused by ground bursts or air bursts, we are confronted with the aftermath of a war that has devastated the 53 largest metropolitan regions of the United States. A third of the population has been killed, half of our industrial capacity destroyed.

When it comes to recuperation, however, we must look to what is left: two thirds of the population and half of the nation's industrial capacity. It turns out, furthermore, that we have lost the more expendable portion of our country—the "A" country, composed of the principal metropolitan regions, as compared with the "B" country of lesser cities and rural countryside. "It further turns out that . . . while the A country cannot survive without a B country, the B country cannot only survive without the A country; it also seems to have the resources and skills to rebuild the A country in about 10 years."

The achievement of such a rate of recovery, however, depends on the assumption "that extensive reorganization could be accomplished within perhaps six months." According to the report, "the initial phase of economic activity . . . would be dominated by reorganization problems . . . Some of the problems are physical, such as the patching up of capital that has suffered only partial damage (for example, electric power grids, open-hearth furnaces without chimneys), decontamination of factories immobilized by fallout, and even the disposal of millions of dead. Other pressing problems are institutional: preservation of the governmental framework, restoration of the monetary system and of decision-making authority in business enterprises, re-establishment of markets for consumer goods and raw materials (though doubtless controlled in certain respects), and activation of the labor force so that people support themselves by regular work (often in new occupations)." The projected recuperation also assumes that the people would not have sustained any long-term psychological disability from their experience, that the human germ plasm would tolerate a prolonged exposure to levels of background radiation far above the present level, and that the environment would not have received any permanent ecological damage.

It is conceded that these questions require deeper study. Recuperation economics, for example, involves some distressing variations on the familiar Malthusian equation. One student has testified: ". . . the relative balance between surviving population and surviving productive capacity has a very important bearing on the problem of economic recuperation. . . . [A] situation could easily arise where the surviving wealth per

capita was greater than it is now. . . . [On] the other hand
. . . most of our population may survive . . . but the destruction of productive capacity may make it difficult to support the
survivors in the long run. Thus the relative importance of the
problems of recovery may be inversely related to the level of
direct population casualties in the war."

Still other questions remain to be studied. One expert has
termed these "the social, psychological, political, and moral
problems of recuperation" and has said "these . . . are currently the hard questions. Many feel they are the dominating
questions."

With all these questions remaining to be studied, it is to be
doubted whether the nation as a whole has accepted the feasibility of thermonuclear war. Whether the present administration has adopted this thesis I do not know. One may suppose
the prevailing view is that the test of this hypothesis may not
be made at our choice. In any case, the first steps in preparation
for the experiment have now been taken. The federal government has launched a $200-million program to survey, mark,
and supply 20 million fallout shelter spaces in the central cities.
The President has personally encouraged citizens to build fallout shelters on their own premises and to stock them for a two-
week stay. Going beyond the results from the computers, the
popularizers of the program promise that 97 per cent will be
saved.

In the President's judgment, the sole function of the present
program is to save the lives that can be saved. Civil defense, he
said, "cannot deter a nuclear attack." There is some dissent
from this narrow concept. Speaking for a great many military
men, General Lyman L. Lemnitzer has said that "civil defense
is a part of our total deterrent," in the sense that capacity to
survive and recuperate is calculated to deter the enemy from
striking first. Still a third position is advanced by some academic and quasi-academic experts on thermonuclear war; they
prefer to believe that civil defense will lend credibility to our

nuclear arsenal, giving it what they call "First-Strike Credibility" based on our capacity to sustain a counterattack.

In the present atmosphere, it is difficult to recall that sixteen years ago the atomic scientists had proved that war was obsolete as a means for arbitrating international political disputes. They did their best at the time to have this widely understood. As Harold Urey pointed out, "atomic bombs don't land in the next block, leaving survivors to thank their lucky stars and . . . hope the next bomb will also miss them." Urey and other scientists "thought the possibilities would be so apparent that when humanity saw what science had done, they would see immediately that here was the end of war." Since 1945 there has been no fundamental change in the physics that underlies this conclusion. No basic discovery has made thermonuclear war either more violent or more feasible. Long before Alamogordo, Urey's heavy-water process had made the heavy isotopes of hydrogen available in abundance. The hydrogen bomb was implicit in the fission bomb. All that was needed was the technology that has come along simultaneously and independently in the United States and the U.S.S.R. and in other countries as well.

To recapture the mood of the nuclear physicists we must take a still closer look at what happens in a nuclear explosion. We shall see that the escalation from kilotons to megatons demands a reconsideration of the premises of civil defense. The nominal atomic bomb that terminated the Second World War is said to have had the destructive power of 20 kilotons of TNT. At Hiroshima the TNT-equivalent blast effect leveled a roughly circular area one mile in radius. The blast effect in this case overrode and obscured the consequences of the other two prompt effects of the nuclear explosion. In the first instant of detonation, the bomb had showered the same area of one mile radius with a lethal pulse of high-energy radiation. This is the "initial radiation" referred to in civil defense literature. During the next few seconds the fireball evolved and showered the same area of one mile radius with thermal energy sufficient to ignite fires and inflict third-degree burns on all human beings directly exposed within one mile of ground zero.

The destructive capacity of still larger weapons is expressed on the same scale of TNT-equivalent explosive power. But this scale has decreasing relevance to the true nature of these weapons as they grow larger. The ranges of the three prompt effects—initial radiation, heat, and blast—increase at different rates with increase in size. In other words, the three concentric circles of destruction and lethality that were coterminous at Hiroshima increase at significantly different rates as technology packs more violence into the nuclear warhead. The initial-radiation circle increases most slowly because this radiation is absorbed and scattered, and it falls so far within the other two that it may be ignored. The circle of total destruction by blast grows faster; its radius increases as the cube root of the increase in TNT-equivalent tonnage. But the circular area showered with thermal radiation grows the fastest of all; its radius increases as the square root of the increase in power. Thus the area engulfed in the incendiary effects of the bigger weapons reaches outward far beyond the perimeter of the blast circle.

The tables show that the 20-megaton bomb, which is 1,000 times bigger than the 20-kiloton bomb has a blast radius of 10 miles (the cube root of 1,000) and an incendiary radius of 30 miles (the square root of 1,000). By the same token, the 50-megaton bomb tested in the Soviet Union must have had a blast radius of about 13 miles and an incendiary radius of 50; a 100-megaton bomb would have a blast radius of about 17 miles and an incendiary radius of 70. If 100, why not 1,000 megatons? Such a weapon would have an incendiary radius of 200 miles.

The conclusion to be comprehended here is that the bigger the weapon is, the more preponderantly it becomes an incendiary weapon. There are two decisive elements in the incendiary effect of the big weapon. The first is that the ignition of many fires at once throughout the 3,000 square miles around a 20-megaton burst is sure to produce a gigantic single fire, a conflagration so huge that it must be counted as a meteorological event—a firestorm. The blast effect would destroy the central city, but the firestorm would incinerate the metropolitan area.

Not much is said about firestorms in the literature of thermonuclear war and civil defense. For perfectly obvious reasons, the effect is not one of those subjected to experimental study in the long series of weapons tests. There was some experience with firestorms ignited by ordinary incendiary bombs in the Second World War: the firestorm at Dresden is estimated to have killed 300,000 people in a single night; at Hamburg, some 70,000; at Tokyo, some 200,000. Blastproof bomb shelters afforded no protection in these storms; their occupants were found suffocated and cremated when the shelters were opened. The firestorm at Hiroshima burned inside the perimeter of the blast effect.

This brings us to the second decisive element in the incendiary effect of the giant weapons. That is the so-called perimeter-to-area ratio: as the radius of the circle increases, the area within goes up as the square of the increase, and the edge of the firestorm moves farther and farther away from ground zero. A number of people at Hiroshima who had been sheltered from blast and heat escaped from inside the circle of destruction before the firestorm took over. It was this experience, programed into the computers, that lowered the casualty estimates in the 1,500-megaton ground-burst attack postulated at the 1959 hearings of the Joint Committee. A far smaller percentage of the population would escape from the vast interior of a 20-megaton firestorm.

Up to this point I have not mentioned fallout in connection with these big weapons. The reason is, of course, that the fire and especially the blast effect of these weapons are maximized by air bursts, by detonating them in the atmosphere high off the ground at altitudes proportioned to the size of the particular weapon and its fireball. Under these circumstances there is no local fallout. A 20-megaton weapon can, of course, be ground-burst. But it would not be profitable to use such a weapon for its radiological effects, because the square-mileage destroyed by its incendiary effect already approximates the area that could be covered by intense fallout. The same logic applies with increasing force to still larger weapons.

In each case the incendiary effect can be magnified still further at the expense of blast effect by bursting the bigger weapons at very high altitudes. Since most of the atmosphere lies close to the ground, there is little loss of energy, and the cone of effective thermal radiation gains a still wider radius at its base. According to one set of calculations, a 1,000-megaton bomb detonated at satellite altitude could set six western—western, not middle western—states afire.

It is evident from the literature that no adequate consideration has been given to the incendiary aspect of thermonuclear war. Fire was not mentioned, for example, in connection with the fallout shelters that were supposed to provide "nominal protection against blast" in the model fallout attacks described at the Holifield hearings in August. Yet any blast effect would be felt well inside the firestorm. It was admitted at those hearings that there has been no research on "what might be called the environmental fire problem," that is, the burning of forests, prairies, and crop lands. It may be that the firestorm is, indeed, unthinkable.

Throughout the literature it is implied that people and property outside the bull's-eye are safe from fire as well as blast. All *they* have to worry about, one gathers, is fallout. The fact is that the only thing they *can* worry about is fallout.

With public anxiety thus directed to fallout, the administration's civil defense program promises fallout protection. The federal effort to establish fallout shelters in the central cities will provide such protection if fallout is the hazard to which the population is exposed. If not, these shelters will trap the urban populations in blast and fire. At the same time, the individual citizen is urged to provide for himself the fallout "protection best suited to his needs." The 60 per cent of the population that has basements readily accessible to it is advised to install a "basement shelter [that] can be built with solid concrete blocks as a do-it-yourself project" for $150 to $200. Again, such a shelter will provide protection if fallout (of the estimated intensity) is the only hazard to which its occupants are exposed. Within the incendiary radius of a big bomb, however, the basement shelter becomes a fire trap.

Even with fallout as the main hazard, there are other things to worry about. At the August hearings on civil defense an expert presented this picture of a householder standing on his own property "about 25 miles from an important, somewhat isolated strategic target." The target comes under a 20-megaton ground burst. "Survival depends on how much this man has found out about weapons effects, about the precaution he needs to take, and above all what he has actually done. For instance, a shelter with a shielding factor of 100 makes the radiation tolerable. Because of the slower rate of delivery of thermal energy from the high-yield weapons, he can reduce effectively the number of calories hitting him if he ducks behind something opaque. After a few seconds the bulk of the thermal energy will have been emitted and he then has about 2 minutes to get to a place where he'll be safe from flying glass and other missiles created by the blast wave which travels at the speed of sound. Depending on the meteorological conditions, of course, the fallout could be expected to arrive in around 20 minutes to an hour and continue to fall for about 2 to 6 hours. Thus it can be seen that the effects of a detonation of 20 megatons as experienced at 25 miles do not confront our man simultaneously. If he knows the sequence of events, and if he knows what he has to do to survive, he has time to act. He does have to act correctly the first time or take the consequences. "At such distances few knowledgeable, intelligent people need be hurt seriously."

It is necessary to add, from the testimony of the same witness, that this man must take care not to look at the fireball as it comes above the horizon: ". . . experiments during the tests above Johnston Island in 1958 show that burns to the retina can occur as far away as . . . 345 statute miles." One must mention also that "the possibility of direct thermal radiation being transmitted by re-radiation into a shelter" is still under investigation.

The idea that fallout constitutes the principal hazard to the civilian population is a derivation from military theory. Remembering Pearl Harbor, our military thinkers are convinced that the enemy will lay the primary weight of his attack on our military installations. We have the word from General Curtis E. LeMay, who commanded the 20th Air Force in our strike against Hiroshima and Nagasaki: "There is no point in going after the civilian population as such." The first attack by the enemy would therefore be what is called a "counterforce" attack, directed at the destruction of our capacity to retaliate. With a substantial portion of our retaliatory force installed in hardened missile bases, the enemy warheads would necessarily be ground-burst, and the civilian population would accordingly come under heavy fallout as a side effect.

To be effective the weight of this attack would have to be considerable. An independent study by a meteorologist at the University of Arizona shows that 300 megatons would have to be laid in a few minutes on the eighteen hardened Titan bases that ring the city of Tucson. The same considerations apply apparently to other communities where missile bases have been installed within logistically convenient range: Wichita and Salina, Kansas; Little Rock, Arkansas; the Rome-Utica complex in New York; Lincoln, Nebraska; Altus, Oklahoma; Abilene,

Texas; and Plattsburgh, New York, among others. With heavy ground-burst attacks directed at such targets, the nearby communities would come under fallout of intensities far above those against which the do-it-yourself basement shelter, supplied for two weeks of refuge, could afford protection. Apparently the siting of missile bases has considerably depressed the prospects of country B. With the distribution of other targets more nearly approximating that of the economy and the population as a whole, one can see the logic in Admiral Arleigh A. Burke's declaration that "in general nuclear war missile forces can no longer attempt to destroy their enemy's counterpart without destroying the corporate body of the enemy state itself."

The elaborate studies of the fallout hazard can be set aside entirely if the attacker should choose to attack the population directly instead of by side effect. As the expert who presented the hypothetical 30,000-megaton fallout attack at the August civil defense hearings said: "So far as initial impact of any attack is concerned, the level of fatalities is extremely sensitive to attack design." The attacker could, for example, adopt the strategy of "counterforce plus bonus." By diverting 10 per cent of the 30,000 megatons, or 3,000 megatons, to civilian targets, he could, according to this witness, "kill as many as 120 million people." He would take as his bonus the substantially complete destruction of United States civilization. The population is a soft target and, as such, highly vulnerable to prompt effects. It takes fewer megatons to kill the corporate body of the state than to destroy the forces that are supposed to defend it.

Civil defense, it is said, "increases markedly our ability to survive war if [the war] is fought by rational methods." But there is little reason to think that a real war will be fought by the rational strategies of game theory that are supplied as inputs to a computer. The experience of history suggests that the first exchange, if "rational," will trigger an unlimited escalation of violence, going on to the final exhaustion and destruction of the installed capacity for violence. We must remember Hiroshima as well as Pearl Harbor.

Not only the United States and the U.S.S.R. but also their allies and satellites and the neutrals in the line of fire face the same dread prospect. We are assured that the empty world of *On the Beach* is pure fiction. But the firestorms of a thermonuclear war could work an irreversible disruption of the social and moral fabric of Western civilization. The kind of society that would emerge from the shelters may be imagined from the kind of society that is preparing to go into shelters now.

The escalation toward the ultimate catastrophe is already under way. We are passing from an era of research and development into an era of intercontinental push-button armaments in readiness for action. The major thermonuclear powers will soon have others in their Jovian company. There will be bigger weapons and more of them, and earth satellites as well as rockets to deliver them. Across the continents and under the oceans, the weapons will be deployed in ever larger number and variety. The danger of the totally irrational accidental war must mount as control over these weapons becomes attenuated over constantly lengthening chains of command.

We are personally witness to this escalation, in the rising tide of callousness and brutality here at home. It is to be seen, at the top level of our government, in the writing off of Tucson and other cities by the siting of missile bases in their immediate environs. It erupts in an ugly way, at the middle level, in the vigilante league of Las Vegas and Bakersfield against the prospective flood of refugees from Los Angeles. It shames our people before the world in the climax of American privatism that prescribes a sawed-off shotgun as equipment for the family fallout shelter.

The civil defense program of our federal government, however else intended, must be regarded as a step in the escalation process. This is a sinister development because it works a psychological subversion of both government and citizenry. It gives the sanction of action to the delusion that a thermonuclear war can be fought and survived. It encourages statesmen to take larger risks predicated on First-Strike Credibility and Post-Attack Recuperative Capacity. It disengages the citizen from vigilance over the rationality and responsibility of his elected officials.

On the other side of the world power contest, in satisfaction of the equations of war-game theory, it invites a Pre-emptive Strike. For the dubious protection it promises, civil defense has exacted a dangerous cost to national security.

It is clear that, in launching its fallout shelter program, the administration has sought to find a compromise. Between the still overwhelming popular reluctance to accept violence as a way of life on the one hand and the pressure to "do something" on the other, the administration has cut its problem down the middle.

The administration has yielded to pressure from essentially two quarters. The first originates with irresponsible politicians in both parties who have adopted fallout defense as a mode of political dynamism. The second and much more significant pressure originates with the military and its commitment to military solutions, backed by the powerful economic interest in those solutions that has come to be the biggest business in the land. But a primary responsibility for this hoax on public opinion must be attributed to those authors of fraud by computer who produced the literature that argues the feasibility of thermonuclear war.

The administration's purchase of this hoax raises two grim possibilities. First, it may have seriously compromised its capacity to rally public opinion in favor of the settlements it is seeking to negotiate at the conference table. Second, in the mood of mounting fear and truculence, the administration may find it has provoked demagogic clamor for a civil defense program going far beyond the present one.

Such programs have been studied and estimated in a preliminary way. The down payment on the cost of taking the nation underground would be $150 billion. But that is only the fiscal cost. The social cost of going underground would not fall short of the total transformation of our way of life, the suspension of our civil institutions, the habituation of our people to violence, and the ultimate militarization of our society. By that time it would surely be difficult to define the ideological conflict over which the war is supposed to be fought. And by that time the technology of thermonuclear war will no doubt be equal to hunting out its targets underground.

If this analysis suggests that a third alternative to the choice of surrender or death may be found in the Garrison State, let me urge a fourth alternative. We must accept the truth that thermonuclear war cannot settle even the most irreconcilable conflict to anybody's satisfaction. With all due caution, at the present stage in the escalation of terror, we must seek the settlement of political differences by peaceful means. Concurrently we must seek an immediate halt in the arms race and thereafter general and complete disarmament under controls that will protect mankind from the resumption of the arms race. The two elements are inseparable; for it is clear that there would be no German problem if we had disarmament and that there can be no convention on disarmament that does not include China.

History has lagged behind the progress of technology, and now an unprecedented emergency confronts the continuation of history. The conflicts that remain from the good old pre-thermonuclear days cannot be arbitrated by war. They must be settled before madness, stupidity, accident, or the arms race itself precipitates the war. If we enter into negotiation in distrust and fear of the other party, we must bear in mind that the other party bears the same distrust and fear of us. If we think they lack our sophisticated appreciation of the menace of thermonuclear weapons, let us recall that they have fresh in memory their 25 million dead of the Second World War. Both sides are driven to the conference table by the same iron compulsion that flows from the thermonuclear inversion of the Golden Rule.

2

On the Feasibility
of Peace

D URING THE PAST FEW MONTHS we have come, quite suddenly, to the end of a strange period in the history of our country. That period may be said to have begun twenty years ago today. Pearl Harbor serves, at least, to mark the formal installation of the war economy as the central institution of the American economic system. Within eighteen months war production secured the full employment of our labor force for the first time since our national bookkeepers had counted a labor force in our population. The enormous appetite of the war economy for goods and services—it has consumed more than 10 per cent of the Gross National Product on the average throughout the past two decades—has never exacted any visible sacrifice of the domestic economy. On the contrary, it has generated an extra demand for consumer and capital goods that has maintained the domestic economy in a state of unprecedented and uninterrupted prosperity.

Today the war economy lends American power in the world the sanction of a ready capacity for destruction vaster than all the violence expended by all of the nations throughout the four years of the Second World War. Yet such is the nature of modern weapons that only a relative handful of our younger fellow citizens need submit to the inconvenience and distraction of service in the uniform of our armed forces. The rest of the population has been free to join in what our publicists have been calling the American celebration. Though "technological unemployment" has begun to exclude some citizens from full participation, there has been full employment at the top of the scale of talent and training. The war economy has at all times directly employed from a third to a half of our engineers and scientists. The rest have been engaged in the regenerative advance of science and technology that has stemmed from the exploitation of science and technology for the ends of national security.

It was discomfiting to recall at times that this age of abundance and adventure rested upon preparation for war. But if science and technology had in truth made war unthinkable, then the enjoyment of abundance and adventure might go on indefinitely.

This period in our history has now come abruptly to an end. On July 25, the President presented the hazards and complexities of the Berlin question to the nation. "We do not want to fight," he said, "but we have fought before." He coupled this declaration with the announcement that he was seeking new funds from Congress to make "a new start on civil defense." For the first time it was made clear to the American people that the assertion of their country's power abroad is now predicated upon their readiness to accept assault upon their home territory. "In contrast to our friends in Europe," the President said, "the need for this kind of protection is new to our shores, but the time to start is now."

Until that moment, civil defense must have seemed a remote and theoretical subject to most Americans. It was a realm of policy, rife with supposition and contradiction, that had pro-

vided employment for lame-duck politicians and elderly ad-
mirals and generals.

The sirens that are blown to clear their throats at stated
hours every day in American municipalities go unheard by
most citizens. The "Shelter" signs in public buildings look like
souvenirs of the Second World War, with the quaint solemnity
of an air-raid warden's helmet of the same vintage. Signs along
the freeways leading out of some of our cities declare that the
route will be "closed in the event of enemy attack," while blue
arrows pointing the way out of some metropolises mark certain freeways as "evacuation routes." Of course, no matter how
they are marked, all of the freeways are choked with traffic.

The President's civil defense program proved to be modest
enough. He was going to ask Congress for funds principally "to
identify and mark space in existing structures—public and private—that could be used for fallout shelters in case of attack
and to stock those shelters with food, water, first-aid kits and
other minimum essentials for survival." What brought the peril
home most poignantly, however, was the advice to citizens to
set up fallout shelters in their own basements. The war economy, it was now clear, could no longer be expected to produce
mere abundance and adventure. The business of the war economy turns out to be war.

The next period of our history poses some dread and insistent questions: Is thermonuclear war feasible as well as possible? Must war furnish the ultimate arbitration of irreconcilable conflicts? These are questions that confront all mankind.
To the agenda, I suppose, most Americans will add another:
Can we get along without a war economy?

In regard to the first question, the state of American public
opinion may be judged from the response to the promotion—
by a hopeful new industry and by the noisy and unstable ampli-
fier of our popular press as well as by the federal government
—of family fallout shelters. There has been little action. Something in the popular wisdom recognizes that the peril goes in-

finitely beyond fallout. To accept the dubious protection of a fallout shelter is to accept that peril as a condition of existence. The questions of the next period of history must be answered first. These questions, like so many in our time, are fraught with technical considerations.

The fallout against which fallout shelters can provide some protection is, of course, one of four effects produced by nuclear weapons. The other three, as the civil defense literature makes plain, are the "prompt effects": the initial radiation, heat, and blast, in the order of their emission from a nuclear detonation. Against these three, the civil defense literature and the announced plans of the government offer no protection. The lives of those "close to ground zero" are conceded to be lost; it is the others—"all the others," the official handouts say—that may be saved from fallout.

In estimating the relative hazard of the prompt effects one must ask: How close is "close" to ground zero? It is curious to note in the civil defense literature the continued mention of the "initial radiation." This is the pulse of gamma radiation emitted from the nuclear reaction in the first instant of its ignition. At Hiroshima this radiation was a hazard to all who were within the range of heat and blast; for the range of the three prompt effects of the "nominal" 20-kiloton fission bomb are the same —about one mile.

These three effects assume quite different orders of magnitude in an explosion in the megaton range. As the weapons get bigger, the range of the initial radiation quickly falls away inside the increasing range of the blast effect. What is more, the range of the blast effect, which increases as the cube root of the increase in power, speedily falls behind the increase in the range of the heat effect, which increases as the square root of the increase in power.

Translating these ratios into numbers, one finds that in the detonation of a 20-megaton thermonuclear bomb the blast effect—the "ground zero" of civil defense imagery—has a radius of 10 miles. But the radius of the incendiary effect reaches out 20 miles still farther. In other words, the result is not a disaster somewhere downtown, with time to get the suburbs into fall-out shelters. The result is the obliteration of the central city by blast and a conflagration that sweeps through the entire metro-politan area.

When the weapon is employed to achieve these results, there is no local fallout. The weapon is burst at a carefully calcu-lated altitude above the ground, just as in the attacks on Hiro-shima and Nagasaki (where there was no local fallout). For bombs of 20 megatons and more, the area embraced by the incendiary effect progressively overtakes and exceeds the area that can be covered by intense fallout.

The incendiary effect of a giant weapon can be greatly mag-nified by bursting the weapon at very high altitude. The ther-mal energy then needs to penetrate only the few miles of dense atmosphere closest to the ground on the way to its vast target. As a footnote to this analysis, it may be mentioned that pre-liminary reports on the world-wide fallout from the 30- and 50-megaton thermonuclear bombs tested by the Soviet Union show them to be relatively clean bombs. There is a reason for making such giant weapons clean; that is, to make them porta-ble. Raising the yield of energy from fusion relative to that from fission reduces not only the fallout (which comes from the fission element) but the total mass that must be delivered to the target. This is the crucial consideration in developing a warhead for an intercontinental ballistic missile.

Local fallout must, of course, be accorded its place as a primary hazard of thermonuclear war. It is generated when a weapon is burst on the ground and at some sacrifice of the range of the blast and fire effects. Apart from the deliberate generation of fallout, there is an important reason for employ-ing ground bursts: to destroy a hardened military target. A determined attack on military targets, directed at the destruc-tion of an enemy's capacity to retaliate, would require an enormous tonnage of weapons and would produce a correspondingly huge fallout as a hazard to the civilian population. It has been estimated that the enemy would have to deliver a salvo totaling 300 megatons in order to knock out the eighteen hardened Titan missile bases that surround the city of Tucson. By contrast, a single 20-megaton bomb burst in the air over Chicago would suffice to destroy the entire metropolis. The first conclusion pressed by this analysis is this: The civilian population is far more vulnerable to prompt effects than are its defenders and is more likely to be exposed to these effects should it be chosen as the target of attack.

Each of the two sides in the present balance of terror is said to have a minimum of 30,000 megatons of weapons in readiness for use. This, in each case, is about ten times more than enough to kill the corporate body of the other. But, given the delivery systems presently available—still primarily manned aircraft—neither one is equipped to knock out the striking force of the other. The civilian populations, therefore, constitute the target against which such forces would be directed and against which they could expect to deliver an attack with success. Such an attack by one side, however, exposes it to the certainty of the same kind of attack by the other. This is the essence of the present stalemate. A second conclusion, therefore, pressed by this analysis is this: If fallout is ever to be a strategic hazard and the fallout shelter a significant arm of civil defense, now is not the time. The fallout shelter campaign makes sense only as a means for public education in—or public habituation to—the peril of thermonuclear war.

The advance of military technology will undoubtedly change this picture in the future. In fact, the picture is changing rapidly now. The two powers are completing research and development on their missile systems and are moving them into production and installation in readiness for use. In the future they may be able to contemplate a "counterforce" attack aimed at the opponent's striking power, as well as a retaliatory second strike or a pre-emptive first strike (that is, retaliation in advance) aimed at the annihilation of the population. As the contestants approach this stage in their progress, the situation is bound to become more unstable. It will be made the more unstable by the entry of other nations in the arms race. When the capacity for mutual annihilation mounts beyond the 30,000-megaton stage and as the number of contestants increases, the danger of war by miscalculation and accident must rise. At some point in the ever less distant future is the point of no return. As C. P. Snow has bluntly summarized it: "We know, with the certainty of statistical truth, that if enough of these weapons are made—by enough different states—some of them are going to blow up."

Nobody who regards the arms race to the finish as our fated future is so foolish as to think that the American civilization and social order can endure in its present state of aboveground vulnerability under the open sky. Survival, if not victory, requires a civil defense system going far beyond the $150 family fallout shelter. Various agencies and individuals, working for the armed forces and on their own responsibility, have been exploring this thicket of unknowns and imponderables. Some of the results of these studies are in print and some have even found their way into the popular press. It is possible therefore to review them and consider what they imply.

One study—Study No. R-322-RC of the RAND Corporation—indicates that substantial underground protection could be provided for the population and the economy at a cost of $150 billion. It is not, of course, suggested that this effort be undertaken all at once. For one thing, the war-game equations show that a crash program of civil defense on such a scale might itself be provocative. The undertaking would accordingly be phased out over a ten- or fifteen-year period. At the end of that time there would be hard-rock "heavy" blast shelter spaces for 40 million people, "medium" blast shelters for 40 million more, and "light" fallout shelters for 170 million people. In addition, some $30 billion of the total appropriation would be invested to take about one fifth of the nation's manufacturing plant underground. It was this study that showed that our country is already endowed with a resource represented by "750 million square feet of usable space in mines with suitable characteristics for industrial or population shelters." Of course, not all of this space is conveniently located. From a long-range point of view, however, it would be possible to pay a premium to the industries that now dig such ubiquitous low-value ores as limestone in open quarries and induce them thereby to mine their ores, where geology permits, near or under centers of habitation.

The model hard-rock shelter is that made possible by the peculiar geology of Manhattan Island, a granitic outcropping of the Laurentian Shield itself. The contemplated shelter spaces would provide 20 square feet per person and would be stocked for a ninety-day occupancy. The report on the study furnishes some significant details: "An engineering calculation of a system of deep rock shelters under Manhattan Island for four million people indicated a cost of $500 to $700 per person depending largely on habitability standards. The shelters were to be excavated 800 feet below the surface, using conventional excavation and mining techniques. They were to be almost completely isolated from the surface, with air purified and enriched with oxygen as in a submarine, with water tapped from the Delaware Aqueduct system of tunnels and treated (or, in an emergency, drawn from internal storage), and with power drawn from diesel generators vented to the surface but isolated from the shelter proper. Occupants would be assigned to berths in a large dormitory, and would receive two cold meals and one hot meal per day, and would draw fresh clothing, take showers, and exercise on a rotational basis."

The report found that in order to get the 4 million into the 80-million-square-foot shelter, there would have to be ninety-one entrances, each located within five or ten minutes' walking distance of every home and office building. The providing of so many entrances turned out to be a factor that would reduce the security of the shelter. This difficulty, however, was solved successfully: "The entrances were sloped tunnels and had 500 psi blast doors at both top and bottom; provision could be made to collapse any single tunnel if the upper door gave way."

The success of this system still required a so-called "strategic evacuation" of the urban population of the country as a whole. But the study found that, with warning time in terms of minutes, "the bulk of the population could conceivably duck in 30 to 60 minutes," especially if it were provided with "a dramatic and unequivocal signal, such as exploding a small atomic weapon at a very high altitude over the city."

The provision of shelter for capital goods offered fewer difficulties to the framers of this plan. The report concedes: "There are differences in the technical problems to be faced— for example, industrial plants that release much heat would require additional cooling equipment, and those with a large volume of material inputs and product outputs would require larger entries and more transport equipment. But there seems little question that either conventionally constructed 'medium' shelters or excavated deep rock 'heavy' shelters could be designed and built for industrial capital." Fortunately, the investigators had at hand a study by the "Army Engineers" which showed the cost of reproducing three specific plants on the surface and in existing mines. The study showed that "a chemical processing plant . . . cost about twice as much underground, a precision manufacturing plant about a third more, and a warehouse about 15 per cent less." Although government bounties might be offered as an inducement to build new plants underground, the investigators thought that "a manufacturer might absorb higher construction costs considered by themselves," since these costs would be fully amortizable. It was felt, "on the other hand, that incidental effects of underground plants on location costs and labor costs could be a more serious obstacle." In the end the report concluded: "Further research in the economical design of plants . . . and into methods needed to induce private firms to accept such locations is needed."

Another student who has looked into these matters finds that they deserve investigation at a somewhat deeper level. "What can be envisaged," he says, "is the following: It is possible to determine within our present economy a sub-economy which provides at least a certain number of interdependent essential activities, free from all luxuries, all frills. It will secure the very barest *but continuing* existence of a part of the population—that part which may be assumed as saved by shelters or by-passed in a large-scale attack. Economic science can make a vital contribution in determining the exact nature of this sub-economy, this 'nucleus' or 'kernel' of our present economic system. Methods for identifying such 'kernels' exist and can be further developed. It is this sub-economy which should be put underground."

As for the civilization that is left aboveground, I am able to report, from my own inquiries in this field, the advice of a distinguished radiation chemist. He says that the incendiary effect of a large nuclear device can be nullified by covering the external surfaces of buildings with aluminum foil and dressing the population in white cover-alls.

At this point in our consideration of these studies of the feasibility of thermonuclear war, at least two lessons should be apparent. In the first place, the extrapolation of thermonuclear violence and of countermeasures to that violence speedily leads us into a realm of underground sub-economies and "sub-topias" that appear no more plausible and no less challenging to human ingenuity than a world without war. One may take as much heart from this observation as one can muster. For, in the second place, it must be borne in mind that this vision of the nation's future has been projected by realists, by experts in the possible, the probable, and the feasible, and by their expert consultants. This is the work of men who have assumed the public office of national defense and whose profession is war. It is their duty to envision the worst—and the best that can be made of the worst circumstances. By profession, they have no other counsel to offer, and, by training, they are qualified for no other.

So long as thermonuclear war remains in prospect—so long as the capacity to wage such war implements the will and power of our nation or any other nation—no part of this extrapolation into a nightmare civilization can be avoided. The extrapolation includes, it should be understood, the conditioning of the population to taking exercise on a rotational basis *before* it goes into the shelters. One cannot cavil at any one of these measures except on technical grounds. On such grounds it ought to be pointed out that the crater of a 100-megaton ground burst might penetrate the Manhattan shelter. Provision can then be made to dig the shelter at a deeper level—taking care to fill in (with solid concrete) the cavern that may have been excavated, prematurely in the escalation of violence, at the 800-foot depth. But so long as the rest of the citizenry accepts thermonuclear war as an extension of diplomacy, they have no choice but to co-operate in measures that will promote the national security. The war of populations can be fought only by the military state.

In his "Farewell Address" to the nation, President Eisenhower put forward wise counsel on the situation that confronts us here. "Until the latest of our world conflicts," he said, "the United States had no armaments industry. . . . But we can no longer risk emergency improvisation of national defense. We have been compelled to create a permanent armaments industry of vast proportions. Now this conjunction of an immense military establishment and a large arms industry is new in the American experience. The total influence—economic, political, even spiritual—is felt in every city, every state house, every office of the Federal Government. We recognize the imperative need for this development. Yet we must not fail to comprehend its grave implications. Our toil, resources, and livelihood are all involved; so is the very structure of our society.

"In the councils of Government, we must guard against the acquisition of unwarranted influence, whether sought or unsought, by the military-industrial complex. We must never let the weight of this combination endanger our liberties or democratic processes. Only an alert and knowledgeable citizenry can compel the proper meshing of the huge industrial and military machinery of defense with our peaceful methods and goals, so that security and liberty may prosper together."

To the military-industrial complex, President Eisenhower coupled another new element in our culture. He said we must be alert equally to the "danger that public policy could itself become the captive of a scientific-technological elite."

"It is the task of statesmanship," he concluded, "to mold, to balance, and to integrate these and other forces, new and old, within the principles of our democratic system—ever aiming toward the supreme goals of our free society."

If alternatives to war are to be found that can keep in view the supreme goals of our free society, then they must have advocates and voices to advance them in the councils of our government. If the feasibility of thermonuclear war has acquired, sought or unsought, unwarranted influence in public policy, then warranted influence, at least, must be sought for the feasibility of peace.

Perhaps the first question for study by responsible American citizens is the third one on our agenda: Can we get along without a war economy? This question can be restated to ask more specifically: How can the country generate $50 billion of final demand to replace the demand of a war economy cut back by disarmament? This is a bigger question than first appears. As the input-output tables of Wassily Leontief show, the $50 billion final demand of the war economy generates more than

$100 billion of total economic activity in the system. In other words, we are concerned here with maintaining not 10 per cent but something more like 20 per cent of the Gross National Product.

One can find many projections of the growth of our economy originating in influential and authoritative quarters. Most of them ignore the possibility of disarmament. They project our growth to 1970 and beyond with a war economy of relatively equal or larger size. But there is one study that grasps the thorny question of disarmament. It was prepared by the Bureau of the Budget at the request of President Eisenhower and delivered to him on the eve of the inauguration of the new administration.

This "Special Study" draws a summary and wholly fiscal picture of the economy and of the federal budget as it might appear after an international disarmament agreement had permitted a cutback of military expenditures to 50 per cent of the 1960 budget. For reasons that are clear to any student of the recent history of the business cycle, no more than one quarter of the reduction in expenditure is allocated to a reduction in taxation. The balance is allocated to various other elements in the federal budget to create final demand offsetting the cutback in military expenditures.

It is interesting to see where these allocations are made. One major appropriation goes to "labor and welfare," raising that line item from $4.4 billion to $19.7 billion. (It should be mentioned that the increase on this and other lines includes a projection of present trends as well as the allocation from disarmament.) The biggest item under this heading is education, up twelve times from 1960 to $7.5 billion. Next biggest is public health, up nearly five times to $3.7 billion. The budget of the National Science Foundation is increased six times to $600 million.

After labor and welfare, the next major heading in the disarmament budget is commerce and housing, with an allocation of $11.4 billion. Here the biggest item is housing and community development programs, increased six times to $3.2 billion.

Third in the major headings comes expenditures for economic and financial assistance programs, principally to the emerging nations. This item is more than doubled over 1960 to a total of $4.1 billion.

All told, the figures yield a federal budget of $92 billion, roughly 16 per cent of the 1970 Gross National Product of $600 billion, compared with the 15.6 per cent claim on the 1960 Gross National Product laid by the last Eisenhower budget.

These figures are, of course, projections and estimates. To make them real, they must find claimants with logic at least as compelling as that of the designers of the $150-billion national underground. What educator is prepared to justify a budget of $7.5 billion for federal aid to education? There need be no water in this figure; the growth and progress of our country in this century stands as a demonstration of the fact that education constitutes the most fruitful investment any society can make. As for housing and community development, this surely ranks as the second most urgent challenge to a generation that has permitted the central cities of our country to be reduced to ghettos and jungles. In the realm of technical and economic assistance, there are already influential claimants for the $4.1-billion sum projected in 1970. As the emerging nations have come forward under their own leadership, they have upset completely the prevailing estimates of their capacity to absorb investment toward the goal of eliminating destitution from its place as the prime subverter of stability in world politics.

There is a heartening lesson in this purely fiscal glimpse at another future. The enormous productive capacity of our society can find significant and fruitful final demands to take the place of the war economy. This lesson, in itself, is crucial to the recognition that peace is as feasible as war. What is now

336

required to implement this finding is action: unilateral action by interested and responsible citizens, by university study groups, by civic leaders, by community associations, by trade unions and industrial trade associations and institutes.

Educators must come forward with programs that will assert the proper claim of our schools and colleges on the productive capacity of our economy. In the repair of the blight on our cities, a host of economic interests hold stakes and responsibilities. None has a greater potential stake than the railroad industry. The commitment to automotive transportation, which makes evacuation of the cities impossible, is subsidized by an $11-billion public subsidy from the federal, state, and local governments every year. Of this total nearly $7 billion goes to capital improvement—that is, highways—a figure equal to 10 per cent of the annual gross expenditure on automotive transportation. By the same reckoning, the railroad system, with $10 billion in annual revenue, should seek an annual capital improvement subsidy of $1 billion to restore, and end the dismantling of, its commuter services.

In the economic assistance program, the machine-tool industry can find the cure for the peculiar instability of its business cycle that has caused its technology to lag behind that of the German and Soviet toolmakers. Perhaps it is in this area that the electronics industry can find at least part of the solution for its disarmament problem. This year, the industry exceeded $10 billion in sales, but with one customer—the war economy—accounting for more than half. The adaptation of missile control systems to the automatic control of industrial processes can help to make advanced technology immediately exportable, and in greater variety, to the emerging nations.

It is not supposed in this Special Study of the Bureau of the Budget that any of these re-allocations would be made short of a disarmament convention that provides controls adequate to shut off the arms race permanently. Dangerous and difficult conflicts still remain to haunt the world from the pre-thermonuclear age, when statesmen could turn them over to the generals. Those conflicts must be settled before the arms race itself brings on the war that will leave no victors and few survivors. This is the task of governments. It is up to the citizens to prepare the peace. Science and technology exploited in the cause of national power has brought mankind to this impasse. War cannot be eliminated from the life of the nations until the genius that thus commands the forces of nature is committed in the cause of man.

A NOTE ON THE TYPE

THE TEXT of this book was set on the Linotype in JANSON, a recutting made direct from the type cast from matrices long thought to have been made by Anton Janson, a Dutchman who was a practicing type-founder in Leipzig during the years 1668–1687. However, it has been conclusively demonstrated that these types are actually the work of Nicholas Kis (1650–1702), a Hungarian who learned his trade most probably from the master Dutch type-founder Dirk Voskens. The type is an excellent example of the influential and sturdy Dutch types that prevailed in England prior to the development by William Caslon of his own incomparable designs, which he evolved from these Dutch faces.

Composed, printed, and bound by
Kingsport Press, Inc., Kingsport, Tennessee.
Typography and binding design by
GUY FLEMING

GERARD PIEL, the publisher of *Scientific American*, was born at Woodmere, Long Island, in 1915 and was educated at Harvard College, where he received his A.B. magna cum laude in 1937. After serving as science editor of *Life* magazine from 1939 until 1945, he became assistant to the president of the Henry Kaiser Company and associated companies, and worked in that capacity in 1945 and 1946. In 1948, in association with two colleagues, he launched the new *Scientific American*, recognizing at that time that communication among scientists and between scientists and the general public would be one of the most pressing needs of postwar America. Mr. Piel, who holds three honorary degrees—Doctor of Science from Lawrence College (1956) and from Colby College (1960) and Doctor of Letters from Rutgers University (1961)—is also a Fellow of the American Academy of Arts and Sciences, a Fellow of the American Association for the Advancement of Science, and a Trustee of the American Museum of Natural History. He lives in New York, is married to a successful New York attorney, and has three children—a son at Harvard, another recently graduated from Harvard, and an infant daughter.

February 1962